RICH
WITHOUT
MONEY

TREVOR AND IRIS LIDDLE

I. LIDDLE
10 TRAVERS STREET, NEW HERRINGTON, HOUGHTON-LE-SPRING,
TYNE & WEAR, DH4 7AA, UK

Published in Great Britain 2002 by
I. LIDDLE, 10 TRAVERS STREET, NEW HERRINGTON,
HOUGHTON-LE-SPRING, TYNE & WEAR, DH4 7AA, UK

British Library Cataloguing-in-Publication Data.
A catalogue record for this book is available
from the British Library.

ISBN: 0-9543268-0-6

© Trevor and Iris Liddle, 2002
Reprinted 2002
Cover design photographs © Phill Dougan, 2002
www.klick.co.uk

Printed and bound by Athenaeum Press Ltd.,
Gateshead, Tyne & Wear, England

This book is dedicated
to our late granddaughter,
NIKI,
who died on the 9th February 2001
at the tender age of sixteen
to cystic fibrosis.
Without her encouragement
I doubt whether this book
would ever have been completed.

ACKNOWLEDGEMENTS

To Denise Robertson, who has helped me every step of the way, a remarkable woman.

To Bill Maynard, who took the time to read the book while still rehearsing for HEARTBEAT. *His comments were: "Picked it up and couldn't put it down. A damned good read and I would recommend it to anyone."*

To Billy Birlison and Jimmy Christie, two very good friends who encouraged me to start the book in the first place.

To Ronnie Potter, neighbour and friend, for his kind and professional help; his mastery of proof reading is immense.

To my friend, Phill Dougan, who provided the photographs for the cover.

And finally to my wife, Iris, who has kept me from falling apart since the passing of our granddaughter, **NIKI.**

Trevor Liddle

CHAPTER ONE

Sitting here writing this book takes me back to 1951 when I had just reached the tender age of ten.

I was brought up by my grandparents in a little row of colliery houses in the North East — County Durham to be exact. There were only about six streets in all. Back to back, each looking into the other's garden or kitchen. I can still see that big old fire range, with its round oven and a fire that never went out. It was my job on a weekend to help my gran to blacklead the range from top to bottom. I used to hate the fire in the summer, but in the winter it was a different story. I would come in from the cold, let down the oven door, sit on a chair opposite with my feet resting on the lid of the oven and be warmed through like toast in no time.

Going up to bed in the winter was great as well. Gran would take out one of the shelves from the oven and wrap it in an old blanket, then she would place it in the bottom of my bed, "Just to take the chill off, our Tom," she would say. I would race up to bed, leave my socks on, and dive under the blankets to get my feet on it before it cooled off.

Northern pit villages were very close communities, mining communities. Everyone knew everyone. They did in those days and a good thing it was too. If ever anyone was in trouble or ill, there was always a helping hand to be found close by.

I'll never forget the time that Gran took ill and had to go to hospital. Mrs. Cleghorn, one of our neighbours, said that I could stay at her house with her two sons, Albert and Jimmy. We were sent to bed early, one night, as Mrs. Cleghorn was expecting company, some distant cousin, a bit of a show-off by all accounts, full of brag about what she had and what Mrs. Cleghorn didn't have.

As it was a bit early when we went to bed we were carrying on, three of us in one bed, pulling the blankets off each other and the new clippy mat that was on the top for extra warmth. Everyone made clippy mats in those days because they couldn't afford carpets and if you were late in getting up on a morning and found your jacket was missing there was a good chance it had gone to finish off someone's clippy mat!

"Who's carrying on up those stairs?" shouted Mrs. Cleghorn.

"It's our Albert, Mam," Jimmy shouted, "he's pulling the clippy mat off us."

Mrs. Cleghorn was glad when her company left and gave us all a good ticking off. "Don't say, 'Our Albert's pulling the clippy mat off,' say, 'Our Albert's pulling the quilt off the bed!' With that she stomped back down the stairs and left us giggling under the bedclothes.

A couple of days later the same cousin popped in and we were packed off up to bed sharpish. We were carrying on, as usual, fighting over the blankets and the clippy mat — Jimmy and Albert were having a tug of war with it, because they both wanted it to keep warm. Jimmy was pulling one end while Albert was pulling the other. It went this way, it went that way. All of a sudden there was an awful sound of stitches snapping where Albert had pulled the wooden frame right out of the hessian. We went deathly quiet and hoped that they had not heard the racket downstairs. No such luck. Mrs. Cleghorn came to the bottom of the stairs and shouted up, "What's all the carry on up there? Come on, answer me!" she shouted.

"It's not me, Mam," said Jimmy, who was always the first to lay the blame at someone else's feet, "It's our Albert, he's pulled the hessian away from the mat, and it's fallen from the bed to the floor!" Albert and Jimmy had taken the mat, frame and all, from where it was standing and placed it onto the bed for warmth; everyone in those days made clippy mats from old discarded clothes because that's all they could afford.

Mrs. Cleghorn's cousin dissolved into fits of laughter and Mrs. Cleghorn didn't know whether to join her or hide her face in shame; in the end they were both doubled up with laughter.

My grandfather was a train driver. He never lost a day's work in his life, that was, of course, until the pit strike. Everyone was affected by this. Times were very hard and we all lived from hand to mouth, never knowing where the next meal was coming from. Sometimes I was lucky and I would be asked to run an errand by some of the well-off folk from the top end of the village. The reward would be pennies, but it was always worth the effort. With the money I received I would race straight down to the fish and chip shop.

Mrs. Moffitt served in the chip shop. She was a rosy faced, kindly sort, who never had a bad word for anyone, except one or two! Mrs. Moffitt had the worst stutter you had ever heard: it took her five minutes to say what could have been said in one. "Wwwhat dddo you want ttthen, young Tttom?" she would say.

"How much will you give me for fourpence?" I asked.

"Wwwell, as it's nearly ttttime for closing, you can have wwwhat's left," she would smile.

"Aw, thanks very much Mrs. Moffitt, that's awful kind of you," I would say. My gran was always saying that you should never forget your manners.

"Dddo you wwwant sssalt on?" she would stutter, shaking the salt all over the chips as she went. This was the tricky bit; if you didn't stop her in time, you ended up with chips looking like Mount Everest.

"Plenty on, Mrs. Moffitt, that's plenty on," I would shout. If you didn't get in with an early shout you wouldn't be able to see your fish and chips for salt.

Holding tight onto my parcel I would dash straight home and share the treat with my grandparents. The way the strike was going it was a luxury to have chips and we made the best of the meal with a few slices of bread.

I came running home from school one day to find that we had company — it was one of Grandad's mates from work. They were laughing and joking on and it was a long time since I had heard Grandad laughing. 'It must be good news,' I said to myself, 'maybe the strike is over!' That would be good news, but as it turned out it was nothing to do with the strike. The man had called to tell Grandad that there was a job at the local dog track, only part time until the strike was over, but at least it would bring in a few pounds. Grandad was to be the doorman.

I was very curious about this job as I had never been to a dog track before, "What will you be doing then, Grandad?" I asked.

He shook his head, smiling, "Just watching the door, Tom."

"What does that mean?" I asked. "I didn't think that a door would need watching! What would you be watching for?"

"Well," said Grandad, "I would have to make sure that nobody gets in the club who's not a member."

I thought that this sounded just a bit more interesting but not a lot and asked out of curiosity, "Can I come, too?"

Grandad rubbed his chin. "Well, I don't know about that, Tom," he said thoughtfully.

Gran, who had been standing by taking it all in, said softly, "Let him go, Bob."

Grandad looked at her and shook his head again but he was smiling, "Well, I suppose it won't do him any harm."

I had started to warm to the idea of seeing all the dogs run, and before I knew it, we were walking through the gates of the track. I couldn't wait, I was so excited. It was the first time I'd been to a dog track, the first time I had seen greyhounds racing. What a thrill it was. Those beautiful, sleek animals, so kind, so graceful, so gentle and SO FAST! I was hooked from that day on. I had a dream now, something to work towards. Next step — to own my own greyhound.

CHAPTER TWO

It was coming up to my birthday and everyone was asking what I wanted. I was really looking forward to it. Did I want this? Did I want that?

"Well," I said, "I would quite like to buy my own present, if you don't mind."

"Oh yes, and what might that be?" asked Aunt Mary who often used to give me a little treat, even if it wasn't my birthday. "Something special?" she asked.

"Yes ... er ... yes. It's something I've been wanting for a long time," I said, fingers crossed that no one would ask what it was to be.

"And what's that?" asked Grandad; too late I thought to myself.

"Oh, it's to be a surprise, Grandad," I said.

He thought about this for a while and said, "Well, it is your birthday. As long as you don't waste the money ...."

"I won't," I interrupted in mid sentence, standing there still with my fingers crossed. "I promise I won't."

Uncle Frank, who had been sitting reading his paper, raised his head so you could just see his eyes over the top edge and said, "Nobody's got money to spare these days you know, what with the strike just settled and things just getting back to normal." Uncle Frank was a miserable so and so, always on about money and never smiling.

Aunt Mary nudged Grandma and muttered, "You know, that man wouldn't spend Christmas if he could help it, he's that mean." I didn't know what they meant at the time, but they seemed to think it was very funny.

Anyway, by the end of the day I had collected seventeen shillings. That was it, nothing could stop me now, I was well on my way to owning my first greyhound.

I had managed to find a job as an errand boy for Mr. Rewcastle, the local butcher. He was a big stout gent, with a bright red face and his boots seemed to be moulded to his feet with stale blood and sawdust. My job was to deliver the meat to the customers on the outskirts of town. The only way I could do this was on the shop bike; a big bone-shaker of a thing it was, and it weighed a ton — I really hated that old bike. But if I was to have my very own greyhound, then I just had to take the bull by the horns — and most of the time, with that bike, that's just what it felt like. A constant uphill battle, day after day, but the rewards more than made up for struggling with it.

Mr. Rewcastle paid me seven and sixpence a week. With tips I could sometimes make up to twelve bob and it wasn't long before I had managed to save four pounds. That was a fortune to me, I had never had that much money in my life and I only hoped I was doing the right thing buying a greyhound!

One night when I was at the dog track with my grandfather I overheard some of the men talking about another track. They were selling off all of the dogs. I was interested and made some discreet enquiries. Mr Mason, a tall lean man with a weather-beaten face from working outside in all sorts of weather, was the owner of the track. He was a kindly man, a good friend of Grandad's and always had a good word for every one, well, almost every one! People in the village had long memories of the strike. Blacklegs who went back to work before the strike was ended were total outcasts and one or two business people who had turned their backs on the strikers were shunned. There was one man in the village that Mr. Mason really didn't like and that was Mr. Pratt, but there again, who did like Mr. Pratt? He was the local garage owner. Tall and thin, he looked a bit like an undertaker, rarely had a cigar out of his mouth and looked down on the working class: he had refused to serve petrol to anyone who was on strike. Not that many of the village folks had cars, but Grandad said there was a principal at stake, hence the boycott of Mr. Pratt's garage after the strike. Mr. Mason's track was called Sunny Side because of the houses that ran alongside with the same name. It was about ten miles from where I lived, and I had never been before. Apparently Mr. Mason had fallen on hard times and with the strike and all he just couldn't keep going.

The strike was a necessity, the miners in the village were being badly paid for risking their lives down the pit and if I had left school, I too would have joined the strike and stood beside my grandad and the rest of the men. Mr. Mason was a friend of Grandad's and I often heard him and Gran saying it was a shame he was in the situation that he was and had no choice but to sell up.

That night I made up my mind that I was going to be the owner of my first greyhound. There was no stopping me now. The next day I raided my moneybox, picked up my precious four pounds — two one pound notes, one ten shilling note and the rest in loose change — and I was soon on my way. Ten miles is a long way and by the time I arrived at the track there was very little left. I saw Mr. Mason coming down the path and he looked a very sad man.

"I'm sorry about the track closing, Mr. Mason," I said quietly.

"Not as sorry as me, lad," he said, shrugging his shoulders. "Anyway, young Tom, what can I do for you?"

I looked up at him and said, "I want to buy a dog."

"A dog?" he said. "Are you sure? Does your grandfather know that you're here?"

"Er ... yes...." I said, again crossing my fingers behind my back, hoping that he wouldn't start asking too many questions.

"Well, I suppose if your grandad knows, it must be all right. Mind you, there's not a lot left."

We walked slowly down towards the kennels, both lost in thought. Then I saw him, a big fawn dog with the saddest eyes I had ever seen in a dog, or in a person. He looked up at me with a slight wag

13

of his tail, but that's all it was, a slight wag. It soon stopped and he lay his head on his front feet as if to say, "He won't take me — everyone walks past me!" The dog looked so pitiful tied to a post with an old piece of rope.

"What's up with him?" I asked, eager for information.

"You don't want him, lad, he's no good," said Mr. Mason, "never been any use since he came out of Ireland — I'm going to shoot him in the morning!"

My heart sank. I asked hurriedly, "How much do you want for him?"

Mr. Mason laughed. "He cost me twenty pounds in Ireland lad. He had a good reputation over there, but he never lived up to it over here. You don't want him, Tom. Come down here and look at this other fellow. He'll do a grand job for yer."

He showed me another nice black dog, but it was no good. I couldn't shift that big fawn fellow out of my mind, nor the thought of him being shot in the morning! "That sure is a fine dog, Mr. Mason, but I like the other one."

Mr. Mason shook his head. "If I let you take that fawn dog home with you, Tom, your grandfather will not be pleased, I'm sure."

I looked up at him. "Yes, I know, Mr. Mason, but it is my birthday money and I should be able to buy what I want!"

Mr. Mason laughed. "You've made up your mind then, young Tom?"

"I have, sir, and I'm determined to walk away with the big fawn dog!" It wasn't like me to be so bold and, to tell the truth, I don't know where it came from.

"How much have you got?" asked Mr. Mason, a slight grin on his face at my boldness.

"Four pounds," I said, adding quickly, "and you did say that you were going to shoot him in the morning."

Mr. Mason rubbed his chin, looked at me and said, "Well, don't say you weren't warned, me lad."

I couldn't believe it. "Really, you mean I can have him, honest?"

"Yes, lad, he's yours. Now take him away before I change my mind."

I took an old belt from my pocket and put it around his neck, rubbing his ears gently as I did so. His big sad eyes looked up at me as if to say, "Thank you." I patted him and stroked him and we set off together down the road. It was a long way home and a long time to think of what might happen when I got there. What would the reception be like when I got home, I wondered?

As I came up the garden path, my grandfather opened the door. "What the hell have you got there, young Tom?"

My heart started to beat faster. "A dog, Grandad," I said nervously.

"I can see it's a dog, Tom, but where has he come from?"

"I've bought it, from Mr. Mason ... you know his track has had to close and I bought it from him," I said quickly.

"And how much have you paid for him?"

"Four Pounds. It was my birthday money," I hastened to add.

"So that's why you've been saving." He shook his head, "Well, he's a sorry sight to say the least. I hope you know that he's going to take a lot of looking after. He'll need lots of exercise and good food, but most of all he'll need lots of love and affection. He looks as if he's been through the mill poor thing. Bring him in and give him a good feed, there's some bread and scraps left off dinner, then he'll need a good bath; after that you can take yourself off to Mr. Miller's farm and ask him for some oat straw."

"Oat straw? Why oat straw?" I asked.

"It's the cleanest straw there is," Grandad said. He looked at me, his eyes sparkling and then said, "While you're up at the farm, I'll clean out the shed in the garden — you can keep him in there."

After a couple of weeks you wouldn't have known it was the same animal. His eyes were bright, his coat was gleaming and most of all he was happy. It was time to take him to the track.

We didn't know what to expect, anything could happen. We placed him in the traps and just hoped for the best. The waiting seemed like hours, but it was only seconds. The traps went up

"Crash", the dogs came out racing, all that is except one! My heart sank. The other dogs had a lead of about six yards on him before he had even pricked up his ears and poked his nose out of the trap. Then all of a sudden he decided to join in. The pack had had a good lead on him and when he caught the leading dog I couldn't believe my eyes. I held my breath, not daring to breathe. In a flash he was five yards clear of the pack. He had won the trial in good time. Grandad just stood there, mouth open catching flies.

"I don't believe what I've just seen!" said Grandad, looking just as excited as myself.

Mr. Chapman, the handicapper, came down to take the dogs markings. "That's some sort of dog you've got their, young Tom, what name are you going to call him?"

"I haven't thought of a racing name, Mr. Chapman."

"Well, you'll have to call him something, young man."

"I just call him Sandy at home," I said.

"That's no use, lad, we've already got a Sandy. What about Flash?" he suggested.

Grandad laughed, "That's about right, Mr. Chapman, the way he passed those other dogs it sounds like a fitting name to me. What about it, Tom?"

"Flash it is," I laughed.

Mr. Chapman was taking a pencil and paper from his pocket to write down all Sandy's particulars, the colour of the dog, his ear marks, any bits of white on him and so on.

Mr. Chapman looked up over his glasses and said, "Well, that's it, young Tom. When do you want him on the card to race?"

I looked at Grandad. I didn't know when he would be able to race, or what I should do next; this was all a new experience for me and I was enjoying every minute of it.

Grandad looked at Mr. Chapman, "Put him on for Saturday, that way all the family can come and see him run."

"Saturday it is then," said Mr. Chapman, "see you then, young

Tom," and off he disappeared to get the rest of the markings for the other dogs.

The excitement and anticipation was too much, I couldn't think of anything else except Saturday. I daydreamed about it, I dreamt about it all night and I talked about it non-stop. By Saturday morning I was so excited I forgot to go to work for Mr. Rewcastle. I was sitting staring into space when there was a knock at the door. It was Mrs. Morgan, a friend of Gran's from the next street. "Is Tom in, Mary?" she asked, "there's a certain Butcher down the High Street wants to know if he's going to show up today!"

I nearly dropped off my stool. I ran so fast down the High Street, if I had been Flash I would have broken all records. Gran's voice was ringing in my ears all the way there, "Him and that dog, that's all he ever thinks about these days."

I flew into the shop, "I'm so, so sorry, Mr. Rewcastle," I panted, trying to catch my breath.

"You only just made it, lad," he growled. He was trying to be tough, sharpening his big knife as he spoke to me sternly. "I nearly gave the job to young Jimmy Jones."

"I'm really sorry. It won't happen again, Mr. Rewcastle. It's just that my dog's running tonight and I forgot all about work." I looked at him sheepishly as I said this, hoping that he would see the funny side and not sack me. I knew he wouldn't give the job to Jimmy Jones — he couldn't ride that old bike!

"Is this dog of yours any good?" Mr. Rewcastle asked. He was a man that liked a wager.

"I think so," I replied, "but mind you, he has to give all the others a few yard's start!"

"He must be a good un, then," he laughed.

"He's the best," I said, with my chest puffed out with pride.

"Right, less of this chatter then, lad. Get cracking with that old bike or you'll never get to the track." He paused, looking over his shoulder at me and whispering, "I'll tell you what. If you hurry up with those errands, I'll give you a lift to the track with the dog."

17

"Really, honest, that's great, Mr. Rewcastle, thanks," I said. I was so pleased. It was really a long walk to the track and I didn't want Sandy to get too tired.

I was back at the shop before you would know it. I even managed to make myself two bob in tips. Mr. Rewcastle was waiting for me tidying things up before he closed the shop. "Well done, Tom," he said, "if that dog is as fast as you then there won't be a problem tonight," he smirked. "Now be off with you — and go straight home. I'll pick you up in about an hour."

I ran home as fast as I could so that I could sit with Sandy in his kennel. He loved me to stroke him and make a fuss of him. I don't think anyone had ever made a fuss of him before. I was whispering to him and telling him how good it was going to be, when Gran shouted, "Tom, your dinner's ready and if you don't come now you won't be going to any dogs!"

"I'm coming, Gran," I shouted, charging into the house.

I hadn't got my behind onto the seat before the garden gate opened and Mr. Rewcastle was shouting, "Is he ready yet?"

I leapt up, knocking the chair over as I went. "I'm just coming, Mr. Rewcastle."

"You are not going anywhere until you've eaten your dinner," said Gran, sternly.

"Oh Gran, I can't. I'm far too excited. If I eat it I'll be sick ... on the new mat!"

"Well," said Gran, "dogs or no dogs, I have not got money to waste and if you don't eat it now then you'll get it for your supper."

"That'll be fine, Gran," I said over my shoulder as I dashed out of the door. I would eat sawdust rather than miss out on seeing Sandy in his first race.

I was just about to close the gate when Mr. Rewcastle shouted, "Don't you need a dog or something Tom?" I couldn't believe it; in all the excitement, I had nearly forgotten the most important thing on the day — Sandy.

We arrived at the track, and the first person I bumped into was

Mr. Mason, the man I had bought the dog from. He did a sort of double take. "That's never the dog you got from me, is it Tom?" he asked.

"Aye, it certainly is, Mr. Mason," I said, beaming all over with pride.

"Well, lad, credit where it's due — you've done a grand job on him; he looks a million dollars."

"Thanks, Mr. Mason, but will you excuse me, I have to declare him now," I said very proudly. Mr. Mason laughed and stepped aside to let me pass.

As I walked Sandy round to the kennels, talking to him all of the time, I was stopped by Mr. Pratt, the local garage owner. "What do you call that?" he snapped.

"Sandy," I said timidly.

"No, stupid boy. Not his pet name, his racing name," he snarled.

He didn't seem like a very nice man at all, but my gran had taught me that you should never forget your manners, no matter how nasty a person you were talking to, so I replied, "Flash sir, why?"

"Well, he's in my race, so that'll be one less to beat," he said sarcastically and marched off.

Grandad, who was nearby had seen all this and asked, "What did Mr. Pratt want?"

"Oh, nothing much, he just said that if Sandy was in his race, then there was one less dog for his dog to beat," I said hanging my head.

Grandad ruffled the top of my hair, "Don't mind him. He thinks that because he's got a bit of brass he has the best of everything, but that's not always the case, son. Anyway, let's get this dog into the kennels before it's too late."

Sandy looked as excited as I was. I rubbed his ears and fussed him and whispered, "Won't be long now, Sandy," as I put him into the kennel.

All the family were at the dog track, including grumpy Uncle Frank. He still hadn't forgiven me for asking for money for my birthday. "So this is what you spent your birthday money on is it?"

"Yes, Uncle Frank, it is," expecting a lecture at any minute.

"Will it win?" he asked. "Not that I'll waste my time or money having a bet. I've got more to do with my money than bet on silly dogs," he moaned.

"Well, Uncle Frank, we'll soon find out, it's his race next."

I rushed off to find Grandad at the kennels. He had Sandy ready. "Well lad, do you want to take him on, or will I get one of the lads to do it for you?" he asked.

"No way," I replied, "I've been waiting for this all week. I'll take him on Grandad."

Mr. Pratt's son came over and said, "Your dog's got no chance, Watson," he sneered. He had one of those faces you just wanted to smack and think nothing of it!

"Who said he's got no chance," I growled back at him.

"My dad, that's who."

"Soon find out," I said, "they're off in a few minutes." I turned my back on him and paraded Sandy around the ring, I felt so proud.

Sandy was running from scratch with Mr. Pratt's dog, the others were all receiving start, up to fourteen yards. This meant that they all had anything from 1 yard to 14 yards start on Sandy and Mr. Pratt's dog.

A voice crackled over the loudspeaker. I nearly jumped out of my skin. "ALL DOGS INTO THE TRAPS," it said, "ALL DOGS INTO THE TRAPS."

I placed Sandy into the trap and held my breath. As the hare picked up speed I thought that I was going to be sick with excitement. The hare flashed by, the traps went up and Sandy came out like a bullet. In seconds he had caught up the fourteen yards and was with the leading dogs. Before the second bend he was up in front of them and in a flash he was crossing the winning line.

"FIRST, NUMBER ONE — SECOND, NUMBER TWO," was the call from the loudspeaker. I was floating on air.

I caught up with Sandy, placed his lead around his neck and gave him a big hug. I was so excited I nearly wet myself. "What about that, Freddy Pratt," I whispered as I walked past, grinning like a Cheshire cat.

Just then Mr. Pratt came towards Freddy and his dog and shouted, "Is he lame, Freddy?" and before Freddy could open his mouth, he added, "He must be, because there is no way any dog can beat my dog that far," he snarled.

"Well, I know a dog that can, and he's not a million miles away from you," I smirked.

"Cheeky young sod," he muttered as he walked away, his head so high in the air that he nearly fell over the hare rail.

There was a huge cheer as Sandy and I approached the paddock. Grandad and all of the family were waiting to greet us. "Well done, Tom, how does it feel to be a winner?"

A bitter voice came from behind. "He was lucky, my dog's gone lame." It was Mr. Pratt.

"Miserable old so and so," someone whispered in the crowd.

Mr. Mason laughed and cried out, "Sour grapes, Freddy, don't be such a bad loser." Mr. Pratt turned on Mr. Mason, but Mr. Mason stood firm. "You've always been the same, Pratty, a bad loser. You have to give the boy some credit, he's done a grand job with that dog. He saved its life and made him into a real dog. If it hadn't been for Tom, I would have shot him."

Mr. Pratt, who was still red in the face and fuming, looked me straight in the eye and growled, "How much do you want for that dog, young Watson?"

"He's not for sale," I said, grabbing Sandy's lead just that little bit tighter. "He's my dog and nobody is going to take him from me."

"Calm down, Tom," said Grandad, "I wouldn't let you sell a mouse to that man!"

Mr. Pratt rounded on Grandad, but Grandad gave as good as he got, and maybe a little bit more. "Remember the strike, Freddy Pratt," said Grandad. "All the shops and factories gave something to the soup kitchens, but not you. Your words were, 'Tell them to get back to work'. Well Freddy Pratt, I've got a long memory and you may

21

be able to buy most things, but you can't buy our Tom's dog!"

"I'll test you, Watson," he said to Grandad taking out his wallet, "twenty pounds, how about that?"

"I would rather starve than let you have him," snarled Grandad.

"Thirty?" said Mr. Pratt.

By this time the crowd were buzzing. 'Should he take it?' 'Should he keep the dog?' "That's a lot of money," someone in the crowd said, "he should think hard about that."

"He's not for sale and that's final — no matter how much you say, Pratty — he's NOT for sale." Grandad turned to me and said gently, "Now, Tom, take Sandy home and make sure you wash his feet." I was off like a shot, just in case he changed his mind.

It was ages before Grandad got home, and he was drunk! Very, very, drunk! Gran was hopping mad. I had never seen Grandad drunk since before the strike. He'd had a right skinful.

"Where do you think you've been till this time, Bob Watson," Gran yelled at him.

"A's been 'aving a little drink with me pals," he slurred, "an I 'ope me dinner's still hot," he whispered to me.

"I can hear you, Bob Watson, you great lout, and your dinner should be hot — it's been in the back of the fire for two hours." Grandad wasn't getting any supper that night!

The next day I was up bright and early to take Sandy for a walk before I went to Sunday school. I was on my way back, ambling along with Sandy by my side when I bumped into young Freddy Pratt; I couldn't resist a comment. "I thought your dog was lame, Pratty?"

"He is," snapped Pratty, his face turning redder by the second. Just like his dad he was, all red and angry when he couldn't get his own way. "Anyway," said Freddy, my dad says he's going to buy me a dog from Ireland and it'll be so good it'll beat yours out of sight. He's even going to pay fifty pounds for it!" said Freddy with a smirk on his face.

"My grandad says it's not the most money that gets the best dog, otherwise, those with the most money would *have* the best dogs and we know that's not true, don't we, Pratty, because my Sandy beat the pants off your dog and that's a fact!" I snapped back at him. He had a way of just getting under your skin that you just couldn't ignore, and you had to have a go back at him.

"Well, we'll soon see when my new dog gets here," Freddy shouted as he marched off down the lane, his face like a smacked baby's backside, all red and puffed up.

I hadn't been in the garden five minutes when Grandad opened the back door and came down the path, he looked awful, all grey and hung-over. "What's Sandy like, Tom?" he asked, sort of quiet like, like the words shook his head when he said them.

"I think he looks a lot better than you, Grandad!" I laughed.

He held his head with one hand, "That won't take much doing, son," he said, "and by the way, here's your winnings from the race. £1-10 shillings prize money."

I took the money, holding it tightly in my hand. "That's great Grandad. I think I'll buy Sandy a coat, it's getting nippy on a morning."

"Aye, lad, you do that," Grandad muttered, rubbing his chin. He obviously had something on his mind, and I had a feeling it was something I didn't want to know. "Thing is, lad," the words seemed to be sticking in his throat, "there's a reason I asked how the dog is doing," he muttered, looking a bit sheepish, sort of shameful like.

"I've bet Mr. Pratt that Sandy can beat any dog he's got in his kennel! The dog we beat in the race the other night is his best dog, so we've nothing to worry about — have we?" He said this all so quickly, the words falling over his tongue like water over a fall, I could hardly take it all in. I looked up at him in disbelief.

"I don't suppose for a minute he mentioned his new dog did he, Grandad?" I asked quietly — hoping but knowing in my bones he had not.

"New dog! What new dog?" said Grandad.

The new one he's sent for from Ireland. Young Freddy told me this morning — fifty pounds he's paying for it."

23

It was just starting to sink into Grandad; what little colour there was in his face drained down to his toes. "I thought that skunk Pratt was keen to bet," said Grandad, looking sicker than he did before. "Sneaky little toad, what a dirty rotten trick." Grandad was angry now and the state he was in, angry must have hurt.

"What was the bet?" I whispered. "How much?" He looked at me, at a point just above my head. He couldn't quite meet my eyes; he seemed to take forever to answer. "Well," I prompted, "what's the matter?" He still couldn't meet my eyes.

"The matter is, lad, that I've, er ... bet thirty pounds. If ...we win, we get the money, but if he wins, he ... er ..." his voice trailed off as he shuffled his feet uneasily, then he blurted it out "... he gets Sandy."

I looked at him in disbelief. Surely, he was kidding, he couldn't possibly have done that. But Grandad wasn't kidding. "How could you, Grandad?" I cried. "How could you?"

"I'm so sorry, Tom, really sorry. I'd had too much to drink, not that that's any excuse, lad — I'm so, so sorry." I just stood there, speechless.

Suddenly, from nowhere, Gran's voice broke the silence. "How could you, Bob Watson?" she demanded. She had been standing by the door taking it all in. "You know how much our Tom thinks of that dog!" Grandad looked at me, guilt etched in every line of his craggy face.

"I'll go and see Pratty, lad, ask him if he'll call off the bet. Don't worry about it," said Grandad trying to reassure me.

"You've got more chance of plating sawdust, Bob Watson," Gran snarled at him as she turned on her heel and stormed back into the house, slamming the door behind her. Grandad winced at the bang, still suffering from his hangover.

Just then, Mr. Mason came down the path. "Morning, young Tom," he said. "How's the head, Bob?" he asked. Grandad shook it very gently, but said nothing. "I heard about your bet with Pratty Bob. He's a real bas....," Mr Mason stopped in mid sentence as he remembered that Gran could appear at any time. "But you know, Bob, I think we have a slight chance of beating him."

Grandad didn't look too excited, but I was keen to grasp at any straw. "How's that, Mr. Mason?" I asked, wiping the tears from my face.

"Well," he said, "just this morning I had a 'phone call from a friend of mine in Ireland, the chap I bought Sandy from to be precise." There was a pause. Mr. Mason was a great one for drama and he liked to keep everyone guessing.

"Well?" I encouraged, still sniffling.

"Thing is," he continued, "he wanted to know if I knew a man called Pratt, as he's from around these parts. Seems that he's just sold Pratty one of his dogs ... the best in his kennel."

"Well that leaves us in a right mess," said Grandad. "I thought you said we might have the beating of him."

"We just might at that," said Mr. Mason. "Apparently, Pratty's new dog and your Sandy were kennel mates in Ireland and my mate out there reckons that we have the better dog of the two," he finished with a flourish.

"Wow," was all I could think of to say. Grandad was still trying to take all of this in. Grandma, who had got over her huff (basically because she was scared of missing anything) stood in the background listening carefully.

"It turns out," Mr. Mason continued, "that the two dogs ran together in Ireland."

"And!" snapped Grandad, him and his hangover getting impatient.

Mr. Mason was grinning like a Cheshire cat now. "According to the Irishman, they are even. They raced against each other twice and won one race each."

"That's an even chance we have then," said Grandad turning to Mr. Mason "Thanks for the information, very grateful we are to have it, I can think of nothing I'd rather see than Pratty getting his comeuppance." Mr. Mason bid his farewells and was off down the road whistling. I started to feel a little better. We had a slim chance, a very slim chance, but at least it was a chance.

"Well, Tom, me lad, we've got work to do now and lots of it," said Grandad.

For the next two weeks I was up at the crack of dawn walking Sandy in all sorts of weather. I had to have Sandy as fit as possible if we were to have a chance of beating Pratty's dog. Sandy's coat was shining, his eyes were bright and he looked a real picture. Then, when I thought that nothing could go wrong, the bottom fell out of my world.

Word on the street was that Mr. Pratt had not only got his dog from Ireland, but he had also hired a professional trainer to go with it. He was a man who went by the name of Tim Murphy, or Tipperary Tim as he was nicknamed, an Irishman with a good reputation for training dogs, if he could keep off the drink that was!

The date for the race was set and I had to give myself a good talking too. It was no use moping about it, I had done my best. Sandy was as good as he was ever going to be and I had to keep my chin up.

With just a few days left before the race, everyone in the village was excited. Me and Sandy were the talk of the place — it was buzzing. Everyone was rooting for us, not a single soul wanted Mr. Pratt to win, they all had long memories and could not forget what he had done to the men and their families during the strike.

Mr. Rewcastle was kind enough to give me some cuts of meat for Sandy. "I hope he wins for you, Tom," he said, as he sliced through a row of pork chops like lightning.

"So do I!" came a voice from the next door shop. That was Mr. Moss, the greengrocer, and as he poked his head round the doorway he had a bag in his hand. "Here's some veg if you want it, Tom," he said, pressing the bag into my hand.

"Oh, yes please, Mr. Moss. That would be most kind; my Gran will be most grateful," I said. "Thank you very much."

"Just you make sure you beat the pants of that greedy bas.... so and so!" Mr. Moss said, biting his tongue and remembering not to swear in the street.

Four o'clock and time to take Sandy for his walk. We were just starting off down the road when a car pulled up alongside — it was Mr. Pratt. I ignored him at first, then a voice came from inside the car, "Enjoy him while you can, young Watson, this time next week he's mine." He laughed through a cloud of cigar smoke as he roared off down the road, throwing up dust behind him. I felt sick with the thought that he might be the new owner of Sandy and a shiver ran down my spine. We had to win, we just had to.

As the day of the race dawned I couldn't eat my breakfast - my stomach was in knots. Would I be bringing Sandy home with me tonight? Would I have to leave him with Mr. Pratt? I couldn't bear to think about it, I had to go for a walk to clear my head.

I was halfway down the lane when I came across Tipperary Tim. He was slouched under the old oak tree, looking decidedly drunk, a bottle of Irish whisky in one hand and his cap in the other. "Top o' the morning t' yer, young fella me lad," he said, "would you be havin' the time upon yer?" he drawled, his Irish voice soft and deep. His breath, however, was strong enough to knock over a bear.

"It's about ten thirty," I replied as I walked quickly by. I didn't think that Mr. Pratt would be at all pleased to see Mr. Murphy in that state.

It was the way my luck was running that day. Just then I bumped into young Freddy Pratt. "Have you seen Tim Murphy?" he demanded.

"No," I said innocently, crossing my fingers behind my back.

"He's not been seen since eight this morning, and my dad's doing his nut! If you see him, tell him he's wanted," Freddy stormed, and marched off in the opposite direction muttering under his breath.

"Yeah, I'll be sure to do that," I said, whispering under my breath, 'If you only knew, Freddy, me boy!' As soon as he was out of sight I ran home as fast as my legs could carry me. I had to tell Grandad.

At the bottom of him Grandad was a good man. He thought about what I told him and said to Grandma, "I wouldn't like to see a man lose his job, no matter who he works for; jobs are hard enough to come by these days as it is. Make me a can of strong tea, Mary, and a drop of the remedy," a sure cure for a man who had drunk too much. Then he turned to me and said, "Show me where Murphy is, Tom, we haven't got too much time we'll try to get him sober before Pratt finds him."

It took the best part of an hour to sober Tim up, but we managed, then we sent him on his way — we had better things to do, we had to make sure Sandy was ready for the track. My stomach was doing somersaults by this time.

Mr. Rewcastle had arrived to take us to the track. "Nervous, Tom?" he asked with a big grin on his face.

"A little," I croaked. I was so nervous I could hardly speak. Grandad looked even worse than me, big worry lines etched across his brow. The only one that was calm was Sandy.

As we entered the track there was a huge cry went up, "COME ON, FLASH," they roared. I could feel my face blushing up, but feeling proud all the same. "Come on, Tom," said Mr. Mason, "I've got every faith in you and Sandy. The love that you have given that dog will pay you back tonight."

It wasn't long before the loudspeaker crackled into life. "DOGS FOR THE MATCH RACE — KING AND FLASH TO THE STARTING TRAPS — AND THE BEST OF LUCK TO YOU TOM AND ER YOU MR. PRATT." Not even the Handicapper wanted Mr. Pratt to win.

As I walked Sandy to the traps Tim Murphy was already there with Mr. Pratt's new dog. It was the first time that I'd had a chance to see the new addition to the Pratt kennel and a smart looking brindle dog he was. "Luck of the Irish to yer, Tom," whispered Mr. Murphy, as he gave his dog a little rub down. Mr. Murphy certainly looked a lot better than he had a few hours before.

"Same to you, Mr. Murphy," I said, but not really meaning it.

"DOGS IN THE TRAPS," came the announcement.

The crowd fell silent, you could hear a pin drop. Then the winding of the hare as it came around in front of the traps. Up went the lids. The noise from the crowd was deafening. The dogs flashed out. I could hardly look, but I couldn't bear to look away. They came round the first bend neck and neck, then King started to edge in front. "He's won from there," shouted Mr. Pratt as his dog took a length's lead into the third bend.

"Come on, Sandy," I was screaming, "come on."

There was only fifty yards to go when Sandy began to catch King up. They were neck and neck as both dogs crossed the winning line. I couldn't believe how close it was — I was praying that Sandy was in front on that line, the thought of Mr Pratt owning Sandy was making me feel sick.

As I walked off the track I asked Mr. Murphy who he thought had won. "'Tis a close t'ing, Tom, it is dat," he said in his warm Irish accent.

My heart was in my mouth, my stomach was in knots, I nearly jumped out of my skin when the loud speaker crackled into life. "PHOTO FINISH." It was unbearable.

"My dog won," shouted Mr. Pratt, "my dog won," trying to convince himself.

"I'll bet you ten pounds," came a voice from the crowd, "that your dog didn't win, Pratty." It was Mr. Mason.

"I'll take that bet," said Mr. Pratt, a large smirk on his face.

"Well that makes me feel a lot better now," said Grandad.

"Why?" I asked, my stomach still tied in knots and feeling as if I wanted to go to the toilet.

"Well, lad," said Grandad, "Mr. Mason's one of the best judges of a photo finish on two legs. He was judge on his own track for over 20 years and that has to stand for something!"

The loudspeaker crackled into life again. There was a deadly hush crept over the crowd. "FIRST NUMBER ..." and then silence. You could hear the angels whisper it was so quiet. There was more crackling "RIGHT." It was working again. The voice from the judge's box boomed out, "SORRY ABOUT THAT — SLIGHT

TECHNICAL PROBLEM — NOW WITHOUT FURTHER DELAY. FIRST, NUMBER ONE, FLASH — SECOND, NUMBER TWO, KING."

The crowd were ecstatic. I could hardly believe my ears. "He's done it, Grandad, he's done it," I said. I could see the look of pure relief on Grandad's face.

"Aye lad. I don't know what I would have done if he had been beaten, but he hasn't and you've won thirty pounds into the bargain."

"We've won," I corrected him, as he ruffled my hair.

"No, Tom. That's your winnings, every last penny of it, all yours. Now come on, lets go and find that Mr. Pratt — I for one am going to enjoy this."

Mr. Pratt was still in the paddock shouting at Tim Murphy. "Call yourself a trainer," he screamed at him, "I could have done a better job myself."

"You were beaten by a better dog, sir," said Mr. Murphy gently. "Why don't you just admit it — the best dog won!"

"Hear, hear," shouted the crowd, "give the lad his money."

"You were lucky, Bob Watson," sneered Mr. Pratt as he counted the money into Grandad's hand.

"You need a bit of luck in this game," said Mr. Murphy.

"And that's what you haven't got Murphy. You're sacked," shouted Mr. Pratt. "I'll train the dogs myself in future."

Mr. Mason burst into laughter. "You! You train a dog! You couldn't train a frog to hop," said Mr. Mason. By this time, the crowd were in stitches. Mr. Pratt was just about to walk away when Mr. Mason shouted, "Hang on a minute, Pratty, haven't you forgotten something?"

"What's that, then?" said Mr. Pratt, with a face like a busted couch.

"Ten quid if you don't mind," laughed Mr. Mason.

Mr. Pratt threw the money at Mr. Mason saying, "There's your tenner, and I hope you lose it on the way home."

"Not much chance of that, Pratty, I'm going to buy all my mates a drink and I don't think I'll get much change, unlike you, Pratty. You would have change from a penny the amount of friends you've got."

Mr. Pratt marched off kicking a tin can in anger and shouting over his shoulder: "I'll see my day with you lot, just you wait and see." He was still muttering under his breath as he disappeared into the street dragging the poor dog and Freddy at the same time.

"Well, Tom," said Grandad, "it's time we had Sandy home."

I looked up at him and said, "You're not stopping behind are you Grandad? Remember the last time?"

Grandad chuckled. "I'm not likely to forget, lad. Your gran never spoke to me for a week; mind you that wasn't too bad either!"

As we walked off, the crowd shouted, "Three cheers for Tom and Sandy." I had never been so proud in all my life: it was something I will never forget.

In the next few weeks Sandy was winning nearly every race that he was entered in. It was approaching the Easter Handicap. Everyone aimed to have their dog ready to win the biggest race of the year: that was everyone's dream. There was thirty pounds to the winner and that was a lot of money.

"I'd like to win that, Grandad," I said with a gleam in my eye.

"Yes lad, so would a lot of other people," he replied. "Some people have being waiting all year for this race. First you have to qualify in four heats."

"What's that mean?" I asked with a puzzled look on my face.

"Well, you have to be placed in the first three in your heat to go into the next round. If you are placed in all of your heats you are through to the final. It won't be easy, you know, lad. Sandy will be giving a lot of start to some good dogs."

"We can do it, Grandad. Me and Sandy are a team." I sat in the doorway of Sandy's kennel stroking his head and he in reply licking my face.

Gran had just started hanging out the washing when Mr. Mason came strolling down the garden path. "Morning, young Tom, morning Bob, missis," he said. "Have you heard the news about Mr Chapman, the track handicapper."

"No, what news?" asked Grandad, taking his cap off and scratching his head.

"Well, by all accounts he was taken very ill at the track last night," said Mr. Mason.

"Oh dear," said Grandad. "That *is* bad news."

"It gets worse," said Mr. Mason, "Twister Thompson's got the job till Mr Chapman's better."

"Who's Twister Thompson, Grandad?" I asked.

" He's a man that a good joiner couldn't nail down straight," said Grandad throwing his cap onto the ground and then kicking it down the path and into his prize leeks.

There now, look what that no good Twister Thompson's made me do now. He's lower than a snake in the grass."

Grandad was just about to start with the curse words when Mr. Mason interrupted, "Why don't you just say what you think about the man, Bob, and get it off your chest."

"Don't you like this Twister then Grandad," I asked, as he bent over his leek trench to retrieve his cap.

"Like him, like him," Grandad was just about to start again when Gran gave him one of her looks; that's all it took for Grandad to stop shouting. Gran stood there with a look that would strike fear into any man that looked her in the face. "Just talking about football, woman," said Grandad.

"Football, my arse," said Gran, slamming the door behind her. It wasn't often Gran swore but she did slip the odd curse word in now and again.

Grandad retrieved his cap and sat down on the old wooden stool. "It's not only that the man's double bent," said Grandad, "he's a good friend of Pratt's. Mind you, he's about the only friend Pratt's got," said Grandad hurriedly.

I was puzzled. "What's wrong with that, Grandad, so what if this Twister is a friend of Mr. Pratt's, so what?"

Grandad looked at me and shrugged his shoulders, "You'll find out soon enough, Tom, when the marks for the handicap come out ."

Sure enough, when the race card was released Mr. Pratt's dog King, was receiving four yards in the handicap. "That's a downright disgrace," said Grandad, thumping his fist on the table top and making his pint pot of tea jump into the air. "At the most we should be giving him one yard. We can't possibly give him four."

"What do you think we should do, Grandad?" I asked, looking for an answer.

"We should withdraw him, Tom, that's what we should do," replied Grandad.

That was just the answer I didn't want to hear. "Is there any other choice, Grandad?"

"Well, you can let him take his chance, Tom, but there's an old saying in the dog game, 'no matter how good your dog is, you can never give a good dog too much start'. The decision has to be yours son. Sandy's your dog, but think on it for a while before you make up your mind."

That night I never closed my eyes wondering what to do? I was up bright and early next day, not being able to sleep, and off round the fields with Sandy. I bumped into Freddy Pratt, out with his dad's dog, King. "Yer wasting yer time, Tom Watson," he said with a smirk, "my dad says that the handicap is cut and dried."

"Your dad's just a cheat," I snapped, the anger boiling up inside me.

"And your grandad's lazy and so are his pitmen friends," he shouted as we stood toe to toe.

I was so mad. "Well, you can give your dad this from me, Pratty," and so saying, I punched him right on the nose with a mighty crack. "I never liked you, Freddy Pratt, and I feel a lot better now," I said, rubbing my bruised knuckles.

"I'll tell my dad about this, just you wait," he sniffled, a trickle of blood coming from his nose.

"And what'll he do — hire a boxer to beat me up? Go home and wipe your nose, Freddy Pratt, before I give you another crack."

Off he went, shoulders hunched, snivelling all the way down the lane. I knew that what I had done was wrong and that I shouldn't have done it ... but it didn't half make me feel good!

That's it, I thought to myself, I will run Sandy and we will win. I was more determined than ever not to let that snivelling little snot and his father run down Sandy and my grandad.

When I got home Grandad was waiting for me at the door; he looked angry, but I couldn't see any belt and that was a good sign, "I've just had Mr. Pratt at my door, young man."

'Oh shit, I thought to myself, I'm in big trouble now.'

"Well, I'm waiting for an explanation. What's all this about you and young Pratty?"

I explained what had happened and what Freddy Pratt had said. Grandad rubbed his chin and thought for a while. "If I had known what he had said to you lad, then I'd have done the same to his father." He looked at me and half smiled, "Did you bust his nose Tom, like his father said?

"I did, Grandad," I replied, not knowing if I was still in trouble. Grandad hesitated for a while. "You did the right thing, Tom, but don't tell your gran.

"Now have you decided yet about running Sandy?"

"Yes," I said, rubbing my chin like Grandad, "I'm going to run him!"

"Then we'll have to make the best of it," he laughed. "It's fresh eggs and sherry for Sandy, nothing but the best. He's going to need all the help he can get," said Grandad. "You've seen the card; in the first heat Sandy's giving fourteen yards start away." You could see Grandad starting to lose his temper the more he went on. "Twister Thompson has made the race as hard as he could to try and beat Sandy in the first heat," he raved, and was just about to thump the table when in walked Gran with one of her looks, and that was enough for Grandad.

There were two dogs in our heat that were known fighters. Twister was obviously trying to knock us out at the first chance he could. The next few days were hard work, keeping Sandy on his toes and working for Mr. Rewcastle at the same time. It was early nights in bed all that week and up at the crack of dawn with Sandy. I loved the early mornings, the birds singing, the sun shining, spring just around the corner.

All that week Sandy got his eggs and sherry as Grandad had promised, his coat was gleaming in the sunlight and he had never looked better. If he was to have a chance of winning the Easter Handicap he would have to be at his best.

The whole village seemed to be taking an interest in the race and lots of people were wishing me good luck.

Mrs. Moffitt from the fish shop stopped me when I was on my way home from school and if you were in a hurry to go anywhere the last person you wanted to bump into was Mrs. Moffitt, "Offf home, Tttom," she stuttered.

"Yes, Mrs. Moffitt, got to see to Sandy, keep him on his toes for the big race."

"Tttom Waaatsson, yyyouv'e got tu bbbeat that Mmmister Prrat if it's the laaast thing yyyou do. Hhhe's the most hhated man in the village." I was just going to say, I have to be off when she started again. "Tttell you a secret, Tttom, that boy of hhis, comes in tthe sshop eevery Mmonday night. Hhhe gggets tthe sssmallest ppportion of fffish and chips I cccan find, and sssometimes they're oooff the nnnight bbbefore." She couldn't talk for laughing, that was my chance to get away.

"Just what he deserves, Mrs. Moffitt, and I hope I can do the same to him on race night; let him have second (plaice), second place, Mrs. Moffitt." It took a little time for the penny to drop but when it did she started laughing again — she was still doubled up when I was half- way up the street.

It was the first day of the handicap and Sandy was in the first heat. I couldn't contain myself, I was that excited. I must have been to the toilet a dozen times in half- an- hour and the worst of it was, there was always someone in, Gran or Grandad, and our toilet was outside in the back yard, no bolt on, so you either had to have a long leg to hold against the door, or be a good whistler or singer.

I had neither of those attributes and the amount of times I was interrupted doesn't bear thinking about.

It was half six, time to set off for the track. Mr. Rewcastle was smack on time as he pipped the horn outside the house. I dashed down the garden to Sandy's kennel, being almost knocked over when I opened his door and having a right job trying to get his lead on. Sandy was as excited as I was. We piled into Mr. Rewcastle's van; me, Sandy and Grandad. Sandy lay straight down, but as soon as we went through the track gates he knew where he was and was soon up on his feet.

We jumped out of the van covered in sawdust as usual. I was brushing myself down when Mr. Mason came by: "By, that dog looks a picture, young Tom," said Mr. Mason, "and he'll have to if he's to have any chance of winning that race tonight the way Twister has handicapped him to get all sorts of trouble. He'll have to be at his best, and have a good bit of luck."

"He'll do it, Mr. Mason," I said, "I've had a quiet word with him."

"I quite believe you ,Tom," he smiled as he walked away towards the bookies.

Two sprints had gone by, and the loudspeaker was calling for the dogs for the first heat, that's what I had been waiting for all week. I walked Sandy round to the paddock and put on his Number One red racing jacket: that's what Sandy was to me ... number one. I was starting to get all excited and hoping I didn't need the toilet again.

Sandy just stood there, not a nerve in his body, "TAKE THE DOGS TO THE STARTING TRAPS FOR THE FIRST HEAT OF THE EASTER HANDICAP," came the announcement. Sandy pulled me onto the track and towards the starting traps. He was as ready as ever he was going to be and if he could avoid the fighters in the race he would have a great chance of winning. "PLACE THE DOGS INTO THE TRAPS, STARTER," was the announcement.

The hare was running, this was it. The traps went up, Sandy came out like a bullet. He had two dogs to pass when one of the fighters started to come over towards him. Sandy sensed it and found that little bit of extra speed to get him out of trouble. He'd missed one of the fighters but there was still one more to contend with and that was in front of him, number four, wearing the black jacket. Fighters weren't fussy which dog they fought with and this one was having a right go at the dog wearing the striped jacket, number six. Twister had done us a good turn. The fighter was more concerned with fighting the six dog and nearly forcing it off the track, which left the way clear for Sandy to come sailing through on the rails. The race was all over bar the shouting — we'd won the first heat. "FIRST, NUMBER ONE, FLASH — SECOND, NUMBER FIVE, INK POT - WINNING TIME - WINNING TIME 27-74." It was a great time.

Mr. Mason came over to congratulate me. "Well done, Tom, that's a cracking time. It'll take some beating tonight."

"We'll see in the next heat," Grandad said. "Pratty's dog is running." No matter how much we disliked Mr Pratt, King was a good dog.

The betting for Mr. Pratt's race was a nonsense; his dog King was thrown in and some of the bookmakers refused to take a bet. The men who had dogs in King's race were so annoyed at the way their dogs had been handicapped in the race, that they went upstairs to complain: "They'll get no change from that feller, Thompson," said Mr. Mason and sure enough he was right. Twister wouldn't even talk to them. He stood at the top of the steps, a short fat spiv type of a man with a pencil thin moustache. This was the first time I had seen him and what I saw I didn't like. He threatened to bar the men from the track if they weren't happy.

"And he'll do it," said Mr. Mason.

As the hare started to move you could hear Mr. Pratt's voice. "Now we'll see a real dog run!" Sure enough, Mr. Pratt's dog won easily. Then came the announcement. "King, the winner of the last

37

race has broken the track record in the winning time of 27-62. However, due to the four yards start it won't count."

"That's two yards faster than Sandy. You've got your work cut out now, Tom," said Grandad. He was right. He had to find two yards before the next round which was the following week.

I'd decided to take Sandy to the beach. He had never been to the beach before and as I climbed down the steep embankment Sandy slipped his lead and made straight for the sea. "Sandy!" I shouted, fearing the worst, but there was nothing to fear, Sandy was running in and out of the water like a child who had never seen the sea before. He would run into the sea and back out when the waves came towards him. We must have spent an hour or more on that beach and we did the same every day until it was the day before the race. That day we just went for a quiet walk in the woods. The birds were singing, the sun was shining: it was a glorious day.

While I was out I met Mr. Hindson who was out walking his whippets. "Grand morning, Tom," he said, "that was some race Sandy ran last week."

"It sure was, Mr. Hindson, but Mr. Pratt's dog will take all the beating," I sighed.

"It's not just Pratt's dog you've got to beat son, you'd best watch out for that no good cheat, Twister Thompson. He'd twist his own mother if he thought there was a few bob in it for him!"

"Grandad has had one or two choice words to say about him Mr Hindson, but nothing I can repeat."

"Well, lad, he used to be the handicapper at the old whippet track before it closed, just after the strike," he went on, "there was no photo finish then, it was the Judge's decision. On this occasion, my little Meg was running at the time, a grand bitch she was. She was up against a dog from the next village and beat it clear by half a length. I was just off to collect my money when Twister shouted from the Judges box 'First, number four, Samson — Second, number two, Meg.' Not a man at the track could believe the result." Mr. Hindson shook his head. "The crowd shouted and jeered, 'CHEAT

CHEAT' but it made no difference. Twister just stood there with a big grin on his face. We found out later," continued Mr. Hindson, "that it was his brother-in-law's dog that he had given the race to — that's the kind of man you're up against."

"He might try and cheat," I said "but he won't stop Sandy from running, and he's fitter now than he's ever been."

"Well, Tom, best of luck — you'll need it," he said as he walked off down the lane. I was more determined now than I had ever been.

Race day, the second heat. We had missed Mr. Pratt's dog, King, he was listed to run in another heat. Grandad said that Twister Thompson was keeping Sandy away from King just in case we beat him. We arrived at the track in plenty of time, Mr. Pratt was there talking to Twister, joking and laughing.

"I hope he's not laughing come final day, Grandad," I sighed.

"God knows,Tom, what they're laughing about, but you can bet the pair of them are up to no good."

It wasn't long before our race. I was giving Sandy a good rub down before he ran. He loved to be rubbed, his back would arch and his legs would stretch and then he'd give a little kick at the ground as if to say, I'm ready.

"TAKE THE DOGS TO THE TRAPS," was the announcement. Sandy was getting all excited. His tail was wagging, his eyes were bright, he looked really well. We walked over towards the traps; when I say walked over, it was more like being dragged. Sandy was so keen to get on with the race he nearly pulled me into the traps with him. The hare was winding up getting faster and faster, only 50 yards to go and getting closer by the second, whoosh the hare went past the traps and up went the lids. Sandy was out like his namesake "Flash" weaving his way through the other dogs like a piece of string, passing one dog then another. Going down to the beach had really sharpened him up. He won the race by four lengths. "FIRST, NUMBER ONE, FLASH — SECOND, NUMBER THREE, MONTY — WINNING TIME 27-62." This was the same time as the track record. I was over the moon. Fancy me, Tom Watson owning a dog with a track record.

"Wwwell dddone, Tttom," spluttered Mrs. Moffitt, who had been watching the race keenly. "I've had a fffew bbbob on him, Tttom. Call into the ssshop for some fffish and chips on your wwway home."

"Thanks ever so much, Mrs. Moffitt, I'll do that," I smiled.

Grandad was as pleased as punch. "Well," he said, "it looks like that training on the beach has done him the world of good, Tom lad."

"Yes and I'm keeping him on the beach until the final," I said with great determination.

The dogs were on parade for the next race. Freddy Pratt was leading his dad's dog, King, around the paddock and kept having a sly glance over to where Sandy and I were standing. You could bet your life that he was wondering if King was going to beat Sandy's time. "DOGS INTO THE TRAPS," crackled the speakers. Freddy hurriedly placed his dog into the trap.

The race was off and running. King, Mr. Pratt's dog, was slow coming out of the traps and got into a little bit of trouble but soon caught up with the other dogs coming through to win by two lengths clear. "FIRST, NUMBER ONE, KING — SECOND, NUMBER SIX, PITLAD — WINNING TIME 27-50." It was two yards faster than Sandy's time.

"It's just as well he's not off scratch," said Grandad, "or he'd be keeping the track record."

"Well, it looks like King's done it again," I sighed, "he must be a very good dog."

"Not that good," came a voice from behind me. It was Badger Baites. He was called Badger because of his white streak of hair.

"What do you mean, Mr. Baites?" I asked.

"Well lad, I clocked him doing the same time as your dog," he said.

"Badger will be right," said Mr. Mason, "he never misses a trial, or a race; a good judge is Badger."

"It's that Twister Thompson up to his old tricks again. He just doesn't want to let Sandy do a faster time than King," said Grandad, who was just about to take off his cap and kick it, but looking round had second thoughts.

"Maybe not," said Badger, "but that doesn't alter the time on my clock; your dog is just as fast as his Tom."

"In that case," said Grandad, "we've still got a fighting chance."

There were two rounds to go, then the final. I stuck to the same routine with Sandy — down to the beach every day and then through the woods on the day before the race.

It wasn't long before the next heat. We were not surprised when we got to the track to see that we were drawn in different heats to Mr. Pratt's dog. "We won't meet him until the final," said Grandad. "Twister Thompson will see to that; that's if we both qualify." A cold shiver ran down my back. I couldn't stand to think about us not getting through to the next round and Freddy Pratt getting there, but I gritted my teeth. I had every faith in Sandy.

"We'll get through, Grandad, don't you worry," I said, full of confidence.

"I'm not," chuckled Grandad, "you're doing enough worrying for the both of us."

We were not too surprised when both dogs qualified easy. The fourth and last round was left to go, then the final.

That week, Mr. Tucker, the school PE teacher, asked if I wanted to play football for the school. "We're a bit short, Tom," he said, "one or two are off sick."

"Who are we playing?" I asked.

"Smith's Grammar," he said. "Mind you, Tom, it's a bit since you played, you might not be as good as you were," he said laughing, "not since you've got that dog and missed a few games!"

"I was never that good, Sir," I laughed, "but I can stop them that think they are!"

"Right then, Tom, bring your kit. Kick off is tonight at 4.30."

I got there at the same time as the team from Smith's Grammar. Freddy Pratt was getting out of his father's car, all the other kids had either walked or caught the bus.

"You're not playing are you Watson?" Mr. Pratt sneered sarcastically.

"Yes," I snapped. "Most of our team are off sick, but it wouldn't take a good team to beat your lot anyway, especially with your Freddy playing."

"Cheeky little sod," he snapped, as he flounced off to the touch line.

We had just kicked off when Freddy came down the wing. He was just about to cross the ball when I tackled him. "FOUL," shouted Mr. Pratt.

"Good tackle," shouted Mr. Tucker, who was refereeing. Freddy got up and dusted himself off.

"That was a foul, Tom Watson," said Freddy, checking himself to make sure he hadn't got his knees dirty for his Dad's new car.

"It's nothing to what you're going to get," I laughed. "I'm going to kick your arse that hard, Pratty, you'll think you're wearing a hat."

Freddy took the warning and kept away from me for most of the game, until the last five minutes. We were winning 2-1. Pratty got the ball and sprinted towards the penalty box. I had to stop him, but it had to be fair. He was just about to shoot when I blocked his shot.

"Well done, Tom, great stop," said Mr. Tucker as he blew the whistle for full time. "You've saved the game, Tom."

I could see Mr. Pratt from the corner of my eye giving Freddy a good ticking off for not scoring in the last few seconds and I could hear him saying, "Anybody, bloody anybody, bar that Tom Watson, but it had to be him!" said Mr. Pratt, as he kicked Freddy up the backside and towards the car.

As tradition demanded, because we were the home team and the winners, we had to cheer the losers. "Three cheers for Smith's Grammar," we shouted, "Hip Hip Hooray."

"Three cheers for Stickdale," shouted their teacher, with very little response, but it didn't make a lot of difference; we knew Smith's

Grammar were bad losers and we couldn't care less!

"Can we go now, Mr. Tucker?" I asked.

"Yes, off you go for your tea, Tom, and well played."

I ran all the way home eager to see Sandy; the days were ticking past and it wouldn't be long before Sandy was racing again. "What's for tea, Gran?" I asked as I entered the house.

"Rabbit pie," she replied.

"Good, I'm starving. I could eat a buttered brick, I'm that hungry."

"What's brought this on lad?" she asked. "You've been off your food all week."

"Had too much on my mind, Gran, worrying about Sandy and the race and all. But I feel a lot better now, plus we've just beaten Smith's Grammar, Freddy Pratt's school, and that's given me a right appetite," and I got stuck into some jam and bread before the rabbit pie.

"You should beat them more often if that's what it does to you," said Gran as she filled my plate with rabbit pie and gravy.

The next few days were spent keeping Sandy fit and happy and also trying to earn a few bob shovelling people's loads of coal that were being delivered by the NCB to the miners, besides doing my job at Mr. Rewcastle's. It was hard work but worth it.

It was the day of the semi-final. If we qualified today we were through to the final. I was starting to get all excited again. Grandad sat in his chair, quite calm, smoking his pipe. A knock on the door broke the peace. It was Mr. Rewcastle. He was taking us to the track in his van. "Ready, Bob?" he asked.

"Ready as we'll ever be," said Grandad, knocking out his pipe on the fire.

"I'll get Sandy ready, Grandad," I said. Sandy could hardly wait to get out of his kennel, but I was starting to get wise to him. If he heard me coming down the garden path he would be ready to jump out of his kennel, so I started to sneak up on him so he couldn't hear me. I had the sneck off the door just lifted and ready to open when

Grandad shouted to get a move on. I was too late, the door burst open, knocking me flat onto my backside. When Sandy saw me he started jumping all over and licking my face.

"He looks well," said Mr. Rewcastle stroking Sandy's head after I'd finally got his lead on. "If he wins tonight," said Mr Rewcastle, "he can have some good mince from the shop. He's going to need something special if he gets through to the final."

"You won't be getting anything if you lot don't get a move on," reminded Gran, laughing.

As we approached the track Sandy stood up in the van. He knew where he was. "If he gets beat tonight, I'll stop going to the dogs," said Mr. Rewcastle as we jumped out of the van, "I've never seen him looking so well."

"Me neither," said Mr. Mason who was standing at the gate waiting for us, "and the good news is," he went on, "they are saying that Jimmy Chapman is feeling a lot better after his illness and will be starting back handicapping soon."

"That *is* good news," said Grandad, "I'm pleased he's feeling better. The sooner we have him back, the sooner we all get a fair crack of the whip. Twister Thompson is now't but a villain and the quicker he's gone the better."

It was Sandy's race next. The loudspeaker crackled: "NUMBER TWO IN THE NEXT RACE IS A NON-RUNNER . THE RESERVE WILL BE BLACK SATIN FROM SIX YARDS."

"He's got no chance," said Mr. Mason. "He got knocked out in the last round. He belongs to Chalky White and he couldn't keep himself right, never mind a dog!" As they went into the parade ring Mr. Mason was having a good look at Black Satin. He shook his head in disbelief and said, "That's not Black Satin!"

"What's he mean, Grandad?" I asked.

"He means lad, that it's not the dog it's supposed to be — it's a ringer."

"Well it can't run then," said Mr. Rewcastle.

"It can if Twister lets it," said Grandad.

44

Twister was looking at the dog's ear identification mark. The dog stood stone still. It was a good looking black dog, not like Chalky White's scruffy mutt.

"It's a ringer all right," said Mr. Mason. "Twister hardly looked at the dog and let him go."

"What are we going to do?" I wailed at Grandad.

"There's now't much we can do, lad," he shrugged. "Who are we going to complain to?"

"DOGS TO THE TRAPS," crackled the speakers.

"I'm off to take a look at the betting," said Grandad. "That'll tell us if it's a ringer or not."

Sure enough, there was a pile of money going on Black Satin. Sandy's price went right out to three to one.

"HARE'S RUNNING." The traps went up and Sandy was out like a rocket. Black Satin started well enough but didn't seem to be running the track too well. Sandy was catching him up and fast. Coming up to the last bend Black Satin moved off the rail. That was just enough for Sandy to get through. He forced his way through, neck and neck they were going into the straight.

"Come on, Sandy, you can do it," I screamed. He started to pull away, half-a-length, then a length, he was really flying. A big cheer went up when Sandy crossed the line in front. We'd done it, beaten the ringer...and Twister Thompson.

As I walked off the track and into the paddock Grandad and his pals were waiting. "Well done, Sandy, well done, Tom."

"I thought we were beat, Grandad," I said, with a sigh of relief.

"We might have been lad, if Black Satin had been round the track before! Some dogs like a look round a track first. It's obvious that dog has never seen this track before. He's what you call 'Track Licked' Tom, and it serves them right!"

"It's all worked out for the best," said Mr. Rewcastle. "We all got a good price for Sandy and there are some very disappointed strangers wandering around this track tonight," he chuckled.

The result was just coming over the loudspeaker. "FIRST,

NUMBER ONE, FLASH — SECOND, NUMBER TWO, BLACK SATIN — WINNING TIME 27-70." I couldn't have cared less about the time. We had done it. We were through to the final.

It was time for the next heat. Mr. Pratt's dog, King, was in it. "TAKE THE DOGS TO THE TRAPS," the announcer called. The betting was heavy on Mr. Pratt's dog.

"They're trying to get back the money they lost on Black Satin," said Mr. Mason. The hare was running, up went the traps and King came out very slow. He was in all sorts of trouble, bumping into dogs, getting knocked back.

"He can't win from there," said Grandad.

"He'll be lucky to qualify, never mind win, chipped in Mr. Mason." Sure enough, he could only manage fourth. Mr. Pratt's face was like thunder. He marched off to the Judge's box.

"What's up with him?" said Grandad.

"I don't know, but I don't like the look of it," said Mr. Mason.

"HOLD ALL BETS," was the announcement over the speaker "THE LAST RACE IS VOID DUE TO TRAP ONE HAVING A SLOW TRAP."

The crowd weren't happy, least of all the bookies. "CHEAT, CHEAT" was the cry.

"I knew there would be trouble as soon as Pratty went into the Judge's box," said Mr. Mason.

"What will happen now?" I asked.

"They'll have to run the race again, Tom," said Grandad, "either tonight, or next week."

The speakers crackled "THE VOID RACE WILL BE RUN AFTER THE LAST RACE TONIGHT IN ORDER TO LET THE DOGS RECOVER." There was a lot of unrest in the crowd and who could blame them.

"The quicker Twister goes the better," said Mr. Rewcastle, "I can't see him getting away with this for much longer."

"But he has," said Grandad, just as Mr. Pratt walked by.

"You're double bent, Pratty," snapped Mr. Mason, "I've seen

straighter cork screws than you are."

Mr. Pratt just smirked and said, "See you in the final."

The re-run was a formality. Mrs. Moffitt's dog, Nat, was lame, not that it had any chance in the first place. It was sheer luck that it had managed to reach the semi-final and the others couldn't run two races in such a short time. Mr. Pratt's dog won and was through to the final.

"What sort of tricks will he be up to for the final?" I asked.

"Never mind him, you just concentrate on keeping Sandy fit for the final. Pratty still has us to beat," said Grandad, with a confident grin.

All that week we were down on the beach. Sandy loved it running in and out of the water. Mr. Rewcastle was true to his word, he brought fresh meat every day. Sandy was being fed like a king. 'I hope that's not an omen, with Mr. Pratt's dog being called King!' I thought to myself. I could have brought the meat myself, but I think Mr Rewcastle liked to talk with Grandad.

"There's an old saying, Tom," said Grandad. "You only get out what you put in."

"He's right, lad," said a voice from nowhere. It was Mr. Mason strolling down the garden path. "Sandy looks a real picture, Tom. If he does get beat, it won't be because he's not fit, and it won't be down to Twister Thompson either!"

"How's that?" asked Grandad.

"Well, after Saturday night's performance, Mr. Chapman got to hear about it and he wasn't best pleased, so he's to be in charge for the final."

"That's the best news I've had for a long time," said Grandad, "at least it will be a fair run race."

"Tom Watson, if you're in that final then you'll need something decent to wear. Get your coat on, there's a jumble sale at the Church Hall." When Gran shouted, if you had any sense, you took notice.

"I am, Gran, coming Gran," I said and off we went.

On the way we ran into Mrs. Moffitt, "Ttterrible cccarry on the ooother nnnight," she stuttered. "I was rrrobbed: my little dog, Nat ssshould have bbbeen in ttthat fffinal," she said, her stutter getting worse the madder she got.

"Never mind, Mrs. Moffitt," I said. "Twister's been sacked and Mr. Chapman is to take over for the final."

"Ththat's gggood news, gggood llluck, Tttom."

"Thanks very much," said Gran, "but we'll have to hurry. We're off to the jumble sale at the Church Hall. I'm trying to get Tom fixed up with something for the final."

"Maybe I cccan hhhelp," said Mrs. Moffitt. "Our JJJimmy's got some ssstuff that's tttoo small for hhhim and after aaall, I've wwwon a few quid on Sssandy this past few wwweeks." We followed Mrs. Moffitt into her house. "Cccome on in," she said, "sssit down." It was a lovely house, all carpets and soft stuff. We were lucky to have mats and they were clippy mats that Gran had made herself. Mrs. Moffitt even had a bowl of fruit and there was no-one ill!

Mrs. Moffitt came down the stairs clutching a bundle of clothes. "Our JJJimmy's a bbbit bigger than TTTom, but I think that you'll find sssomethin' in this lllot to fffit him."

"I'm very grateful," said Gran, "do we owe you anything?"

"Nnno, not aaat all," said Mrs. Moffitt, "JJJust wwwin that fffinal."

"We'll do our best, Mrs. Moffitt, and thanks ever so much," I said as we walked off down the path.

"Yes, thanks again, Mrs. Moffitt," said Gran as I closed the gate and waved goodbye.

"You've done real well there, our Tom," said Gran, "you'll clean up a treat for the final night."

Sure enough, final night came and I looked a treat. Mr. Rewcastle came as usual to take us all to the track. "My word, young Tom, you do look smart tonight," he said, winking at Grandad. "You'd best squeeze in the front with your grandad and me. We can't be getting them new clothes all creased and messed up with sawdust."

"I'll sit in the back with Sandy like I always do, thanks just the same," I said, as I tried to clean some of the sawdust from the van floor.

"Come on, then," laughed Mr. Rewcastle. "Get cracking or we'll be late."

As we got to the track the butterflies started in my stomach. This was it, this was what I had been waiting for all week. The final of the Easter Handicap.

"Good luck to yer, Tom," shouted Mr. Murphy, who Mr. Pratt had sacked.

"Thanks, Mr. Murphy, we'll need it." I went through my usual routine with Sandy, rubbing him down with some sort of liniment that Grandad had given me. I'd asked him on several occasions what was in the bottle and where had it come from, but I always got the same answer, 'that's for me to know, and you to find out'.

That was the thing about the dog game, if you had something that would help your dog, it was a closely guarded secret and not for the ears of someone else. Grandad had always told me I would learn by my mistakes and he would teach me the rest and the Golden Rule in the dog game was you told nobody now't!

One more race before the final. Mrs. Moffitt's dog, Nat, was running and I think Mr.Chapman the handicapper had given her dog a big chance because of the way she was cheated in the semi's by Twister Thompson.

Mrs. Moffitt always liked to take her dog on herself, but on this occasion she had asked me, "Dddo me aaa fffavour, Tttom, take Nat on for mmme. I've ssspilt some hhhot fat on my fffoot, and it's gggoing mad." I didn't like leaving Sandy, but I felt obliged, after all, she had given me the clothes that I was wearing.

"It's all right, Tom," said Grandad, "I can look after Sandy, after all, I have had dogs before," he smirked looking down on me. I gave Sandy a pat on the head and handed him to Grandad, took Nat from Mrs. Moffitt and on to the track we went. Nat rubbed her nose against my hand, she was a nice little black bitch about 48lb in weight. I suppose that's why she was called Nat, on account of her size.

I placed Nat into the traps and she went in like a dream. 'Let's hope she comes out the same way,' I thought to myself. The hare flashed past and sure enough Nat was out like a shot. I could hear Mrs. Moffitt screaming at the top of her voice, "Cccome on mmmy bbbeauty, yyyou can dddo it," and sure enough Nat won by 2 lengths. I hurried from the track to be greeted by Mrs. Moffitt, "I knew ssshe cccould do it," she said, hugging the bitch and kissing me all over. I was glad when Grandad came over to rescue me.

"Come on, Tom, plenty of time for that when you get a bit older, then you won't be too keen to get away!"

"He's rrright, Tttom," said Mrs. Moffitt, "wwwait tttill you ggget older."

"CAN WE HAVE THE DOGS FOR THE GRAND FINAL," came the announcement, a timely intervention if ever there was one. Sandy was all excited, wagging his tail and barking.

We made our way over to the traps, Freddy Pratt, with his dad's dog, King, and him all dressed up in a brand new suit. "Hey, Watson," he shouted, "your gran been getting a club out, or has she been to the jumble sale as usual." He was referring to the clothes I had on. I was thinking of something to say back to him but my mind was blank, I couldn't think of anything but the final.

"DOGS IN THE TRAPS FOR THE EASTER HANDICAP AND GOOD LUCK TO ONE AND ALL." Sandy couldn't wait to get into the traps, it was all down to him now. "HARE'S RUNNING."

The only thing I could think of was could we give Mr. Pratt's dog, King, four yards. We were about to find out. The traps went up, both dogs came out well. King had soon taken the lead from the other dogs and we were a couple of lengths behind him. "Come on, Sandy," I yelled. "Come on." Coming round the last bend Sandy was catching him, but could we catch him before the winning line? Twenty yards to go and Sandy was putting everything into catching King. Two yards before the winning line and Sandy gave one massive last effort and got up on the line by a neck. I was jumping for joy and twirling Sandy's lead round in the air, but not for long. The crowd went silent. The silence was frightening and went on for ever. There was a small group of people just past the winning line. I ran as fast as I could.

Sandy was lying on the ground, motionless. "What's wrong with him?" I screamed, the tears pouring down my face.

"I'm so sorry, Tom," said Mr. Scott, the track vet, " I'm ... I'm afraid he's dead."

"NO, NO, NO," I sobbed, "he can't be. He's my Sandy. Make him better, Mr. Scott, make him better, please," I begged, tears falling from my chin. I was sitting on the track in a dream, my arms around Sandy, his head resting on my lap.

"He's had a heart attack, Tom. There's nothing I can do for him. I'm really sorry," said Mr. Scott, patting my head as he left the track..

A stunned silence in the air. Grandad was standing there with tears in his eyes.

"Take our Tom home, Mr. Rewcastle," he said, his voice shaking with emotion.

"No, no," I shouted, "I'm not leaving Sandy, you can't make me go."

"You can't help him now, Tom," said Grandad gently. "He died doing what he loved most...racing. We'll see to him, Tom, you get off home with Mr. Rewcastle." That night I never slept a wink, or I thought I hadn't, but I must have cried myself to sleep When I woke the next morning I looked out of my bedroom window at Sandy's kennel, the tears starting again. Grandad had brought Sandy home and buried him at the bottom of the garden. The grave, freshly dug, stood out amongst the flowers. On top of the grave was the Easter Cup.

I couldn't bring myself to set foot on a dog track for four years, after that.

CHAPTER THREE

Four years on and I had still not been anywhere near a dog track. I couldn't shake the memory from my mind. That fateful night when Sandy broke his heart winning the Easter Handicap for me, my heart was broken too.

I had filled the time in with football and athletics. I became a good athlete, representing the school for the 100 yards and the hop, step and jump. It was about the only thing that would get me to school. I loved sport, but hated all the other lessons. I'd be off more times than I'd be there.

When the time came to leave school and start work the pit was the only option open to me. Grandad had been to see Mr. Grainger, the Overman at the pit. I was to start work on the Monday after leaving school. Grandad took me up to see Mr. Grainger in his office. He was a nice enough man, with two fingers missing on his left hand. Grandad had told me all about them and I wasn't to stare.

"Now then, Tom," Mr. Grainger said, looking over his specs at me, "you want to be a pitman then?"

"Yes Mr. Grainger," I said, nervously.

"Can you read, lad?" he asked.

"Er... yes," I said a bit hesitantly

"You have to be able to read to go down the Pit," he went on. "You have to be able to read the signs telling you which way to go." How I wished that I'd gone to school more often and not just for the sport. Mr. Grainger passed me a sign to read. "What's that say?" I was lucky, I knew the sign.

"No Smoking," I said with a great sigh.

"Good lad," said Mr. Grainger. "Start on the screens on Monday." I thanked him and shook his hand as we bid him good-bye. On the way home I had to ask Grandad what the screens were, I hadn't got a clue.

"That's where the stones are sorted from the coal lad," he said. "Boring job, but it's a start."

On the Monday there were five of us starting, all doing the same job. It was hard and dirty. No pit baths for us, just the tin bath in front of the fire. Grandad used to pop out for a pint and Gran would nip in to a neighbour's for a cup of tea while I got bathed. It was nice in front of the fire, especially in the winter.

I had been working on the screens for some six months or so when it was time for my underground training. It was hard but interesting. I made lots of friends. You had to team up with someone to do a job, all part of the training. I'd been left with a lad called Billy Grant — no-one else wanted to partner Billy. He was a great big six footer with carrot-ginger hair and freckles. I think a lot of the lads were just scared of him. He was built like a brick outhouse, but we became great mates going out together after work.

But times weren't easy. Grandad had taken ill and had to lose work; there was one less wage coming in. I had to try and find some extra work, which wasn't going to be easy!

Mr. Chapman, the handicapper from the track called in to see how Grandad was doing. "Hello, Tom, how's it going?" he asked looking pleased to see me.

"Not good, Mr. Chapman," I explained, "with Grandad being ill it's hard to make ends meet."

"Well, there's a job at the track if you're interested."

"No thanks, Mr. Chapman," I said without hesitation, "I've not been to the track since I lost Sandy."

"I know, lad," he said, trying to cajole me into accepting the job, "but if I'd been knocked down crossing the road and got hurt, it wouldn't mean that I'd never cross a road again, would it?"

"You've got a point," I said, shaking my head, "but it's hard, you know."

"I know, but at least think about it," said Grandad.

"It will bring in a few bob," said Mr. Chapman, chivvying me along a bit.

"What's the job then?" I asked, just out of politeness really.

"We need a trapper," said Mr. Chapman. "Jim Slack is leaving to go in the army. It's thirty bob a meeting if you're interested."

"We could do with the money, Tom," said Gran quietly. I realised then that I had to put my feelings to one side; I couldn't turn down the chance to bring in the extra cash and it might stop Gran from looking so worried all the time ... and I owed Gran and Grandad a lot.

"OK, I'll do it," I said with a heavy heart.

"Great! Good lad, Tom," said Mr. Chapman rubbing his hands together. "Start Monday night," he said. He bid his farewells to Gran and Grandad after a warm cup of tea and was off down the lane whistling to himself. "See you Monday, Tom," he shouted as he went on his way.

Next day at work I was telling Billy all about my new job.

"Wow Tom, that's great. Extra cash in hand and a night out too. I've never been to a dog track," said Billy, looking like a kid that had never been to the seaside. He went on and on; in the end I gave in to him and told him he could come along with me. Billy couldn't wait for Monday. Mind you, there was never a chance I could have gone without him. I was a bit more apprehensive than I let on and I didn't know what to expect. All that weekend I was very unsettled, moping about the house, not eating my food and wondering if I was doing the right thing.

Race night, and Billy was knocking the door down. "Are you in there, Tom, you haven't changed your mind have you?"

"Not much chance of that Billy, you're an hour early and determined to get me to the track."

"Come on, then," said Billy, looking like a kid that was going for his first bike.

"OK, OK, there's plenty of time, we'll take a slow walk up," and off we went. It was a waste of time trying to walk slow with Billy; you'd think we were in a walking race. We arrived in plenty of time. As I looked up and saw the lights around the track it all came flooding back and I doubted whether I could go through with it. I stopped for a while to gather my thoughts. If I didn't go in there would be no money and if I did go in, how would I feel?

Billy made the decision for me by pushing me forward, "Come on, Tom," he said grabbing my arm, "you've got a job to do and you don't want to let anyone down, do you?" Billy was right.

It was strange walking through those gates again after so long. The first person I bumped into was Mr. Mason. "Is ... is that you Tom?" he said, looking pleased to see me.

"It is that, Mr. Mason," I said, smiling and shaking his hand.

"Well, there's a sight for sore eyes I can tell you. I'm right glad to see you, Tom, How's your grandad?"

"He's still quite poorly, Mr. Mason."

"Call me Frank, lad, you're old enough now. I'm sorry to hear that he's not well. Give him my regards."

"I will that, Mr. Mason, I mean Frank."

"Anyway," he asked, "what's brought you here?"

"The bus," laughed Billy, who had been quiet up to now.

"Take no notice of him Frank, Billy only gets out on a weekend, then the men in white suits come and throw nets over him and take him back to the funny farm."

"Huh, very funny," snapped Billy.

"Aye, about as funny as the bus," I laughed.

"Point taken," said Billy, shoving his hands in his pockets and looking a bit sheepish.

I turned back to Frank who was looking at the program, to explain that I had the job on the traps.

"Well good for you, lad. It won't take you long to see that nothing much has changed. Same old faces, same villains," said Frank. "Talk of the devil and he will appear," muttered Frank from the side of his mouth, as none other than Mr. Pratt came into view.

"Never thought I'd see you here again, Watson," Mr. Pratt snapped.

"Well, you'd better get used to it. I'm working the traps."

"I'd have thought you'd had enough with the last carry on: after all, it was only a dog," he sneered. I lurched forward to have a crack at him.

"Steady on, Tom," said Frank, taking a hold of me by the shoulders. "He wasn't worth it then and he's not worth it now." I shrugged my shoulders and turned my back. I couldn't bear to look at him.

Billy looked puzzled. "Is someone going to tell me what the hell all that was about?" he asked. Frank explained to Billy about Sandy and what had happened to him. When he'd finished it took him and me to hold Billy down, "I'll kill him, the useless, sarcastic old toad," said Billy, "I'll kill him." Pratty looked like an undertaker four years ago, now he looked like Joe the ghost.

"Don't worry about it, Billy," I said, "there's more than one way to skin a cat. I'll see my day with Mr. Pratt. My time will come." The meeting went off without a hitch. I'd done okay and it was nice to be back on a dog track. I hadn't realised just how much I'd missed it.

The next day at work Billy had my head in a spin. Dogs this, dogs that, he had caught the bug. "Why don't we get a dog, Tom," he kept saying, "can we, can we?"

"I don't want a dog, Billy," I told him over and over.

"But we could have fun, we could you know," he went on.

"It's not all fun, Billy," I snapped.

"I know, Tom, I'm sorry. I'd forgot about what you said last night about Sandy."

"It's okay, Billy, but just don't keep going on about getting a dog."

It was time for the Stickdale Feast, an occasion that everyone looked forward to, both young and old. The feast had been a tradition for over a century and was always accompanied by the fair and, as tradition demanded, the Council roasted an Ox for the townsfolk. Billy, as usual, was excited beyond his age.

"Are we going to the feast, Tom, are we?" said Billy like a big kid.

"Yes, if you want to Billy, but keep out of trouble."

"I will," he said with a glint in his eye. "I will, no problem," he repeated.

We were lucky that night at work and finished early. "What time tonight?" shouted Billy as he ran down the road.

"7.30 outside the bank," I shouted back as he disappeared into the distance.

When I arrived home Mrs. West was sitting in the front room talking with Gran, or I should say, talking at Gran. Mrs. West was the biggest gossip in Stickdale. She could talk anyone under the table. She was that bad her husband would volunteer to do a double shift just to avoid her nagging!

"How are you, Tom?" she asked.

"Oh, just fine, Mrs. West," I replied, trying hard to remember my manners. The problem now was how to get rid of her so that I could have a bath! She sat there for two hours. Gran dropped loads of hints, but she just kept sitting and talking; I don't think she missed anyone out in the village. I was getting desperate.

"I see the police were at the Morgan's when I came up the street," I said, to no-one in particular.

Mrs. West's eyes lit up at the thought of some new gossip "Go on," she said.

"Well, someone was saying that Mrs. Morgan had hit Mr. Morgan with the frying pan."

"Is it serious?" Mrs. West asked.

"It could be," I said, desperately trying not to laugh out loud, "they were putting handcuffs on Mrs. Morgan ... er ... so they say." I didn't get a chance to go any further. Mrs. West was up and out of the chair like a whippet.

"Tom Watson!" said Gran. "That was cruel." Gran was smiling

all over her face.

"Well, I thought she was in for the night and I need to get ready," I said, "as it is I've only half-an-hour to get bathed and get out of here. Come on, Gran, pop next door for ten minutes won't you?"

"All right, Tom, all right, I'm going," sighed Gran as she wrapped her shawl around her shoulders. "She must be someone special," she smiled.

"Matter of fact, it's only Billy, but it won't be anyone if I don't get my skates on."

I was ten minutes late meeting Billy. "What kept you, Tom, I had almost given up on you?"

"It's a long story, Billy, I'll tell you later and if we want a sandwich from that Ox we'd best get a move on."

We started running down the market place when someone shouted from behind. It was Tubby Bell. "Wait for me, lads," he shouted.

I was running backwards as he caught us up and as I turned around I bumped straight into someone and knocked them flying. "I'm ... I'm sorry Missis," I said, stooping to pick her up and dust her down at the same time.

"What do you mean, Missis," she yelled, with a volley of words and a tongue that would shame a viper. "I'm only fifteen," she screamed as she knocked my hands away and dusted herself down.

"I'm really sorry, Miss," I said sheepishly.

"Well...," she half laughed, "it's just as well you didn't call me Missis again or I'd have slapped you one."

I had never bothered about girls much, but there was something about this one, her spirit, her strength of character and her good looks. It must have been love at first sight; it was for me, anyway.

"What's your name?" I asked quickly, before she had the chance to walk away.

"Jill. Why?"

"Well, Jill, to make up for the inconvenience I've caused you, I'll treat you to the fair if you like?"

She looked at me through her eyelashes and gave a cheeky grin,

"What's your name, then?"

"Tom," I replied quickly.

"Well, Tom, by the time tonight's over, you'll regret saying that you'd treat me to the fair. Come on, then," she said, pulling at my coat.

We went on every ride at the fair we could, some twice, and Jill was right. By the end of the night I was as sick as a dog. Billy had long disappeared with one of Jill's mates, a tiny, pretty thing called Rose. They looked a bit odd, her so small and petite and Billy, six foot two and ginger with it. As they passed by later, Billy shouted, "Having a good time, Tom?" He smirked as he looked at the gaunt look on my face.

"Oh yes," I replied, "I always go this shade of green when I'm having a good time."

Rose nudged Jill and looked at her watch, "It's time we were off home, Jill."

"Where's home?" asked Billy.

"Mordale, why?"

"That's just the next village to us, we'll walk you home, won't we Tom."

I nodded in agreement, I was so pleased that he had said walk, I don't think I could have got on a bus. I'd have been sick on anything that moved. After seeing the girls safely home, we made a date for the following week. Jill and I saw each other as often as we could. Billy was still seeing Rose. It was sometimes difficult to make arrangements though. Billy and I had finished our training and were now working shifts. Then, there was my extra job at the track. I had avoided telling Jill about the dogs because I had no idea how she would feel. Some people weren't too keen on dog racing and I didn't want to take the chance. I need not have worried, fate was on my side in the shape of Billy. He couldn't keep a secret if you stitched his lips together and he had told Rose all about the dogs. Of course, Rose, being Jill's best friend, had to mention it and as expected both Jill and Rose turned up at the next meeting.

"It's the first time we've been to the dogs," said Jill, looking all excited.

"Well, you know what they say about first timers."

"What's that, then?" she asked, her eyes sparkling.

"You always win the first time, just to get you to come back again."

We were having a smashing time, until an argument started on the track. Surprise, surprise, Mr. Pratt was having a go at someone. We turned round to see what was going on and saw him having a right set to with old Mr. Storey.

"What's his problem?" asked Billy.

"I've not a clue," I said, "but I'm sure that sooner or later we'll find out!"

Billy was watching closely. "Is...is that the bloke who had a go at you, Tom, when you first started on the traps?" he asked, never taking his eyes of Pratty.

"That's him, thinks that because he has lots of money he can insult anyone he likes."

"I'll give him a crack, that'll keep him good and quiet," said Billy, inching forward.

"Much as I'd like to see that Billy, he's not worth it," I sighed.

The argument went on between Mr. Pratt and Mr. Storey, "My dog's the best trapper in the country," Mr. Pratt was bragging.

"My Daisy's the best trapper on this track," argued Mr. Storey, who sounded as if he was a bit the worse for the drink.

I turned to Billy over my shoulder and said, "I just hope old Storey doesn't start betting with Pratty." No sooner the thought than the deed. Before anyone knew it the pair of them had struck a bet. A ten pound match over 100 yards and Mr. Storey's dog had more chance of knitting a jumper than beating Pratty's dog in a dash. I had to think of something to help old Mr. Storey and put Pratty in his place at the same time, but what?

They walked off to the Judge's box to arrange the race and to draw for traps. There was an announcement over the loud speakers.

"LADIES AND GENTLEMEN — CAN I HAVE YOUR ATTENTION PLEASE. NEXT SATURDAY, THERE WILL BE A MATCH RACE BETWEEN MR. STOREY'S DOG, DAISY, AND MR. PRATT'S DOG, MINTY. — THE RACE WILL BE OVER 100 YARDS — DON'T MISS IT."

By this time Mrs. Storey was doing her nut. "Now you've gone and done it, you old fool," she shouted at Mr. Storey. "You and the demon drink, I always said it would get you into trouble," she went on. " How on earth are we going to find ten pounds, we'd be lucky to scrape up ten bob in a month of Sundays," she wailed and from past experience I knew that Mr. Pratt would want his pound of flesh, no matter what!

I interrupted when Mrs. Storey stopped for breath and enquired as to what trap they had drawn, "What trap 'ave we drawn?" said Mr. Storey to his wife, his words starting to slur.

"Trap one, Tom," said Mrs. Storey. "Pratty's drawn three," she said over her shoulder as she herded Mr. Storey off home.

"That man is downright awful," said Jill, who by this time was close to tears. "You can't let him win, Tom. You have to do something, do you hear me?" she snapped.

"What can I do?" I asked

"Well, you'd best think of something, Tom Watson, or you and me are finished!"

"That goes for me, too," said Rose and the pair turned on their heels and left the track.

Billy looked distressed. "You've got to do something now, Tom."

"I know Billy, but what? What are we going to do?" I said, as much to myself as to Billy. Scratching my head as Billy watched the girls disappear into the night, I sighed. 'I just don't know,' I muttered, 'I just don't know.'

"Well you're the dog man," said Billy, "think about it!"

All weekend I sat in, getting under Gran's feet. I was racking my brains to try and come up with something to help Mr. Storey and to make sure that I got to see Jill again. Gran was getting fed up with me being in the house all the time. "What's up, lad, you and Jill been fighting and rowing?" she asked.

"No, Gran," I sighed.

"Well I can't be doing with you sitting around doing nothing when I've work to do. Now lift your feet while I mop this lino and mind you don't slip when you walk on it."

Slip! That was it! It was as if someone had lit a candle in my head. I knew how Daisy might beat Mr. Pratt's dog. I jumped up from the chair nearly slipping on the lino as Gran had warned. "Gran, I could kiss you to bits," I laughed as I proceeded to fasten my boot laces.

"If I'd known that mopping the lino was going to put a smile back on your face I'd have done it two days ago. Now be off with you, Tom Watson before you're wearing this mop for a hat."

Next day at work I explained my plan to Billy.

"Will it work, Tom?" Billy asked, eager to hear more.

"It has to Billy, it just has to," I said, "if it doesn't, no more Jill or Rose. Plus, Mr. Storey hasn't got two ha'pennies to rub together, and, of course, getting even with Pratty will be nice — I owe him from way back."

The night before the race me and Billy cut out a piece of old lino the same size as the trap bottom and off we went to the track. Making sure there was no-one in sight we placed the lino in the bottom of trap three, Pratty's trap, and covered it with some dry, soft sand. All we had to do was make sure that the traps stayed the way that we had left them. We scattered sand in the bottom of both traps to make sure there was no difference between them.

Billy was starting to get excited. "Here, Tom, we could have two bites at the cherry with a bit of luck — win a few bob and get even with that Pratt bloke."

"We could do with a bit of luck, Billy," I said, "especially with Grandad no better."

"We'll pool our money," said Billy, "How much have you got?" he asked.

"Not much," I shrugged, "I gave most of mine to Gran on pay day."

Billy shook his head. "Never mind, I've got a bit of scrap metal to weigh in, that'll give us a few bob for a bet." Next day Billy called in. "Hey, Tom, I've done really well out of that scrap," he shouted.

"How much?" I asked, expecting him to say twenty-five bob or so.

"Seven pound and four shillings," he said, smiling.

"How much? I didn't think you had that much scrap, where the hell did that lot come from?"

Billy started to blush, "Er ... here and there," he said, sheepishly.

"Come on, Billy, where did the scrap come from?" I asked. Billy's face was as red as a letter box and him with that mop of ginger hair looked a right picture,

"Well," Billy went on, "Dapper Pringle, the scrap man, has been cheating me and all the other lads that take scrap to him to weigh in for years and ..."

I prompted Billy, "Come on, out with it."

"... well I sort of ...." Billy was finding it hard to find the right words.

"Come on Billy, what have you been up to?"

"... I nicked his own scrap and sold it back to him," he said quickly.

"That's wrong, Billy," I said, half wanting to laugh.

"No more wrong than what you'll do at the track tonight," he said in a huff.

Billy was right, there was no difference, but what the hell, both Pratty and Dapper weren't the very best of people, especially that no good Mr. Pratt.

"OK, Billy, point taken," I said, as Billy put that big daft grin back on his face.

"Do you think Jill and Rose will turn up?" said Billy, changing the subject.

"I hope so, Billy." I'd only known Jill a short time but my gut feeling was that she'd like to think Pratty would get what he deserved, and by some miracle, or mishap, Mr. Storey's dog would win.

We arrived at the track just that little bit early, to make sure that everything was all in order. The traps had not been touched, the sand in the bottom was as I'd left it, the problem was Mr. Storey's dog. Was it good enough, even with the help I was giving it from the traps? The match race was the first race on the card and the whole village had turned out to see it.

Mr. Mason was just coming through the gates at the same time as Jill and Rose. I walked towards them, fingers crossed they would speak. Jill and Rose looked the other way, so I pretended that I hadn't seen them. "Hello, Mr. Mason, nice night for it," I said, risking a glance in Jill's direction.

"A nice night it is, Tom. I've come to see that match race, but I can't see old Storey's dog doing much against Pratty's."

"Well," I said, rubbing my chin. "You never know what might happen. This is dog racing, and you should know more than most of us, that there are no certainties in this game."

"Do you know something I don't, Tom?"

"Not really, Mr ... I mean Frank, but you know when you have one of those feelings, you know the feeling, Frank, when things don't seem to add up!"

Mr. Mason thought about this for a moment, he'd been in the dog game a long time and knew not to ask too many questions, "If you fancy anything later on, Tom, give me a shout."

I had never forgotten the good turns Mr. Mason had done for me and he had sold me Sandy. He was just about to walk away, when I pulled him to one side.

"I would be obliged if you could do me a favour," I asked. "When you go to the bookies, put me ten pounds on Mr. Storey's dog, will you?" Frank looked surprised. I continued, "If I let Billy do it, somebody might say something and if they say something to Billy that they shouldn't, they might regret it."

Mr. Mason knew there was something up, but had the good sense not to ask. "I'll do my best, lad. The bookies were shouting 10-1 for Old Storey's dog that on paper has no chance, and 1-10 on for Pratty's dog," and off he went looking to place the bets.

"DOGS IN THE TRAPS — DOGS IN THE TRAPS," crackled the announcement. The hare was running. Mr. Storey's dog flew out of the traps like it had wings. On the other hand, Mr. Pratt's dog looked like it was on skates. It couldn't get started, the lino and sand had done their job and by the time Minty, Mr. Pratt's dog, had got himself together, it was too late. Quick as a flash, Billy grabbed the lino from the trap that Mr. Pratt's dog was in, rolled it up tight and hid it under his coat, then disappeared off to a quiet corner of the track and stuffed it up an old drainpipe.

By the time Billy got back all hell had broken loose. Mr. Pratt had been up to the Judge's box complaining about a slow trap. "You're not whingeing again, are you, Pratty?" said Mr. Mason.

"There is no way on earth that Old Storey's dog could beat mine," snapped Mr. Pratt.

"It just did," shouted someone out of the crowd. By this time Mr. Chapman, the handicapper, had come down from the Judge's box.

"There is only one way to settle this. Come on," he snapped, everyone coming to attention at the tone in his voice. I started to get a lump in my throat. 'Oh God, please don't let him run the race again,' I prayed to myself.

"Yes," he snapped again, "the only way to settle this is to try the traps again." I could only just manage to stifle the huge sigh of relief that coursed through my body.

"That's no problem, Mr. Chapman," I said helpfully, "I'll go and set the traps up now, shall I?"

"Will that satisfy you, Mr. Pratt?" Mr. Chapman asked.

"I suppose it will have to," he said grudgingly.

I set the traps up and released them. They both came up at the same time, much to Mr. Pratt's disappointment. Mr. Chapman looked happy and said, "I'm quite satisfied that the traps are fine. What about you, Mr. Pratt?"

"There is still no way on earth that that dog could beat my dog in a fair run race." By this time he was steaming. He stood there scratching his head and eyeing me up and down as I stood there, a slight smirk on my face. He knew that something was amiss, but he couldn't for the life of him work out how he had been stitched up. He turned on his heel and stormed out of the stadium gate, kicking it on the way out. I just stood there as if butter wouldn't melt.

"There goes one very unhappy man," said Billy who by this time was almost crying with laughter.

Mr. and Mrs. Storey couldn't believe their luck. "I told you my Daisy was the best. I told you she could beat that mutt of Pratty's," Mr. Storey said, his chest puffed out like a banty cock.

"Yes, Mr. Storey, you were right, all along," I agreed. "That's a fine animal you've got there. But a word of warning. I wouldn't go betting anyone else if I were you."

"Don't you worry yourself about that, Tom. I'll keep him right," said Mrs. Storey. At least they were happy and a bit richer as well. Little did I know that Mrs. Storey had pawned her wedding and engagement ring to raise the £10. I may have cheated Mr. Pratt, but it didn't half feel good, and was well worth the effort.

Out of the corner of my eye I spotted Jill and Rose coming over. "I knew you would think of something, Tom," said Jill, her eyes bright as diamonds as she gave me a big kiss right on the lips.

Billy puckered up next to me, "Don't I get one," he laughed.

"You'd best ask Rose. You're not getting one from me," said Jill."

"Why not?" asked Billy, holding his heart and pretending to be hurt.

"Because you don't work the traps, not that Tom has done anything wrong," she added quickly, giving me a sly wink at the same time.

"Never mind, Billy," came a voice from behind us, "I'll give you a kiss." It was Mrs. Storey and she had no teeth in.

Billy screamed, "No thanks, Mrs. Storey, I was only joking."

"So was I, you big, daft lump," she said, laughing till tears rolled down her cheeks.

We had a real good night that night. I had Jill back and Mr. Mason put us on to another couple of winners. All in all, Billy and I won seventy pounds each. I gave Jill ten pounds to spend on herself. She argued that she couldn't accept that much, but I insisted. I had won a few bob and I wanted her to enjoy it. I loved winning on the dogs, but I got just as much pleasure giving it to the ones I loved.

I saw Jill home and went straight to the fish and chip shop.

"Tttell me you dddid wwwell tonight, Tttom," said Mrs. Moffitt, smiling at me over the counter, her cheeks red as usual.

"Not too bad, Mrs. Moffitt. Mr. Storey's dog beat Mr. Pratt's dog in a match, that's all."

"Tom Watson, I'vv'e gggot more channnce of ssstopping ssstuttering, than Mr. Storey's dddog hhhas of beating Pppratty's."

She was a wise old lady and knew that something had gone on, but I had no intention of letting her badger any information from me that might get back to the track, let alone to Gran and Grandad. I quickly changed the subject and I think Mrs. Moffitt got the message, but there was a much bigger problem to overcome — how to stop Mrs. Moffitt covering the fish and chips with salt. She started to parcel them up and before I could get a word in, her hand was shaking the salt as she was stuttering. "PLENTY ON," Mrs. Moffitt, "PLENTY ON," but it was too late, once again my fish and chips looked like a scene from a Movie: MOUNT EVEREST. I thanked Mrs. Moffitt and bid her good night.

"Gggive mmmy rrregards to your gggran and gggranddad," she stuttered, "and ooonce aaagain, nnnice one on Pppratty," she shouted, with a sly wink as I left the shop.

When I entered the house it was nice to see Grandad was downstairs. "You look a lot better, Grandad," I said pulling off my coat and putting down the fish and chips on the table.

"I feel quite a bit better, lad," he replied

"Well enough to manage a fish supper, I hope. Mrs Moffitt has sent two fish lots, and she sends her regards to you and Gran."

"That's very good of her," said Gran. "She's always been a good woman, Mrs. Moffitt. It's just a shame about that stutter."

"Oh," I said, "by the way, I've had a bit of luck tonight — me and Billy have won a few quid."

"Good for you, son," said Gran, ruffling the top of my head. Sometimes I think she still thought I was about ten. "It's about time you had a bit of luck, what with you working two jobs and all," she said, sitting herself down with her fish and chips still in the paper and placing them on her knee beside the fire. "I don't think I'll need any salt on, Tom, will I?" she grinned.

"Not really, Gran, no," I replied, shaking as much salt from my fish and chips as possible and it was nice to see Grandad back on his feet and getting stuck into his fish supper.

We had all enjoyed our suppers and I thought it was about time I sprang a little surprise on Gran. "You know that coat you've been wanting in Doggart's Store, Gran?"

"Yes, lad" she sighed, "a bit of a pipe dream though at the minute."

"Well, not any more, you can go down in the morning and get it and while you're about it, get something warm for Grandad as well. And I don't mean a hot pie from the pork shop neither." Gran just sat there, open mouthed.

"But ... but we can't afford it, Tom," she went on. I handed Gran forty pounds. Her eyes nearly popped out of her head.

"Where on earth has all that money come from, Tom? You can't have won that much. Where has it come from?" she demanded.

"We did win it, Gran," I assured her. "Me and Billy put our money together and backed Mr. Storey's dog."

"Are you sure? You haven't done owt wrong, have you?" she went on.

"No, honest, Gran, ask Mr. Mason, he put the bet on for us."

"Well as long as you got it honestly, that's okay." I stood there fingers crossed like I did when I was a ten year old. "Well I'm really glad, Tom. I can pay off a few bills now and I hope you and Jill have made it up too!" It was nice to see both Gran and Grandad happy. I would say a good night was had by all, except one!

The next day at work, Billy was jumping through hoops, he was so happy. He had some great news, his dad had managed to get a swap for his house with Mr. Kidson down the road from Gran; he was going to move into our street. I didn't know if that was good or bad!

As well as moving nearer to me, it also meant that he wouldn't be late for work every day. We only had two fields to cross to get to work and even if Billy did oversleep, he didn't have far to go.

On the day of the move we were wandering home from work. Billy had to be reminded that he was moving that day, he was setting off in the wrong direction, big thick lump that he was. In the distance we could see Dapper Pringle with Billy's mam's furniture stacked onto his horse and cart.

"Hurry up, Tom," said Billy, setting off to run the rest of the way and shouting up the road to Dapper, "We'll give you a hand to unload, hang on five minutes." That suited Dapper, who was not a man who revelled in hard work.

The whole street was out, most of them just being nosy, looking to see who was moving in and what sort of furniture they had. Dapper started the unloading and everyone lent a hand in one way or another, all except Mr. Morris. A dose of Epsom salts couldn't work him. I can remember one time Mrs. Morris shouting to him to dig the garden. "Dig the garden," shouted his mother-in-law "I think he'd rather pick up a rattlesnake than pick up a shovel, the lazy good for nothing," she said, shaking her head in disgust as she went indoors.

Mr. Morris just sat there, the original Andy Cap, not moving a muscle until everything was off the cart. "I'd have given you a hand lads, but me back's playing up, you know." Just then Mrs. Morris appeared and had heard Mr. Morris complaining about his back.

"The only thing wrong with your back is you can't get it off the bloody bed, but let me tell you this, Alf Morris," and by this time she was steaming, "the day you die, I'm going to have you cremated and put your ashes in an egg timer. If you won't work when you're alive, you'll bloody well work when you're dead," and with that she gave him a swift kick up the backside and into the house.

The whole street was in an uproar, laughing till they cried. Billy's mam and dad must have thought they had come to a right old street.

"Don't worry," said Gran to Billy's mam, "it's a good street to live in really. Everyone helps each other if need be, apart from some," glancing a look to Mr. Morris's house.

Billy and his family settled in well over the next few weeks, not a problem to be had, then one day a few weeks after the move, Billy came running into our yard, hammering on the back door like the devil was chasing him.

"What's up," I asked, "is your house on fire?"

"No, it's worse than that, Tom," he panted. "Our ...our Jack Russell, Tadger, has killed next door's rabbit!" Billy was in a right panic.

"How do you know that, Billy?" I asked, trying to calm him down and let him catch his breath.

"Because he brought it into the bloody house, that's how!" he went on. "I've had a look at the hutch and the door's wide open."

"So what are you going to do?" I said with a grin on my face, Billy pacing up and down as if he'd robbed a bank.

"It's now't to laugh at Tom, I'm in deep shi ... trouble," Billy was about to swear but stopping in mid verse in case Gran was knocking about.

"Did the Shipley's see your dog kill the rabbit?"

"No, I don't think so, I don't think there's anyone in."

"Well, there's your answer."

"What?" said Billy looking at me as if I was daft.

"Get rid of the dead rabbit and get yourself up to Dapper's; he keeps rabbits, he's bound to have one that looks like theirs. Buy one from him and stick it in the hutch before they come back; no one will ever know the difference."

"Good thinking, Tom," said Billy and off he went like a shot.

Later that day there was a knock on the back door. It was Billy once again. "You won't believe this, Tom," said Billy. "Mr. Shipley's just been round."

"Has he found out?" I asked. "No way, but you'll never guess," said Billy, catching his breath.

"Come on then, what won't I guess," I asked.

"Well, it seems that Mr. Shipley got up earlier than usual this morning to go and visit his sister," Billy went on. "Before he left he went out to feed the rabbit, except the rabbit was dead in the hutch, so he buried it at the bottom of the garden; our Tadger must have been watching him. When he got back he came straight around to see me. 'Billy' he shouted, 'have you seen anyone in my garden lad.' I thought 'shit, he's found out,' so I told him no, never seen a soul in his garden and before he could say anything else, I told him the dog had been in all day."

"That wouldn't make him suspicious Billy, would it? "

"No, no way, Tom," Billy replied, "I asked Mr. Shipley why he wanted to know if anyone had been in his garden, trying not to look too guilty and had there been any trouble? 'Trouble is lad,' said Mr. Shipley, 'that the rabbit died this morning and I buried it at the bottom of the garden and now the bloody thing is back in its hutch and running round as if it's got a new lease of life!' "

Me and Billy couldn't stop laughing, I wish I could have seen Mr. Shipley's face when he saw that rabbit as large as life in its hutch. An hour later we were still laughing, after all the trouble Billy had gone through and all for nothing.

CHAPTER FOUR

It was spring time, the birds were singing and it was a beautiful morning. Billy and I had just finished the night-shift; it was six-o-clock in the morning and you could smell the fresh air. We bumped into Mr. Soppit with his greyhound, Monty, as we walked home.

"Grand morning, Tom, Billy," said Mr. Soppit, stopping to have a chat.

"Smashing day," we replied together. I leant over to rub Monty's ears; he was a bonny brindle dog with just half a tail, an accident at the traps ... not when I was trapper I hasten to add.

"It's about time you were getting another dog, Tom," said Mr. Soppit.

"I'm not interested, Mr. Soppit, not since Sandy died."

"You know you can't go on brooding forever, Tom. There's another Sandy out there waiting for a good home, same as he was," said Mr. Soppit, glancing at his pocket watch.

"That might well be the case Mr. Soppit, but there will never be another Sandy."

"You never know, Tom, you just never know," he said, making his way off over the fields.

I knew what was coming next, I could have bet money on it. "Let's get a dog, Tom, let's, let's." Billy was like a kid when he wanted his own way.

"I've told you before, Billy, I don't want a dog, so let the matter drop. OK."

"OK, Tom, OK," grumbled Billy mouthing some select curse words under his breath.

All that week Billy went on and on and on about a dog. He was driving me crazy. If it wasn't for the fact he was so big I would have cracked him one by now, but I wasn't that keen on hospital food.

"We can't afford a dog, Billy, they cost too much to keep and if you can't keep a dog right, don't keep a dog at all. My grandad told me that and he's right."

"We'll work overtime from tomorrow then," said Billy, adamant that we would have a dog, and he wasn't prepared to give in that easy.

Billy was true to his word. We worked overtime all that week, but the problem was the following week. We were on first shift and that meant a four in the morning start. That weekend I spent as much time as I could with Jill. I explained to her what was happening and why we were working so much overtime and, to my surprise, she was all for it.

So there I was, Monday morning, half-past-three, knocking hell out of Billy's back door. There was no response. Billy had overslept again. I shouted and shouted until he woke, then popped his head out of the window to confirm he was up. As usual in that shift I set off without him. I'd only been gone five minutes when I heard a familiar sound, "Wait for me, Tom, wait up, Tom." This was the same procedure each morning without fail. As I turned, all I could see was the familiar figure of Billy in the soft mist, then, all of a sudden nothing! "Oh shit, ouch, that hurt." Billy had tripped over something. When he eventually caught up he was swearing like a trooper. "I nearly broke my bleeding neck on that bloody sleeper," he snapped, rubbing his knees and elbows, and trying to fasten his boots at the same time.

"Well," I said, "if you weren't so late on a morning and in so much of a hurry, you'd be able to watch where you were going."

"You know I'm no good at getting out of bed on a morning, Tom, specially this early," Billy moaned.

"Well then, don't complain when you fall down then."

Billy may have taken some starting on a morning but once he

was at work he worked like a horse and he was just as strong. We had been working overtime for a good few weeks and had saved twenty pounds. "When are we going to get a dog, Tom, when?" said Billy.

"When the time is right and not until," I replied.

"I know where there's a good dog for sale," he said, a big smile on his face.

"Oh aye, and where would that be?" I asked.

"Jimmy Horton's got it."

"Not that black dog, Pit Lad?"

"Yeah, that's it," Billy shouted, getting all excited.

"That dog couldn't run a message, never mind win a race," I laughed.

Billy's chin hit the floor. "Well I was told it's a good dog," he snapped.

"And who told you that, Billy?"

"Jim Horton's brother," Billy replied.

"Say no more, Billy, say no more. You've got a lot to learn about the dog game and the first thing is, don't believe everything that people tell you, especially a dog man! So much for your judgement. It's just as well you're not the one buying the dog, and it's no good going in the huff, Billy." That was one thing I'd learnt about Billy, he was like a big kid. If he couldn't get his own way, he'd sulk.

"I'm not in the huff," he grunted, "I'm going for me dinner," and off he went, slamming the door behind him.

The following day it was work as usual. First shift, half-past-three and there I was again, hammering merry hell out of Billy's back door and not a sound from inside to be heard. I set off without him as usual with the mist floating about two feet above the ground, a bit thicker than usual. I'd been gone a couple of minutes when I heard the usual, "Wait up Tom, wait for me," and then the crash and swearing as Billy tripped over the same sleeper that he had tripped over every morning of every week we were on first shift.

"I'm going to shift that bloody thing before I kill myself," Billy ranted, stooping to pick up the sleeper; it must have weighed at least ten stone.

"I wouldn't do that, Billy," I shouted. "I think it's a marker for the old pit shaft it's next to."

"It is," said Billy, "but the shaft's fenced off and everyone knows where the shaft is anyway," he went on.

"Do what you like, Billy, anything to keep you happy." Billy picked up the sleeper and threw it down the shaft like a match stick. You could hear it bumping from side to side. Billy turned to walk away from it and stopped suddenly!

"What's that noise, Tom, can you hear it?" I stopped to listen. There was a 'Swish, swish, swish' noise going along in the grass, getting faster and faster, closer and closer. "What is it?" Billy asked again, looking a bit scared into the bargain. I was starting to feel a bit nervous myself. We were brought up on legends and myths about old miners that had died in the pit and roamed the fields surrounding the old shaft. To be honest I think it was a bit of scare-mongering from the grown-ups to keep the kids away from the shaft.

The noise was getting louder, swish, swish, swish, and getting closer. All of a sudden, something white flashed past us. Billy screamed, "Shiiit, what the hell was that?" his eyes nearly popping out of his head as the white blur whizzed passed us and straight down the old shaft. It was a goat that had been tied to the sleeper to stop it wandering, a look of sheer terror on its face as it passed. Billy and I nearly had a heart attack each and I don't think the goat was too happy either! The old shafts were full of water and rubbish. As we looked down into the darkness we could just see the white shape of the goat splashing about. The sleeper it was tied to had lodged itself in the side of the shaft and prevented the goat from being taken to the bottom.

"We can't leave it there," I said to Billy, "we'll have to try and get the poor thing out." We spent the whole morning getting that bloody goat out of the pit-shaft and ended up losing a day's pay. The Overman at the pit, Mr. Simms, wasn't too pleased at me and Billy losing a shift so he stopped all our overtime and that put the spoke in buying a dog, not that I lost any sleep over that.

Billy left the mines shortly after that and joined the army. I was in two minds whether to go with him, but I had Gran and Grandad to think of. Jill and I were getting on so well that joining up with Billy was out of the question. Billy could be a pain in the arse at times, but I missed that big lump of a man something terrible.

CHAPTER FIVE

The next four years were spent courting. I had gone out with Jill from the age of fifteen and she was the best thing that could have happened to me. We both had a lot in common and loved to go to the dogs. We had saved up enough money to get married, but I didn't fancy us living with Jill's mother, or my Gran, so we bought a caravan and asked Mr. Mason if we could put it on his land. Mr. Mason had plenty of space on the old track. It was such a shame to see it the way it was now, all overgrown and forgotten about. A few years back, before the strike, it was a thriving business. Now all that was left was a few old kennels and bits of equipment strewn about the place; a sad, sad sight.

We were married a few weeks after buying the caravan and moved straight in. We'd offered Mr. Mason ground rent, but he'd refused. "I can't take rent from you, Tom," said Mr. Mason, "I don't provide any services."

"We'll have to do something in return, Mr. Mason. I'm not happy with the situation the way it is."

"It's not necessary, lad," he said, shaking his head.

I thought about it for a while and then suggested a deal that would suit both parties. "If you won't take money, Mr. Mason, how about a couple of bags of coal now and again. I'm classed as a householder now and I'm entitled to free coal and there's no chance we'll use our full entitlement in this caravan."

"That sounds just the job, Tom." Mr. Mason stuck out his hand and we shook on it. "We have a deal, young Tom," he said, rubbing his hands together, "and that leaves both parties happy."

Jill and I were as happy as could be in that caravan, both of us working and saving at the same time. I'd been given a dog from a friend of Mr. Mason, a little blue dog. He wasn't that good, but we had some fun with him. We called him Misty because of his colour.

I'd bought a motor bike to go to work on and at the weekend, when Misty was on the card to race, Jill and I would get on the bike with the dog stuck in the middle. We used to get some real queer looks from folk as we went past, but they soon got to know us and looked forward to seeing the three of us on the bike. It became a bit more difficult when Jill became pregnant, so I swapped the bike for an old car.

The first day I drove the car I ended up in a field and had to get the farmer to pull me out with his tractor. He was a friend of Mr. Mason's and had a good laugh about it. There was no tax, no insurance and no full licence and if I'd have been caught by the law, God knows what would have happened! I soon learned to drive and passed my test in no time. It was a lot more comfortable than the bike, no more getting wet and no more three on a bike, which would be handy when Jill had the baby.

It was June the sixth. I had just finished my shift at the pit, arriving home about six forty-five in the evening to find Jill had gone into labour. I sent for the Doctor and then got word to Jill's mother, Doris. She arrived before Doctor Clegg and was I pleased to see her. This was a strange situation for me, having been brought up by my grandparents and had not been in a household where anyone had given birth. I was getting into total panic, pacing up and down the path outside the caravan.

Just then, Tommy, Jill's dad, came up the path. "Any news Tom," he shouted, but before I could answer him, he said, "It's all right Tom. I know nothing's happened by the way you've worn a trench in that path." I was still walking up and down when he was talking to me. "Calm down, bonny lad," said Tommy. "I've been through this situation five times; it gets easier after the first four." Tommy turned to me with that toothless grin and gave me a little wink. "Don't worry, son, everything will be all right." Just then we could see a car's headlights coming down the dirt track. "That sounds like the Doctor's car," said Tommy. "I can tell by the way he's trying to get the gears. Forty years he's been bloody driving and he still can't get those gears right."

Sure enough it was Dr Clegg; he pulled up five yards passed the caravan still trying to find the right gears. "Bloody gearbox," he mumbled, followed by "Bloody cow shit,"as he stepped out of the car and took a stride towards the caravan. "What the hell are you doing living in the middle of a field like a gypsy?" he shouted as he tried to wipe the cow muck from his shoes.

He was just about to sound off again, when Doris shouted from inside the caravan. "Instead of mumbling on about the bloody gearbox and cow's do da, my daughter's in here, in agony, and if you don't move your arse, someone else will be in agony with her." And she meant it.

With that, Dr Clegg took off his shoes before entering the caravan and got down to the business he had come for. It wasn't long before we heard the sound we had all been waiting for, the cry of our first child. I just stood there, not knowing whether to sing, shout or scream at the top of my voice; it was an experience I had never had before. I just stood there dumb struck, when Doris popped her head out of the caravan door.

"Well, young master Watson, you have a son."

"Is ... is Jill all right?" The words seemed to be sticking in my throat.

"Jill's just fine," said Doris, a big smile on her face; after all, it was her first grandchild.

"And ... the baby?"

"Both fine, why don't you come in and see for yourself," said Dr Clegg. I stepped into the caravan, legs feeling like jelly, and had to sit down before I fell down. "I don't know who looks the worst, you Tom, or Jill," said Dr Clegg.

Tommy was standing at the caravan door looking in. "No contest," he said, as he pointed his finger in my direction. "I hope I didn't look that bad when our Jill was born!"

"You did, and you've never bloody changed," said Doris, having her daily crack at Tommy. Tommy just stood there not saying a word. It was pointless anyway, he couldn't win!

As my legs seem to come back to me I stood up, leaned over the bed and gave Jill a big hug. The lump was there in my throat as usual and a tear in my eye. "Go on, Tom, pick him up, he won't break," said Jill handing the baby over.

"Don't forget, Tom," said Jill's dad, "grandads get to hold their first grandchild as well."

That night Tommy suggested we go out and wet the baby's head. I was a non-drinker and not too keen on the idea. "Go on," said Doris, "one or two drinks won't hurt and I'll stop in with Jill. Besides, it's an excuse for some people to go on the booze," she said, giving a scowling look at Tommy.

"Excuse," said Tommy, "no way do I need an excuse, I go out when I want, and I come in when I want."

"Over my dead body," said Doris, folding her arms and staring Tommy in the eye. Doris was a very domineering woman, Tommy was just the opposite, anything for an easy life,

"Just kidding, sweet one," he mocked, "just kidding."

We did go out that night and we did get drunk, much to my regret. I remembered nothing of getting home or who's home I was in. It turned out Tommy had taken me back to his house and Doris had stayed with Jill.

The next few months were strange, Jill being at home looking after the baby, whom we had decided to call Colin, and me working all hours God could send trying to make up for the loss of Jill's wages. It was hard, but we were no strangers to a bit of hard work. I'd struck up a friendship with a farmer in the village who I'd done a bit of work for, and decided to buy a few vegetables; turnips, cabbage and potatoes. I'd scrounged an old pram, slung a door across it and that was it — my transport; potatoes in the bottom, a bag of cabbage on one side and turnips on the other, and off I'd go on a weekend, knocking at the doors selling my veg. We had good days and bad days and on bad days I knew what was for dinner — whatever I had left in the pram, but at least it kept us fed and we made a few bob.

Colin was only a few months old when Jill fell pregnant again; it wasn't planned, it was just one of those things! We weren't over the moon at first, but warmed to the idea as time went on. Jill was fingers crossed for a girl, not that she had said so, but the hints were there like, 'that's a nice name if we have a little girl,' she'd say, or, 'look at that beautiful dress'. I'd always agree with Jill, just to keep the peace. Jill was a lot like her mother, Doris, and I'd learned from Tommy that agreeing with them was the best policy, even if you didn't agree!

The months went by and Jill had another little boy, I could see the slight disappointment in her face, but that lasted a matter of seconds. "Well," said Tommy looking down at the new arrival, "what's his name going to be?"

"Tommy, after his dad and grandad," said Doris, with her stern voice.

"We are going to call him Bobby," I said, "after nobody."

"It's Tommy," said Doris, her tone of voice changing by the second, as Tommy made a quick retreat before the sparks started flying.

"It's Bobby, Mam and that's final," said Jill. If anyone was a match for Doris it was Jill.

"There's plenty of time before he's christened to change your minds," said Doris, a look of determination on her face as she left the caravan.

The discussion of the name went on for weeks, without the argument getting too much out of hand, and Doris always looking as if she was getting her own way.

The big day had arrived, all the family, relatives and friends had turned up to see the baby christened, but deep down the majority had turned up to see the outcome of the baby's name — was it to be

81

Tommy or was it to be Bobby?

We all piled into the church and you could here the whispering as you walked down to the font. "I bet it's Tommy," came a whisper from the aisle; other's were saying, "Jill's a chip off the old block and I can't see her giving in to her mam that easy." We handed the baby over to the vicar and after naming the Godfather and Godmother came the moment of truth. "I name this child..." there was an almighty hush, you could here a pin drop, "... Bobby." Doris and Tommy both looked at Jill, the church was full of whispers, then there was a silence that seemed to go on for ever. Doris moved towards Jill and I feared the worst, but Doris opened her arms and with a tear in her eye gave Jill a hug. Not a word was spoken and there was a big sigh of relief from both Tommy and me. Little did they know that I had seen the vicar the night before and told him under no circumstances was the baby to be called anything else but Bobby.

CHAPTER SIX

The next three years flew by. Both boys, Colin and Bobby, were thriving, doing what all boys did, fighting, getting into mischief, the usual, but their main pastime was football; give them a ball and that was them set for the day. We were very happy and thought that nothing could go wrong. Then the rumours started, rumours that the pit was going to be closed. If it was true, it would have a devastating effect on the community. The men held a meeting with the union representatives.

Bob Todd was the main man and stood for no nonsense from anyone. "What's going on? What's the situation?" someone in the hall shouted.

Bob cleared his throat and put up his hands so that everyone would quieten down and listen to what he had to say. "It's like this, lads. Three of the top brass from the Coal Board are coming up to talk to you. They want to close this pit down. They say it's running at a loss." There was a lot of muttering from the crowd. Bob put his hands up again. "They have said that no-one will be out of a job, but there's a catch; you have to be willing to travel and that is where the problem lies! If you don't travel, you get the sack. It won't be too bad for some of you younger lads," said Bob.

"What about the older ones?" was the question from the audience.

By now Bob was in full swing. He banged his fist on the table and went on. "I'll tell you what'll happen to the older men. They will be thrown on the scrap heap. They will have outlived their usefulness. And I'll tell you another thing. When they say travel, they don't mean a bus ride away. They want you to travel to bloody Stoke and Yorkshire to work and leave your families up here. Now what you all have to do is go home and discuss this with your wives, families, kinfolk or whoever you like, but you must all think long and hard. It's a big decision, no matter what you decide." With that he finished the meeting and we all wandered off home

Jill and I talked and talked but in the end we knew there was only one answer; I had to go where the work was. The majority of young lads decided to give it a go. Little did I know that it was going to be the worst mistake of my life.

We decided on Stoke-on-Trent. As we were the new lads in the area we were given the worst jobs in the pit. The people were none too friendly, very clannish, not like the folks back home in Durham. I got Jill and the kids down after eight months. I couldn't bear to be parted from them any longer. We stuck it out in Stoke for another three years before we decided to leave and head for South Yorkshire.

I had managed to arrange a transfer with the NCB and some housing was arranged. We had three boys now and landed up in a brand new council house. The kids loved it. There was a big football field close at hand and there wasn't far to travel for school. Jill liked it because it was only five minutes walk to town where there was a market three times a week and if Jill loved anything better than me and the kids it was the market. Within a couple of weeks we had settled in and made new friends. The lads I was working with seemed to be a lot friendlier than the lads in the other coalfield. We all got on well, and best of all we discovered where the local dog tracks were.

I was doing well at the pit earning a lot more than I did in Stoke and feeling much more content. Things were going great. I had palled up with a local lad called Charlie, who would gamble on two flies crawling up the wall. He was a single lad and had no responsibilities. He was a bit of a loner but we got on like a house on fire. We decided to buy a dog or two from a chap called Billy Evans. Billy went over to Ireland to buy dogs regular and you could always find a bit of time with the majority of the dogs he brought back to sell.

He was due back from Ireland that weekend, so Charlie and I went to his kennels to see what he had brought back. We arrived at Billy's house and walked down to the bottom of his garden. "Now Charlie, what can I do for thee?" he said in his broad Yorkshire accent.

"We've come ter see what tha's brought back from Ireland," said Charlie in his equally broad accent.

"And who's thee mate?" he asked, nodding in my direction.

" Tom Watson from Durham," said Charlie.

"A Geordie lad, eh?" said Billy. "There's a few of you lads down here now. What brings thee ter these parts then?"

"Work Billy, work," I replied, "NCB is closing my pit back home and it won't be the last the way things are going."

"Well at least thar had the guts to get up off of your arse and look for work. Coal Board's now't but a ounch of bloody Tory's," said Billy starting to get into politics.

"Never mind work," said Charlie, "let's see what thar's got in here," he said, walking over towards the kennels.

"Thar can tek thee pick from them, sixty-five quid a piece," said Billy.

I pulled Charlie to one side. "Tell him we'll give him sixty-five quid for a dog and a bitch."

"I can hear thee well enough, Geordie," he laughed "and it's not on. Anyhow, which two did tha fancy?"

There were a couple that had caught my eye; a fawn and white dog and a little dark brindle bitch. The dog looked like a hat rack, his spine and ribs showing through and the bitch was not much bigger than a whippet. I pointed out the two I fancied to Billy. "That skinny coloured dog and that little bitch," I said trying to make them look worse than they were.

"Tell thee what Geordie, give me eighty quid for the pair," said Billy holding out his hand to clinch the deal.

"Make it seventy and you've got a deal," I said, holding out my hand.

"Yer a hard man to deal with, Geordie Tom, but I don't think you've got the bargain of the year there." We shook hands and the deal was done.

Charlie didn't look too impressed. "What's thar done, Tom. They look like two right scrubbers," and he was right!

"Yes, they do, Charlie, but give me three or four weeks with them and then see what you think; don't judge a book by its cover."

When we arrived home the dogs went straight into the bath. The muck and fleas that came out of them you wouldn't believe. The dogs had everyone in the house scratching. The bath was just a start, now we had to get some good grub into them. The pair of them wolfed their food down as if it was their first meal for days.

"What about some names for them?" asked Jill.

"Hungry," said Charlie, laughing at his own joke.

Jill laughed and said, "We'll call the bitch Milly and the dog Patch."

Both Milly and Patch licked their bowls clean, looked up as if to say...that was good, now show me to my bed. We led both dogs down to the kennel, took off their leads and watched them snuggle under the straw as if they had been here all their lives.

CHAPTER SEVEN

The next few weeks were hard, trying to build the dogs up and working at the same time. I had found out a little about the bitch's characteristics. She loved the kids and liked being made a fuss of, but she didn't like people shouting at her. She would go all quiet and moody but at least we knew how to treat her. The dog was just the opposite; very laid back. You could drop a bomb next to him and it wouldn't bother him a bit. We had already graded them at the track before they started to shape up.

We had entered both dogs for a Saturday afternoon's racing at the Lowgate track, a ramshackle place but very friendly. No matter what marks the dogs were off, we knew we had plenty in hand due to their poor condition when we graded them in. The bitch had the hardest race, giving five yards start. The dog was in a level break.

"How much are thar having on, Tom," asked Charlie, rubbing his hands together.

"I'll have £20.00 on the bitch," I replied, "and we'll see what happens after that. What about you?" I asked.

"The lot," said Charlie without batting an eyelid.

"You must be joking," said Jill, but I knew he wasn't. I hadn't known Charlie that long but when he said he was having the lot on, he meant it!

"I'm having fifty quid on bitch, and when she wins I shall have the lot on dog." There was no arguing with Charlie, that was the way he was, and he'd made his mind up.

Billy Evans was there with a good looking black dog. "Now Charlie, Geordie, Mrs. Geordie, nice day," he said, tipping his hat.

"No, not bad Billy," said Charlie, "I see we've got one in same race."

"Aye, my black dog and that bitch ah sold thee. A hope thar's not thinking of backing it," said Billy, looking very confident that his black dog would be too good for that skinny little bitch he had sold us.

"Why?" said Charlie.

"Because it's got no chance; it can't give that black dog of mine four yards."

"We'll just have to wait and see," said Charlie. "Wait until after the race."

It was our race next. Jill had the job of parading Milly; the bitch always seemed happier with a woman. Charlie was doing the betting and I was looking after the kids. All of a sudden there was one mad rush at the bookies. Billy Evans had gambled his dog off the boards leaving no price at all for his black dog, Fred, "This must be a handy dog," said someone after nearly being killed in the rush. Charlie was still at the books not a care in the world about the amount of money going on Billy's dog, Fred. Milly's price went from two's to five's.

"Five Eighty's" Charlie shouted as the hare was running.

"I thought you only had fifty quid, Charlie?" shaking my head in amazement as to where the rest of the money had come from.

"I did, but a kid owed me a tenner and with your £20 that made it eighty."

"You should have held a tenner back for the dog, just in case the bitch gets beat."

"It wayn't get beat," said Charlie, quite confidently. "Ah can feel it in me watter."

The traps went up and Milly came out well. It was the first time she had been in a handicap race and I didn't know quite what to expect. There was no need to worry, she was weaving in and out like a piece of string. "She'll get where watter can't," said Charlie jumping up and down and shouting at the same time. "Come on, Milly, thar can do it." She only had one dog to pass. Billy Evans' black dog, Fred, who was running up the inside rail.

Now, I said to myself, will she wait for the rails or go on the outside? There was no hesitation. Straight past on the outside she went and won by six lengths.

"FIRST, NUMBER ONE. SECOND, NUMBER THREE," crackled the tanoy.

The kids were jumping up and down with excitement, after all there was only Colin that had been to a dog track and he was too young to remember.

"Well done, Geordie," said Billy Evans, thumping me on the back. "We were beat fair and square. Thar's done a grand job wi that little bitch, she looks like mecking a good un."

"Thanks Billy, I hope the other dog you sold us is as good."

Jill came off the track to rapturous applause from the kids and Milly wagged her tail in response to the kids pampering her. "Didn't she run great, Tom?" said Jill, smiling and as proud as punch.

"Better than I thought she ever would," I admitted, "and she was staying on." The kids were all over the bitch and she was lapping up all of the attention.

Charlie wandered over with our winnings, a grin from ear to ear. He had collected from the bookie's £480.00. "Theres your Tom's £120.00," he said, handing a large wedge of cash over to Jill.

Her eyes lit up. "It's a long time since I've seen this sort of money," said Jill, you could just see a twinkle of a tear starting to form in her eye. "That's just the job, Tom," said Jill, "the kids can all have new shoes now."

"No, No," shouted Charlie. "Wait till Patch runs. I can buy shoes for the kids when Patch wins." Charlie was always the optimist.

"The kids have to come first, Charlie. It's OK for you, you have no ties. Put me £70 on Patch and that leaves me £50 for the kids' shoes and one or two things that they need."

"Thar must be barmy, Tom," said Charlie starting to get all frustrated, "he can't get beat."

"Anything can happen in a race, Charlie, you know that."

"Well, thar'll not put me off, Tom, I'm having lot on."

It was pointless trying to stop him. "Do what you want Charlie, it's your cash, but I still think you should keep a little back, just in case." It was no good, Charlie had made up his mind.

There were five minutes to the race. Jill had decided to parade the dog. She thought that as she had been lucky with Milly she might also be the same with Patch. Charlie was up and down like a yoyo in front of the bookies. Everyone knew he was going to back Patch. The bookies weren't going to be half as generous as they were with Milly. There was very little activity in front of the bookmaker stands. When you had a new dog race like we were in, you had a lot of non triers because no one knew the strength of the other dogs, therefore there was a lack of interest in the betting.

The hare was running, Charlie had to bet the dog quick; the best price was only 2-1. The traps went up and Patch came out well. He went two lengths clear at the first bend. "Go on, my son," Charlie shouted." The kids were jumping up and down and screaming the place down. Patch was six lengths clear coming round the last bend when he stumbled and started to slow down. The other dogs were starting to close the gap.

"He's dodging," someone shouted.

"No, he's not, he's as honest as the day," Charlie shouted back.

"If he's honest then I'm a Dutchman," answered this voice in the crowd.

"Tek no notice of him," said Billy Evans. "He's a right nutcase. He'd cause trouble in an empty house," he went on, "his name is Dodger Smith." By the time Billy had explained about Dodger Smith the other dogs had passed Patch. There had to be something wrong.

Sure enough, as Jill walked him off the track, it was plain to see that he was limping. As we got him to the car to wash his feet I could see that he had jumped a toe, it was twice the size of the others. "Bad luck, Geordie," said Billy, "he'd have won by a mile."

"Thanks, Billy, but that's dog racing for you. You have to take the good with the bad." I picked up Patch and carried him back into the track.

"Where's thar goin'?" asked Charlie, a look of confusion on his face.

90

"I'm going to hose his toe down with cold water to try to keep the swelling down," I replied.

The next day I was up at the crack of dawn to see how bad Patch's toe was. It wasn't quite as bad as I had first thought; the cold water had done its job. Three or four weeks and he'd be as good as new. The bitch on the other hand was raring to go. She had come out of the race very well and was ready for her next encounter.

"When are we goin' ter race Milly again, Tom," asked Charlie.

"Next week," I replied. "We'll try to grade her in at another track, nice and steady."

"What's thar going' ter use to steady her down, Tom?" asked Charlie.

"Well I'm not going to give her anything to harm her, Charlie, if that's what you think. We'll try a little bit of grub and see what that does. After all, she's only a small bitch and it might just work."

Sure enough a feed did the trick. Milly just qualified and we had plenty in hand.

The boys had settled in nicely at school and had made it into the football team. Colin and Bobby in one team, Peter in the other. There was only one problem. If both teams were playing on the same day, Jill and I had to split up, me watching one team and Jill the other, but it was great fun. The kids enjoyed it and we were as proud as punch of them all.

We had just come back from a match one night when there was a knock on the door. It was a boy called Jed from down the street. "Er, can I borrow one of your lads' bikes," he said rather hurriedly.

"I'm sorry lad," I explained, "but there's only one bike and it's not too good as it is."

"That's OK," he said, "it'll do."

I was suspicious of him and asked, "Why do you need the bike?"

"Me dad's fallen down the stairs and I've got to fetch the doctor," he said, looking at the floor.

"I'll 'phone from next door," I said, "that'll be quicker."

"Er ... no, I've got to go on the bike," he said looking a bit red-faced.

I knew by now that something wasn't quite right, so I told him that I would 'phone for a doctor for his dad if he had fallen down the stairs, but he couldn't have the bike. With this he just shrugged his shoulders and walked off back down the street. We had been sitting for about fifteen minutes, eating our teas, when Peter, the youngest of our boys, looked up at me and said, "Dad, I knew Jed was telling lies."

"And how do you know that son?" I asked.

Peter looked at me as if I was daft and said, "Well, anybody could work that out Dad ... where was the doctor going to sit?"

Jill and I just looked at each other and burst out laughing, the other two kids were on the floor. Every time we looked at each other that night we laughed till we cried.

Milly was back on the track and winning all over the place. She was very versatile and could sprint or stay and turned out to be a real good bitch. We had her entered at Lowgate track where she had won her first race.

The handicapper had been hard on her because of the good time she had done and the way she'd run, but Milly had improved a lot since she'd won at this track. There was one dog in the race she had to beat; a dog named Sparrow, who'd won his last two races.

We sat on the lawn, Charlie and I, looking at the dog card. "Thar ken's whose dog that is, Tom, dun't tha?" said Charlie, pointing to Sparrow.

"No, I don't. Whose is it?"

"It belongs to that good for now't, Dodger Smith." Charlie hadn't got the words out of his mouth when Dodger came down the garden path.

"Now Charlie, how's thar keeping?"

"No better for seeing thee Dodger," replied Charlie.

"I hope we're not goin' to fall out over that do at track t'other week. It were only a bit of fun," went on Dodger. "Anyhow, I'll get straight to point, thar's got bitch in same race as my dog and we both can't win same race, can we?"

"What's thar trying to say Dodger?" asked Charlie.

92

"Well, my dogs a danger to thine," said Dodger, a glint in his eye. "If ah stop mine and back thine, we'll all be better off."

"How's thar mek that out?" asked Charlie, looking a bit uncomfortable at his suggestion.

"Because your bitch will be a better price than my dog so I'll stop mine for yours."

"What about the betting?" I asked as Dodger seemed to be referring all of his questions to Charlie.

"Aye, Dodger, who's gonna do that?" asked Charlie.

"Get who tha wants," said Dodger, "I'll give thee my cash so thar knows everything's above board. OK? Here's my £40 and I'll see thee at track," and off he went, lumbering into the distance. He was a big lad, about eighteen stone and mouthy with it, with a red face and fair hair.

"What's thar think, Tom?" asked Charlie.

"I don't trust him one little bit," I said, "but we'll have to wait and see tonight." The way I looked at it, we were going to bet Milly, anyway and Dodger's dog was a big danger; we had to take the chance!

By the time we got to the track Milly was jumping out of her skin. Charlie had arranged the betting with some lads that he could trust and everything seemed to be going to plan. It was getting close to our race. Dodger was all over the track with a grin like a Cheshire cat on his face every time he saw me or Charlie.

"I don't like this, Charlie, I don't like this at all, something's up."

"What's thar mean, Tom?" he asked, looking puzzled.

"Dodger looks a bit too smug for my liking." It was too late to do anything now, the bookies had started to bet. Two to one Sparrow, three to one Milly. Then crash, there was one mad rush, and Milly's price had gone.

"Who's backing the bitch, Charlie?" I asked, having grave doubts about the whole job.

"Ah dun't know, but it's none of my lads, Tom."

Ted Barnes, one of the lads who was doing the betting for Charlie and I, came over to see what had gone wrong. "None of my team have done this," said Ted, "we were just waiting, ready to go in, when a load of strangers stepped in and took the market. Milly was still on at evens." Ted shrugged his shoulders "We might as well take what's left," and off he went to lay what bets he could.

The hare was running and the traps were up. Milly was out like a shot passing dog after dog, Dodger's dog was tailed off, God only knows what had gone down that poor dog's throat and I had a sneaky suspicion that Dodger had also got to some of the other dogs. Milly did her job and won the race easy.

Dodger was all smiles when he came over, a big fat grin spread all over his fat greasy face. The temptation to punch him was nearly too much. "Well done, Geordie," he said, "bitch ran well. What price did thar get, Charlie?" he asked over his shoulder.

"Thar kens what price we got, evens," Charlie snarled at him, "someone shopped the betting."

"Don't look at me, it's now't to do wi me," said Dodger holding his hands up. He was about as convincing as someone trying to sell ash-trays for motor bikes!

"Just give him his money, Charlie, and let's go home. There's always another day." It was plain to see that Dodger had sent in a strange team to bet the bitch. He had managed to get two bites at the cherry. Three to one and evens. I swore then and there that I would see my day with Mr. Dodger Smith.

It wasn't long before we had Patch back on the card. He turned out to be nearly as good as the bitch. We had him entered in a race at Lowgate Track, a level break. Lots of people still remembered him from his last race when he took a big lead and got beat. Some thought he had been dodging, as did Dodger, so there was a big question mark over his honesty. We knew the real reason for this was because of his injury but the bookies weren't sure. They must have been listening to the punters at the track because his price was generous at 4-1. Charlie had £30 and I had £20.

That fat slob Dodger Smith was at the track. "No trouble, Tom," said Charlie, "I know you've sworn to get even for that other job but today is not the day." I assured him that there would be no trouble that day, not from me, anyway.

The traps went up and like a flash Patch was well clear. He was coming round the last bend ten lengths clear when someone shouted, "He's stopping again."

It was that fat so and so Dodger Smith. I turned on him and shouted back, "The only place he's stopping you fat toad, is in front." Patch went on and obliged, winning by twelve lengths. When the result and time came over it was only two lengths short of the track record.

We were delighted as we counted out our winnings in front of Dodger, just to rub salt into the wounds. As we were counting the cash we were approached by a well-dressed man and woman. They were a nice couple, in their forties I would say. "Congratulations," said the chap. "Your dog ran very well. How old is he?"

"He's not two until next month," I said.

"Is he for sale?" said the man,

"I hadn't thought about it," I said. I was a bit puzzled by their interest.

"The thing is," he went on, "the wife and I have just lost our own dog through old age. We kept him after his racing days were over and your dog is just like him." All the time we were talking his wife was bending, scratching Patch's ears and talking to him. "I'll give you a fair price for him," he went on, "and I promise he'll have a good home for life."

I turned to Charlie, "What's to do?" I asked.

"It's up to thee Tom," he said, "see how much he wants to pay."

Before we could discuss a price the man said, "I was thinking about £150.00. Does that seem fair?"

Charlie, who just liked the sound of money, grinned and said, "It seems fair to me. What about thee, Tom?"

"Well, as long as the dog gets a good home." The deal was done. All I had to do was to go home and explain to Jill, who had stayed home to look after Peter who wasn't too well. Jill was none to pleased when I told her, but as the night went on and I explained that Patch had gone to a good home she was a lot happier.

CHAPTER EIGHT

I had always wanted to go to Ireland but had never had the time or the money. Things, however, were starting to change. We had won a good few quid with Milly and we still had some of the money we made on Patch. I discussed the idea with Jill and she was all for it. The annual pit holidays were coming up and it seemed like the right time to put things into motion. Charlie was as excited as I was as neither of us had ever been out of the country.

We made arrangements to borrow a van from a friend of Charlie's, a chap called Paddy Conners. He was as Irish as you could get and a real nice chap. He liked a drink and he could swear like a trooper but he had a heart of gold and was harmless. His best mate was a big Blackfoot Indian, a coloured gent from Canada called Mick Shorfeiled. They were like Siamese twins; I think they were related through drink! There was a knock at the door one night, about two weeks before we went to Ireland. It was Paddy and Mick. "Any chance of meself and Mick coming to Ireland wi't you Tom," said Paddy in his soft Irish accent, "we'll pay half the fare and the petrol?"

I could hardly refuse, after all, it was his van. "I'll have to talk to Charlie first," I said.

"Dat's OK Tom, but I've had a word with him meself and it's all right with him if it's all right wi't you."

"In that case," I laughed, "there's not much point in me saying owt else!"

"Yer a good man yerself, Tom," he said, "you won't regret this."

"I hope not, Paddy, I hope not," I said shaking my head, but something told me I just might.

Everything had been arranged. The van was serviced and filled with petrol, we had a change of clothes and something for the dogs to eat on the return journey. All that was left to do was pick up Paddy and Mick.

I had visions of all sorts going wrong with our passengers and felt quite uneasy. We had arranged to pick up the pair of them at 8.00pm. At 8.30pm there was no sign of them. I was starting to get fed up and worried; we had a ferry to catch. "If they are not here in ten minutes," I said to Charlie, "I'm setting off without them."

All was quiet for a couple of minutes then Charlie said, "What's that racket?" I couldn't bear to look. We turned and looked out of the back windows of the van and there in the distance were Paddy and Mick, singing their lungs out, as drunk as skunks and trying to hold each other up.

"Top o'the mornin' tu yer, Charlie, me boy, have you been here long?" slobbered Paddy.

"Too bloody long," I snapped. "Another ten minutes and we'd have gone without you! Get in the back of the van before I change my mind." They scrambled into the back of the van still singing and oblivious to my temper. Paddy apologised and kept on singing.

We had a long journey in front of us and had lost valuable time; we needed a clear run if we were to catch the ferry. I had no sooner thought that things were going quite well, if you could put up with Paddy's singing that is, when all of a sudden he stopped singing. "Stop the van, Tom," said Paddy. "Quick."

"What's the matter?"

"I need to use der toilet."

"Er ... me too," said Mick.

That set the pattern for the night. Every hour, on the hour, the singing would stop and so would the van. By the time we had arrived at Holyhead the ferry had long gone. It was by now 4.00 a.m. and there wasn't a hope in hell of finding digs at that time in the morning. We had to sleep in the van and it was bloody freezing.

Paddy and Mick were sleeping it off in the back of the van, snoring like a pair of hogs, oblivious to the fact that we were still in England.

We had to wait until 7.00 a.m. before we could board the next ferry. I was cold, tired and hungry and couldn't wait to get warm and something inside me. I drove the van onto the ferry and made straight up the steps to find out where the breakfast room was. Paddy and Mick made straight for the bar and ordered two pints. They weren't best pleased when they had to wait until the ferry had sailed; the bar couldn't open until then.

I decided to try and get some sleep but it was pointless, the ferry was full and everyone else had the same idea. We made enquiries about a cabin but they were all taken. We had to get some sleep somehow but there was nothing to be had.

One of the crewmen overheard me talking. It turned out he was a Geordie as well. "Can I help you, lads," he asked. We explained that we needed to get some sleep after the long journey, "Well, the only option left is the Flea Pit," he said.

"What's the Flea Pit?" I asked, desperate for a bed, but not sure I wanted to know.

"It's forty bunks on the bottom deck, but it's only five bob a bunk."

"It'll have to do, Charlie," I sighed, "I'm shattered and we have a long way to go when we get off this boat."

"Oh, just one more thing," said the crewman, "sleep with your shoes on and your hands in your pockets down there; there's some funny folk about, you know."

"I know," I said. "We came with two of them," pointing to Paddy and Mick. The crewman got the message and just laughed.

It seemed like no sooner than I was asleep than it was time to leave the ferry. I must have slept like a log but everything was intact, boots, money, etc, Charlie and I were climbing the steps to the wash room to freshen up when we heard a sound which was becoming all too familiar. Paddy and Mick were singing their hearts out. I turned to Charlie and shook my head, sure enough it was Paddy and Mick at the Bar.

"I bet we'll have some fun and games with these two when we

get off this boat," Charlie said, and I had a gut feeling it'd be more trouble than fun.

It was a long way to Limerick but the views and the scenery were out of this world. We stopped at a little cafe for something to eat and to stretch our legs. Paddy and Mick had sobered up and started to count the cost of their booze-up. Mick had £84 left and Paddy had £30. We had something to eat and set off to continue our journey. It was one of those days when you just felt like driving and taking in the view, the sun was shining and I was looking forward to the sale.

As we arrived in the city it was like something from another era. Everything was old-fashioned. The pubs had green paint on the windows except for six inches at the top so you could see if your friends were in. The butchers had the meat hung outside the shop and there were lots and lots of second-hand shops.

The first thing to do was find somewhere to stay. We stopped someone in the street and asked about digs.

"I'll take over from here," said Paddy and after making some inquiries he had been advised to seek out a Mrs. Malone's.

She was a big red faced woman with arms like a wrestler. "How long will yer be staying lads?" she asked.

"Just two nights, if that's OK," I replied.

"Be javers, yer can stop as long as yer like, just don't get drunk and go messing up me nice clean house."

Charlie and I looked at each other and then looked at Paddy and Mick. "You heard what Mrs. Malone said, you two."

"We surely did," said Paddy with an impish grin on his face.

"Well, as long as yer have dat sorted out," said Mrs. Malone, "will yer be havin' a bite to eat. I've just taken some soda bread from the oven."

"Soda bread," said Charlie, "what's soda bread?" Mrs. Malone explained what soda was, not that it would make any difference to Charlie, he could eat a rusty can!

"That's very kind, Mrs. Malone," I said, "if it's not too much trouble. We don't want to put you out."

"Put me out, not at all, I'm doin' this all day long," said the lady. "After all, I have ten lodgers and they all need feeding."

After washing our hands we sat down to eat — it was the best bread I had ever tasted. We had it with home-made fruit jam that Mrs. Malone had made herself.

"That was delicious, Mrs. Malone," I said wiping the crumbs from my face and relaxing into the chair.

"Ah, tis notin' just a bit of soda bread and stop calling me Mrs. Malone, Molly's the name if you don't mind," she said as she busied herself clearing the table. "Are you boys down fer the sale?" she asked out of curiosity.

"Me and me pal are just along for the ride," smiled Paddy. "Tom and Charlie are the men for the dogs."

"I hear that there's some good dogs up for the sale," said Mrs. Malone, "but yer have to be careful what you're doing. There's some tricky sorts out there you know," and with that she set off to the kitchen muttering to herself, then stopping and turning round. "You lads have got to watch what you're doing," said Molly pointing her finger at me and Charlie.

We went to bed that night after giving Paddy and Mick a good warning about not coming in drunk and to my surprise when they came in they were stone cold sober.

The next morning, after having one of Molly's huge breakfasts of fried bread, bacon, egg and mushrooms, we were off to the sale. I was so excited. It was the same feeling I had when I'd first bought Sandy.

Charlie and I watched all the trials, making little notes about the dogs we liked and those we didn't like. After the trials there was a break for something to eat. Charlie and I were still full from Mrs. Malone's breakfast so we sat down and compared notes, watching all of the activity going on around us. It was a whole new experience for Charlie and me and we were really enjoying ourselves.

The break had finished and the sale was about to start. "Will you bring Lot 1 to the stand," came an announcement over the speakers.

As we settled down to watch, a tall, red-haired man sat down next to us. "Would you two be Tom and Charlie?" he said, looking at the both of us and not knowing which of us was who.

"That's right," I said, surprised that anyone would know who we were. "Can I help you?" I asked.

"Tis me what'll be helping you, young man," he said as he sat down beside us. "Molly Malone has sent me along to keep an eye on the pair of you and see you come to no harm.

"That's very kind of her," said Charlie.

"Tis notin at all, tis just the way the woman is, kindness herself," he said, making himself room on the long seat that had been provided.

The first few lots had been sold and the majority of the cheaper lots had gone to one man. It looked like it was going to be very difficult for Charlie and me to buy the dogs we wanted. By now our tall, red-haired friend had introduced himself. He was Dermot and he kept us full of information about the people who were buying and those that were selling.

"Do you see dat chap who bought the last lot?" He pointed to a greasy looking man who looked as if he hadn't been washed for a week.

"He's an agent from England who buys a lot of dogs for Spain. He'll buy anytin' under £40.00 and the poor dogs have a hell of a life. No-one likes him at all," Dermot went on. It was getting close to the lots that Charlie and I had marked off. I had to think of something to stop the agent buying the dogs that Charlie and I had marked in the catalogue. Meanwhile, the best dog in the sale was about to come onto the bench; it had done the fastest time of the day and would bring a big price. The bidding started at 400 guineas. I turned to Charlie and said it would be nice to have something like him in our kennel.

"You might at that," said Charlie, looking rather pale "Mick's bidding for him."

"Mick! But he's only got £84 left."

"Yer right, Tom, and there looks like trouble at mill today," said Charlie. "We'd best keep our distance from Mick and Paddy."

The bidding was brisk between Mick and a well-dressed chap,

who we learned from Dermot was a well-known trainer from one of the London tracks. The dog sold for 525 guineas and was knocked down to Mick. My stomach dropped to my feet. There was loud applause from the crowd and lots of people shaking Mick's hand. The dogs had to be paid for at the end of the sale and I had no idea how Mick was to perform this impossible task. It didn't bear thinking about. Besides, I had more on my mind than how Mick was going to pay for his dog. There were only three more lots before one of the dogs that I fancied came onto the bench. I turned to Dermot. "What's the agent's name?" I asked.

"I tink his name is Mead." he replied.

I turned to Charlie and said, "Go outside, ring this number and ask to speak to Mr. Mead."

"What number?" said Charlie looking puzzled.

"This one on the bottom of the catalogue," I said, "it's the number of the track."

"What then?" asked Charlie looking very vacant.

"Then you ask for this fellow Mead to come to the 'phone. When he arrives, keep him talking for as long as you can. Tell him you want to buy five or six dogs. That'll keep him busy."

Charlie had been gone for ten minutes and there had still been no announcement of a 'phone call for Mr. Mead. "Lot 39 to the bench," was the call from the stand.

'That's ours,' I said to myself.

Just then there was an announcement: "Mr. Mead to the telephone please. Urgent call for Mr. Mead." He was off, faster than some of the dogs he had bought earlier that day.

The dog on the bench wasn't much to look at but I had a feeling he'd be all right.

"Who will start me off with twenty guineas?" said the auctioneer looking round for a bid. No-one raised a hand. "All right then," he sighed. "Where do you want to start with this fellow? Have we got a bid anywhere?"

I shot my hand up. "Five guineas," I shouted.

"Well 'tis a starting point," said the auctioneer, "who'll raise it to ten." No-one was interested. I heard someone in the crowd say that the dog had run three times and had three seconds on his card and that he might be dodgy but I wasn't going to be put off. I was going on my own judgement and by my instincts.

"Take the dog down," the auctioneer said, "he's going home to race for his owner."

"Ten guineas," I shouted, before the dog was taken from the bench.

The auctioneer turned to the owner. "It's up to you Mr. Leach."

The man studied me for a while, then nodded. "Put him on the market," said the owner, shaking his head in disappointment.

"I've got ten guineas here," the auctioneer continued, "do I hear fifteen?" Just then I saw Mead crossing from the office and getting closer.

'For God's sake,' I thought, 'knock that bloody hammer down.'

Mead had just sat down in his seat and was about to indicate a bid when Dermot stood up right in front of him. The auctioneer hadn't seen Mead and knocked his hammer down. "Sold to the gent on my left." The dog was mine. Mr. Mead wasn't too pleased and ranted and raved at Dermot but to no avail.

As the sale went on Mead bought most of the cheaper lots and it looked like we weren't going to buy another dog. Then came Lot 79. It was a nice black dog who had fallen over in his trial. Mead was straight in with five guineas. We matched him bid for bid until it went up to seventeen guineas. The auctioneer looked at the owner who shook his head. Mead then bid twenty guineas. The owner still said no. "Take him down," said the auctioneer, and with that the old gent went off in the direction of the kennels.

Two or three lots went by but were well out of our reach, and to be honest not what I fancied. "Well, Charlie, it looks like only one dog for us this time."

Just then there was a tap on my shoulder. It was the owner of the little black dog. "Do yer still want him, Sir? Are yer still interested in the feller?" the man asked.

"We are, very much," I said, "but we can't afford to pay twenty guineas."

"Forget about any twenty guineas; will you still give me the fifteen you bid?"

"Yes," I said puzzled, "but I don't understand."

"Well it's like dis," said the old gent, "I wouldn't sell dat man Mead a dog to save me life. I tink a bit about dis dog and I couldn't bear tu tink of him over in Spain. If you lads want the dog, he's yours for fifteen guineas."

We paid the money and shook the old man's hand as he wished us good luck with the dog; he even gave us back two guineas for luck. We made our way to the office to pay for the other dog and collect his papers, and from there to the digs. When we entered the office, Mick and Paddy were paying for the dog that he'd bid for with a cheque. We didn't want to be seen within a mile of those two and made a hasty retreat backwards through the door. God knows what was going to happen when the auctioneer found out the cheque was no good.

We waited until Mick and Paddy had distanced themselves from the office and disappeared before we went in to pay for our one purchase and crossed our fingers that the man behind the desk didn't associate Charlie and I with the two clowns that had just left the office. We loaded up the dogs and headed off to the digs to pick up Paddy and Mick. We were on our way when we caught sight of the two of them wandering into the pub, we waited a few minutes, hoping they'd gone for a quick pint before we set off. There was a large crowd starting to gather outside. It didn't look good. "It looks like they're going to be lynched, Charlie," I said, fearing the worst.

"What's thar going to do, Tom?" asked Charlie, a worried look on his face.

"Well we can't leave them here, Charlie, we'll just have to go in and get them out." This was something I was not looking forward to.

As we approached the pub there was a load of kids jumping up at the window. We feared the worst. "Well, Charlie, there's only one thing for it. We'll have to go in and get them." The pub was packed to overflowing and Mick and Paddy were centre stage, right in the middle.

We were trying to get near to them when we heard two old Irish gents talking. "Do yer know who dat dark feller is Shamus," said one of the old gents to his mate.

"No, Flynn, I don't at that," he replied

"Dat there is Cassius Clay's brudder!"

The old man stood up on his stool and looked at Mick and studied him for a while before replying, "Be Jesus, Flynn, you're right, he looks just like his brudder, so he does."

"Aye," said his pal, "and if we sit in here long enough, dem TV cameras are going to be here to see him!"

I caught hold of Charlie's arm and whispered, "Try and let them know that we are leaving in half an hour." Charlie going one way and me the other. I forced my way outside just as the TV crew were pulling up. Charlie was a couple of seconds behind me.

"It's no good, Tom," shouted Charlie, "there's no shifting them. Mick's buying all the drinks and paying by cheque."

"Well, it's time for us to vanish and quick; they'll just have to make their own way back to Yorkshire." And with that we brushed past the T.V. crew and into the van. There were more and more people arriving at the pub as the news spread.

We set off down to Mrs. Malone's as quickly as we could. We didn't want to stay a minute more than necessary. One last feed with Mrs. Malone's wonderful soda bread, the dogs safely loaded into the van and we were on our way. It was a good two weeks before we saw Paddy and Mick again and to hear their side of the story you'd think they were a pair of saints and had done no wrong. It was obvious the cheque was going to bounce and instead of ending up with a dog they ended up with a massive hangover.

CHAPTER NINE

We had been back in England about two weeks, had graded in the new dogs and were quite happy with their progress, but we were short of cash as usual. Jill had kept Milly on her toes and had entered her for the Summer Handicap. She had a good mark but we had no money. Jill was happy to run Milly just for the prize money as she said it was a shame not to when she was so well, plus any money we might win was always welcome.

We were discussing the situation of whether to run for the prize money and not have a bet or wait for another day. Just then the door burst open. It was Charlie. "You'll never believe what I'm going tu tell thee, Tom," he said with a grin from ear to ear. "Me dad forgot to tell me when we got back from Ireland."

"What did he forget?" I encouraged. Charlie had a tendency to forget what he was talking about while he was talking about it.

"This!" he said, throwing £100 down on the bench. "I won it on the coupons. It were there on top o' sideboard and he forgot to tell me! This means we can have a bet on Milly at weekend, 'cos I owe thee a few bob, Tom," he winked.

"That's great news, Charlie, it couldn't have come at a better time." Maybe, just maybe, our luck was changing!

As race day approached we had a visit from Dodger Smith. I still felt like I wanted to punch him on sight for the last stroke he pulled on Charlie and me.

"Thar's not welcome here," said Charlie with a look of pure hatred in his eyes.

"How's thar mean, Charlie," replied Dodger looking all innocent.

"Thar kens what I mean, that carry on last time when thar stitched up me and Tom."

"That were just pure bad luck that, Charlie," said Dodger as if butter wouldn't melt in his mouth.

"Bad luck my foot, more like having the pi.. taken out of you." I had just been about to swear when I saw Jill from the corner of my eye.

"Tom Watson," she said, "I'll have none of that if you don't mind, not when the kids are knocking about." Jill was saying little but taking it all in.

"I didn't, I didn't swear."

"No, you didn't, but you would have had I not being standing there."

"I'll tell thee what I'll do for thee, Geordie," said Dodger. "Your bitch will be no more than 2-1 to win race. I'll give thee 3-1 now and thar dun't have to win."

"D'unt trust him," said Charlie, "he's now't but a snake in grass and that's an insult tu snake."

"Hold on just a minute," said Dodger, "at least hear me out. The situation is this. I think your bitch is the best thing on card and so do a lot of other people. I've spoken to all of the lads who have dogs in your race and they know they can't beat your bitch."

"So what's that got to do wi us," said Charlie still looking daggers at him.

"Well, it's as simple as this," Dodger went on, "they'll all be wanting to bet your bitch before the race and you'll be lucky to get even money."

"He has a point, Charlie," I said reluctantly, 'but I still wouldn't trust him as far as I could throw him,' I thought to myself. "What's the plan, then?" I asked.

"That's more like it, Geordie. We're getting somewhere now. This is what we do. All lads that's got a dog in your race will meet at my house an hour before the race is due tu go off. We'll pick out a dog that's going to be a big price and stop the rest — in other words, prevent five of the dogs from winning," said Dodger.

"What about the 3-1 you offered us," said Charlie, "what if the winner is 5-1?"

"Then you'll get 5-1," said Dodger. "Anyhow, think on it Geordie, it's time I was off. I've got dogs to see to," and off he trundled like a tub of lard.

After he'd gone Charlie and I had a right set too. "Thar knows thar can't trust him, Tom," he said, "I dun't know why thar's goin' along wi' it. I would have thought thar had more sense," he ranted on.

"If you're quite finished Charlie, let me explain. The reason I'm going along with it is because I see the opportunity of getting even with our fat friend, Mr. Dodger Smith."

"And how's thar goin' tu do that," asked Charlie with a smirk on his face.

"Simple, Charlie, I'm going to beat him at his own game!"

"How's thar mean, Tom. Ah dun't understand."

"Well, I just happen to know what sort of capsules Dodger uses to stop his dogs." At least, I hope I do!

"So," said Charlie getting more curious and impatient by the second.

I went on to explain that Dodger used a drug in a green and black capsule and that we would have to try and obtain a capsule that looked the same, from old Ernest in the village. Ernest kept more pills and potions than any chemist. Charlie still didn't understand.

"It's simple, me old fruit, as they say in Yorkshire," I laughed. "We empty out the capsule and put in some icing sugar, so when I get the capsule from Dodger I swap them over and give Milly the wrong one." You had to cheat in the dog game but drugs was not the way.

Everything was arranged. We had sorted out the betting with one of our mates and told him not to back Milly until Dodger had backed the dog he thought was going to win. We had managed to get a capsule identical to the ones Dodger used; it hadn't crossed my mind that he would use anything else. If he did, we, or should I say

I, would be right up the creek without a paddle. I prayed that Dodger was true to form as I made my way to his house.

As I arrived, the other lads were there with their dogs. They were an unsavoury lot to say the least. Dodger opened the door and beckoned us all in. "Right," said Dodger, "you all know the score. I'm going to stop all the dogs bar one and that's Nicky's." The dog Dodger was talking about couldn't run a message he was so slow. "Right, lads," he went on, "I'm going to give you all a capsule; you just make sure it goes down the throat, right." I had my own capsule in my hand ready for the swap. The palms of my hands were starting to sweat and I could feel the capsule sticking to my palm. I was all set for doing a runner if they weren't the same pills or if anything started to go wrong. One by one he gave the capsules to the lads and watched them put them down the throats of the dogs. Much to my relief I had already swapped mine when he was watching one of the other dogs.

As Dodger came to me, I was just about to put the capsule down Milly's throat when he grabbed my hand. "Hold on a sec, Geordie." 'Shit!' I thought, 'He's twigged on.' I had one of those feelings like a kid when you've been caught nicking sweets from the shop. I looked at Dodger and thought, 'This is it; he's sussed out what's going on.'

"I'll do your dog," he said. He took the capsule from my hand, still sticky with sweat, and proceeded to put the capsule down Milly's throat himself. A sigh of relief entered my body.

"Why my dog, Dodger, why not the other lads' dogs?" I asked.

"Because I ken these lads, Geordie, and I dun't trust thee," he said.

"It's a bit late for trust when you've just dropped that pill down my little dog's throat."

"I had tu mek sure that job were done right, Geordie, and I feel a lot better now," he said, grinning all over his fat face.

"Well," I smiled, "if this job goes wrong, then it's down to you, Dodger."

"That's all right, Geordie, cos it wain't go wrong, will it?"

"It had better not, for thy sake, Dodger, cos 'ave got a lot of money on this race that dun't belong tu me, right, and if it gets beat, tha'll be eating thee dinner through a straw in hospital," said one of the other lads. He looked a real hard case, not the type you wanted to cross, and I couldn't help feeling sorry for Dodger if my plan worked and his didn't. It didn't bear thinking about.

By this time, Dodger was looking very sick at his mate's suggestion and without reply changed the subject. "Er, next thing is the betting, lads," he announced. "Let's have all the cash sorted out." They were all betting £50 and £60. When it came to me, I gave Dodger £15. I begrudged giving him that but I had to make a show. "Is that all thar's havin' on, Geordie?" he asked, with a sarky grin on his face.

"It's all we have. Charlie lost the rest at the betting shop trying to win a few more quid," I explained.

"Aye, that's typical of Charlie, but it leaves more for us," he said. I thought to myself what a greedy man he was and how the greed would be his downfall.

It was time to leave. I regretted leaving the £15 with Dodger but we had to show that we were going along with his scheme. As I got to the track with Milly I made straight for Charlie to see that our little plan was all set. All was well; all we had to do was sit tight and watch the fun and games.

The dogs were called for the race and Dodger was like a cat on hot bricks. The bookmakers started to bet; Milly was the favourite and the dog Dodger and his team were backing was 5-1. There was an almighty rush at the bookies and the 5-1 odds were soon gone. Every time a new price went up, it was taken, with Milly's price going out to 7 and 8-1. The bookies had caught on that there was only one dog trying. Ted, the lad who was doing the betting for us, went in at 8-1. There was such a volume of money for the other dog that our bets went on mostly unnoticed. Ted, of course, had been very careful and not put too much on with any one bookmaker.

The hare was running and Dodger was grinning all over his face. He was trying to add up the amount of money he was going to win with his pen and notepaper. The traps went up and Milly was out like a shot.

She was soon clear of the field and it was obvious to all watching that she was going to win the race. The dog Dodger had put the money on was a long way second to Milly, the others were strung out like runner beans. As Milly crossed the line, I looked up and caught sight of Dodger. His face was like thunder. He and his mates made straight for Charlie and me.

"Keep cool, Tom, and try and look disappointed like them," Charlie advised.

Dodger demanded to know how Milly had won the race. "Don't ask me," I said. "You gave the dog the pill because you said you couldn't trust me and it was *your* pill we used on the dogs." Dodger was speechless for once and one or two of his mates started to turn on him. I thought it was time to make a quick exit. Charlie and I made our excuses and left. We had arranged to meet Ted back at our house so no-one would see us sharing out the money.

All in all, we had won £800. Charlie and me had £40 a piece on and Ted had put another £20 on. It was a good job, very well done, but the most satisfaction for me was getting revenge on Dodger. The £320 I had won was just the icing on the cake, or in the capsule if you like, but it would help with the bills and provide a few treats for Jill and the kids too.

CHAPTER TEN

It was 5 o'clock in the morning, time to go to work. Jill would see to the dogs until Charlie came down to take them for a walk. I was half-way through my shift when John Norris, the Pit Deputy, came and asked if I would move to another part of the coal face. When I asked why, he explained that one of the younger lads, Smithy, had bust his hand and had to go home. I picked up my tools and set off to the new job. As I left, John said, "Watch yourself along there mind, Tom, it's a bad roof."

He was right, it was a bloody mess down there; bad timber, water running down from the roof. I just wished the job was done and I could be on my way home. I started to advance the roof supports over to the other side when there was an almighty rumble. I looked up and nearly choked on the dust. The roof was falling in. I was buried up to my shoulders in no time and couldn't move at all. All I could see was big lumps of rock falling from the roof, something I would never forget.

I didn't think that I would ever be able to get out of there alive. My life started to be replayed to me in flashes, the good times with Jill and the kids, the bad times, although to be honest it was more like *hard* times than *bad*. Would I ever see Jill and the kids again? Would they ever be able to get me out? I started to shout at the top of my voice. I shouted and shouted for what seemed ages, but was probably only a few minutes at most. Then I heard a voice coming through the noise and blackness, and it was better than winning the pools.

"It's all right Tom, we know where you are, we'll have you out in no time." It was Sharpy. He was one of the biggest men in the pit and as strong as three. After a couple of minutes I could see his shape in the distance. He was a mountain of a man, six foot five and nineteen stone. I have never been so glad to see anyone in my life. He was moving huge slabs of rock like they were pebbles on the beach.

It was a good hour before they pulled me free. As they moved the last piece of rock, I went cold. I couldn't feel my legs. The worst fears came into my head and I started to panic, "Don't worry Tom," said Sharpy trying to comfort me, "we'll soon have you at the pit top; let the doctor have a good look at you then."

The first aid officer arrived and Sharpy told him about my legs. He tried to comfort me further by saying that it was probably because I had been trapped for so long in the same position and the blood wasn't circulating. He was more concerned about getting all the blood cleaned up from my face and head so they could see how bad I was cut. As they cleaned all the dust away it became obvious that I would take a lot of stitching up. This was, however, still the least of my worries; I was still concerned about my back and my legs. The pain was really starting to get to me.

As I arrived at the hospital I was rushed straight into X-ray and then down onto the ward for the stitches. The X-ray didn't show up any serious damage and I was less worried now. The injection they had given me to kill the pain had started to work.

I put my feet gingerly from the bed onto the floor and started to walk, a bit uneasy at first, but getting there. "It's not too bad," I gasped at the doctor, "can I go home?"

"You still have a lot of bruising, Mr. Watson, all around your back and your legs, but there's not a lot we can do for you at the moment. I suppose it'll be all right, but you must take it easy." I assured him that I would. I'd have told him anything; I just wanted to go home.

I thanked the doctors and the nurses for all their help and started to make my way to the door. One of the sisters, looking a bit like Attila the Hun in a blue dress, stopped me. "And where do you think you are off to, Mr. Watson?" she asked.

"Home," I said. "The doc said it was OK, honest," I replied. "Ask him!"

"You can't go unless you go in an ambulance," she snapped.

"It's OK, I can manage, I feel fine," I said. I didn't want to turn up in an ambulance and frighten Jill and the kids half to death.

"I'm sorry," she said. "Hospital rules. If you want to go home; you go in the ambulance. If not, you stay in hospital. What's it to be Mr. Watson?"

I thought about it for a minute. If I stay in hospital Jill will think it's worse than it is. I had no choice. "The ambulance it is, then," I said, smiling in mock defeat. Sharpy went back to the pit to collect my clean clothes, which meant the rest of the day off for him, because it was too late to go back underground.

As the ambulance drew up outside our house you could see the curtains and nets twitching as the neighbours tried to get a look to see what was going on. Jill came to the door as white as a sheet.

"My God, what's happened to you?" she cried.

"It's all right, Mrs. Watson," the ambulance driver explained. "Tom's had a bit of an accident at the pit, but he's OK."

"It's enough to give someone a heart attack," she said, fighting back the tears. The injection I had for the pain was starting to wear off and as I stepped down from the ambulance I got such a sharp, hot pain up my spine that I thought I had been shot, but I managed to walk down the steps and into the house without letting it show to Jill and the neighbours.

During the night I was in so much pain that Jill had to send for the doctor. He was of the opinion that I had damaged a disc in my back and that I would be off work for some considerable time. This was just what I didn't want to hear. I was doing well at work and we were just starting to get on our feet. It was a real knockback.

The next few weeks were pure hell. I wasn't getting any better and we were starting to feel the pinch, money wise. There was only one thing for it, I would have to try and get back to work. I was nowhere near being fit enough but I had to try. The doctor tried to persuade me not to go back but I was determined to give it a go.

I was placed on light duties in the lamp room, filling the oil lamps and checking the wicks. A tedious job but it was better than sitting at home not earning a wage. After a few weeks of light work I was feeling a lot better and asked if I could go back to my old job. That turned out to be a big mistake. I hadn't completed my first shift when my back gave in, I couldn't move a muscle without shooting pains. I was in agony. Once again I was carried up to the pit top on a stretcher.

Over the next few weeks I was in and out of hospital like a yoyo. First they tried traction, that didn't work, then I was put in plaster cast from the neck down to my left ankle. They left one leg free so I could move around a little. The worst thing was trying to use the toilet. Can you imagine how difficult it was trying to sit on a toilet in a plaster cast from your neck to your waist, then down to your left ankle?

The cast had to stay on for four weeks. I was so glad when it was time for its removal, not only to see if it had helped my back, but because the thought of lying in a bath again for as long as I wanted was an inviting one. Jill came to the hospital with me to see if the cast had been a success. Having the sheer weight of the thing removed made me feel a whole lot better.

Jill was straight in at the doctor wanting to know the result. "Do you think it has been a success, Mr. Black?" she asked.

"It's very hard to say at this stage, Mrs. Watson. He'll have to take his time for the next few weeks before we can make any judgements."

"And what if it hasn't worked?" asked Jill

"We'll just have to cross that bridge when we come to it," was his reply. "I want to see you back here in six weeks time, Mr. Watson, and whatever you do, don't lift anything heavier than a newspaper!"

Over the next couple of days I started to take little walks to strengthen my legs. It was hard at first and I soon got tired but after a couple of weeks I was starting to feel much stronger. Charlie had been keeping the dogs going with help from Jill. She had been a saint throughout all of this. She saw to the kids, saw to me, and looked after the dogs as well. I wasn't allowed to do anything. If I tried to lift more than the paper and she caught me all hell would break loose.

"If you keep this up, Tom Watson," she would screech at me, "you'll end up in hospital with more than any bad back." I soon got the message.

I had been back to the hospital for more X-rays but when the results came through the doctor explained that it wasn't good news. The cast had not done what they had hoped and the X-rays showed that at least one of my discs was damaged.

"What's the next move?" asked Jill of Mr. Black, the doctor.

"Well, if he keeps getting this much trouble," said Mr. Black, "the only option left open is surgery."

"And will that cure my back?" I asked.

"There are no guarantees, Mr. Watson, it's a 50/50 chance, that's all."

"I'm no gambler," said Jill, "but I don't care much for those odds."

"No," I said, "neither do I, Mr Black. I think I'll take my chance the way I am for the time being."

It wasn't long after that I was back in hospital and this time I had a visit from a man from the NCB. He explained that he was the NCB doctor and he had come to examine me. After the examination he read all of my hospital records then came back to my bedside. He was shaking his head as he came into the room. "I'm sorry, Mr. Watson. I don't bring good news with me. I'm afraid that with the state of your back you won't be seeing any more of the pits. I'm afraid I'm going to have to retire you."

I was gobsmacked. "You can't!" I cried. "I'm only a young man and I've a wife and kids to feed."

"I'm sorry, Tom, but I have no choice. I can't be held responsible if anything should happen to you while working for the NCB." My world ... like the pit ... had caved in around me. I sat there in total shock as the truth began to hit me.

I used to look forward to visiting times from Jill but not on this occasion. How on earth was I going to break the news to her? How would she take it? At 2 o'clock the visitors trooped in. I could see Jill and Charlie walking down the ward, and as soon as Jill got to the bed she knew something was up. She knew me too well.

Before Jill could ask any questions, Mr. Black came over. "Mr. Watson," he said. "I must apologise for not being here when Dr. Wade came to examine you. I was on call. I'm so sorry. I can only apologise."

He was just about to leave when Jill asked, "Who's Dr. Wade?"

"Oh, he's the doctor from the NCB," replied Mr. Black and off he went to continue his rounds.

"Well," said Jill looking me straight in the eye, "what did he want?" I had to tell her, she would get to know sooner or later and it had to come from me. After the initial shock wore off and the news sank in Jill just leant over, gave me a big kiss and said, "Don't worry love, we'll get by somehow," and somehow I had the feeling she was right.

CHAPTER ELEVEN

Autumn had arrived and the leaves were starting to fall from the trees. Winter was just around the corner. There was one consolation of being retired from the mines, I still received my coal allowance. At least we would be warm over the winter, if nothing else. Money was as scarce as rocking horse droppings but as long as we had the dogs we were in with a chance.

Both dogs were entered for weekend races, but at separate tracks; the dog at Lowgate and the bitch at Doncaster, and both dogs were in with a chance. Charlie and I had eight pounds to our names after the entry fees. Poor Charlie was going to have to climb the fence to save paying in. I was now well known at most of the tracks and didn't have to pay the bookies until after the race, that's if the dog was beaten. It saved the bookie from giving you a ticket and it saved you standing around sorting out the cash. If you had a bet the bookie would put it down in the book as 'hat' or 'myself', they used anything that they could relate to you. They always put me down as Geordie. The race was about to start.

Our dog was two and a half to one with Honest Jim. "Two and a half eight quids Jim," I shouted.

"Thar's got that, Geordie," he said as he turned to watch the race.

The traps were up and Pip was out like a flash. "Go on my son, thar can do it," Charlie screamed at him. He was coming up to the last bend and was well clear as he passed the winning line.

"Get the money quick, Tom, and we'll make straight off for Donny," shouted Charlie who was off to pick up the dog. I stood in the queue, the bet worked out in my head. Two and a half times eight pound was £20. Plus the eight pound still in my pocket. I was next in line to be paid.

"Right Geordie, that'll be two and a half half quids; twenty-five bob."

"Hang on a minute there Jim, I think you've made a mistake," I said, starting to get a bit worried.

"How's that like?" he replied, a slight smirk on his face.

"I bet two and a half *eight* quids."

"No, no, Geordie, it was two and a half *half* quids." The argument went on for quarter of an hour. There were plenty who heard me make the bet and told Jim so but he wouldn't listen. By this time, Charlie was back to see why the delay, mad as hell at being kept waiting. When Charlie heard what had happened, he saw red, and tried to crack old 'Honest Jim' right on the nose. Big Sharpy, who was standing there, had to use all his strength to stop him.

"It's no good," I said to Charlie, "flattening him won't get us our money." As Sharpy dragged Charlie away, I turned to the bookie and said, "I promise you one thing, Mr. Honest Jim, you'll live to regret this. Mark my words, you'll regret every hair on your head," adding sarcastically over my shoulder, as I turned to leave, "Oh you can't, can you, you're bald!"

The next few weeks were hard. Money was still scarce and it was getting close to Christmas. We were clutching at straws, hoping that Jill would win at the bingo or that Charlie might win big on the horses. I was still hell bent on getting one back at Honest Jim but we couldn't do it without having a few quid behind us. Someone upstairs must have been watching over us because one fine morning, in a brown envelope, there was a big fat cheque for £70 from the Inland Revenue. I didn't have a clue why we had been sent it but I wasn't going to look a gift horse in the mouth.

We entered the dog at Lowgate that weekend. Jill had taken out the money she needed for the bills, food and stuff, and that left me with a tenner. Charlie had his wages from work so we both had a bit of cash to spare.

"What's the job then, Tom? How's thar goin tu skin that bookie wi the money we've got?"

"I'll tell you how, Charlie. We're going to give him the money."

"How's thar mean?" screamed Charlie. "Thar must be barmy Tom. Thar's seen card, Pip's in same race as bookie's dog and we can lick that easy."

"That's right, Charlie," I smiled. Charlie was getting impatient.

"But what odds will we get? Evens at best. That won't skint him, or win us a fortune, so what's thar gunna do, Tom?" By now Charlie was pacing up and down like a caged tiger.

"Well, here's the plan," I went on. "You know that it's the Christmas Handicap and the first three go through to the next round." Charlie nodded. "Well, what we have to do is make sure we don't win, but that we do qualify to go through."

"Easier said than done," said Charlie scratching his head. "How's that goin' tu work that miracle?"

"You leave that to me Charlie. If things go wrong then it's down to me."

"Aye, thar's boss, Tom. I'll just have to trust thee on this one. I didn't think thar could pull off that job wi Dodger, but thar did. So, like thar says, it's down to thee."

We were all at the track for the first round. Jill, the kids, Ted and Sharpy; it was nice to see them all again. The kids were told to shout for Pip and Milly when they were running and to stand next to Honest Jim when they were shouting. Pip was the first to run. He was in with the bookie's dog. I'd given Charlie strict instructions to make sure that he paid the bet on with Honest Jim, the bookie who had robbed us. Pip was on at six to four, better than I thought we'd get, but that was because the bookie had backed his own dog.

Charlie went in. "Fifteen to ten Pip, down to Charlie, paid on," said the bookie.

Pip came out well and was soon up with the leaders. "Ah hope thar's done job right, Tom." Charlie was starting to get a bit anxious now and to tell the truth I was starting to feel the same way. Pip was only two lengths behind Captain, the bookie's dog. If he won the race all my plans had gone up in smoke. Please God, don't let Pip win. I tried to remain calm and yet had to look excited for the benefit of the bookie and the punters. The dogs were coming round the last bend, Pip was starting to tire. As they flashed past the post Pip was beaten into third place. I looked up to the sky: "Thank you Lord," I muttered under my breath.

Honest Jim looked down from the wooden box he was standing on. "I don't know why thar backed Pip to beat Captain," he said. "He'd no chance and I'll tell thee summit else, Geordie, I'll win Christmas Handicap with him as well." Charlie, by this time, was as red as a beetroot and dying to say something. I had to get in quick.

"Thar's probably right at that, Jim," I answered before Charlie opened his mouth and put his foot in it. The main thing was that Pip was through to the next round.

It was time for Milly's race. If things went as smoothly as they did in Pip's race, I thought, we were halfway there. Milly opened at two to one, that was a price we didn't expect to get. "There's summit wrong here, Charlie," I said.

"How's thar mean, Tom, it's a good price."

"Aye, too good if you ask me," I replied.

We were standing talking when there was a rush for number five, a dog called Teapot. Sharpy was standing behind us. "Does thar ken who's doing the betting for that dog?" he asked.

"I've not a clue, Sharpy, who is doing the betting?"

"Well, I'll tell thee, Tom, it's thee old mate, Honest Jim. He's had someone bring it in for him."

I hadn't reckoned on Milly's race being hot and hoped that I had judged the race right. Anyhow, it was too late to do anything about it now, the hare was running. Milly was up there with them when she ran into trouble and got knocked back into last. 'Come on girl,' I thought, 'just pick yourself up and run into a place'. She had started to pick up a few places, one at a time, and coming into the last bend she was neck and neck with the three dog for third place when she missed her footing and stumbled. She was out of the race and out of the handicap.

"Bad luck, Geordie," grinned Jim the bookie rubbing his hands with glee, no doubt thinking about the money he had won on his dog Teapot.

Sharpy, his huge frame bursting out of his clothes, was standing next to me when the comment was made, and he was not a man to cross.

"That were your dog, Jim," he shouted for all to hear.

"Don't be so silly and go away," said Jim trying to ignore him.

Sharpy was not a man to be argued with, especially if he was losing money. "That bloody dog is yours and what's more I'll prove it," he said. He set off round to the kennels. "Hey, you," he hollered, "aye, you with the number five dog. Who does that dog belong to and I don't want any slaver about it being your dog." The man could see that Sharpy meant business. If Sharpy said it was Christmas in the middle of June you would start singing carols. He dragged the man round to the bookies like a sack of potatoes. "Now son, last chance," he said, "it's you or him, your choice." The lad was shaking like a leaf by this time.

"It's his dog not mine," he stammered. Sharpy let him go, and he was off like a shot. Mind you, if I was being threatened by Sharpy I'd have done the same!

"That's all I wanted to hear," boomed Sharpy. He picked Jim up by the lapels and shook him like a rag doll. Then he took all of his equipment, his betting board, his box and his bag and threw them all over the wall and onto the track.

With the commotion that was going on and the large crowd gathering, the Manager appeared. Someone had informed him that there was a small disagreement going on. That must have been the understatement of the century. After we explained about Jim putting his own dog in the race, the manager looked from Jim to Sharpy and back to Jim again. "If this is true about Teapot, Jim," said the Manager, "and I can't prove it now, 'cos the other lad's done a runner, it would be wise if the connections didn't run him in the next round if you get my drift." Jim knew he was in the wrong and left it at that.

The Manager then turned on Sharpy who was standing there looking as innocent as a choirboy. "And as for you, my lad," he started, "if you weren't so bloody big I would have you thrown out. As it is," the Manager went on, "I doubt if I could find anyone big enough or daft enough to have a go. So just you behave yourself or I'll have to send for the Bobby." With that he turned on his heels and walked off.

He hadn't got more than ten yards before Sharpy exploded with laughter; he was in near hysterics. The last time someone sent the Bobbies for Sharpy two of them ended up in hospital. Through his tears of laughter, he said, "Well Charlie, Tom, we may have had some good luck and some bad, but all in all we've had a bloody good laugh tonight and that's done me the power of good."

When we got home the first thing to do was to check the dogs' feet. Both dogs were sound which was a big relief. Now we could go ahead with the plan. Pip was still in the handicap so he was all right. Milly was out, so the next best thing was to enter her for an ordinary race on the same night as the handicap heats. All in all, this would probably work out better because if Pip and Milly had been drawn together in the next round that would have been one hell of a headache, not knowing which dog to bet.

The next round heats had been drawn. Pip had missed the heat that Captain, the bookie's dog, was in, so we just kept to the same plan: back him with Honest Jim and hope he gets through to the next round. The plan was the same for Milly. Just steady her down a bit, not enough to hurt her, but just to make sure she didn't win. You only had to shout at Milly to make her think she was in your bad books and she wasn't the same bitch. Both of the races went off like clockwork. Charlie backed both dogs with Honest Jim and paid on. Pip was third and Milly was fourth in their respective races. Honest Jim's dog won his heat, but he was only five yards faster than Pip. I knew in my heart that we had more than five yards in hand.

The only problem was, we were still short of cash. Charlie, bless him, was working all the hours that God sent in overtime at the pit trying to get as much money as he could because when Charlie fancied something, it was either all or nothing.

It was only three weeks to Christmas and both Jill and I were starting to worry about buying presents for the kids. They all had their little lists written out and at the top of each list was a "Bike" but there was no way we could afford to buy one between them, never mind one each. We had to try and sit them down and explain the situation. They were good kids and they didn't kick up a stink, but you could see the disappointment on their faces.

Colin, the eldest, tried to ease the situation. "I'm ... I'm not that worried about a bike, Mam," he said, "we still have the old one."

"Who wants a bike, anyway," laughed Bobby, trying to help out.

"I do," said little Peter, the youngest, tears welling up in his eyes.

"Look, Peter, you know Dad's been off work," said Colin, trying to explain. "We'll get what Dad and Mam can afford." He gave Peter a look that shut him up. It was hard to tell who was the most upset, me or Jill.

Bobby looked up at his Mother, "Why are you crying, Mam?" he asked

"I'm not, Bobby," she said, wiping the tears away on the back of her sleeve. "I've ... er just got something in my eye."

She was a good mother and it was breaking my heart to see her upset this way. I was starting to fill up myself. I had a lump in my throat the size of a football. "Never mind, lads," I said, trying to swallow that football, "you never know what Santa might find for you lot, you just never know," hoping under my breath something would turn up.

Jill was up off her seat saying, "Come on, let's have you young 'uns up to bed, school tomorrow." She was still upset so I said that I'd tuck them in.

As I was saying goodnight, Bobby sat up in bed. "It's all right

Dad, if we don't get a bike, honest," said Bobby. And I think he meant it too.

"We'll do our best, boys, you do know that, don't you?"

"We do, Dad, we do," they all said together. The lump started returning to my throat as I said, "Goodnight, lads, sleep tight, mind the bugs don't bite, and if they do ... bite the buggers back!"

I was now more determined than ever to make sure the job came off. The following week was the last round before the final; we *had* to qualify. We had drawn the same heat as Captain who was favourite to win the handicap outright. Milly had been eased in her race which was just what we wanted. Charlie and I had scraped together what money we had. It wasn't much but it was just enough to make the bookie think that both the dogs were trying. Pip ran second to Captain but he was only beaten by three lengths, his fitness was beginning to show through. Milly ran third, but a fair race. We were now through to the final with Pip; the plan was working like clockwork. The only problem was the money to bet the dogs. Charlie said he would have £100 by the end of the week and that half of it was mine. I thanked him but told him I couldn't take it. There had to be another way. I had to find my own money to bet the dogs. All that week, as I was training the dogs, my brain was doing overtime, but to no avail. I just couldn't come up with anything.

It was the day before the final. I may not have the money to bet the dogs myself, but I made sure that they were super fit for Charlie to have his money on. It was Friday afternoon and I was sitting about the house feeling depressed but trying not to show it to Jill. She was looking like the cat that got the mouse with cream on, singing and laughing at the same time. "It's no good Tom, I can't keep it to myself any longer," she laughed, "your face is as long as a fiddle."

"Well, what's all the secrecy?" I asked, my face starting to brighten up too. It had to be good news the mood she was in.

"You won't go mad when I tell you now, Tom, will you?" she asked.

"What's up? No I won't," I assured her. "Just tell me." I was starting to worry again now.

"Well I might as well come straight to the point," she said. "I've cashed in an insurance policy for £120. You needed the money to back the dogs and I couldn't see you without a bet, not after all the work you have put in on those dogs and all the money that's gone on with Honest Jim. I just couldn't let that skunk get away with what he did."

She stopped for breath, her eyes filling up. She always started to cry when she was mad. "I was saving that policy for a rainy day," she said, "but who cares about the bloody weather, anyway," she snivelled.

She was still snivelling when I stood up and put my arms around her. "Wipe those tears away, woman, or you'll have me in the same state," I said as we both gave each other a big hug.

It was the day of the final and both dogs were fit and ready. The kids had strict instructions not to shout or upset the dogs, especially Milly. Charlie came down to sort out the money. I suggested to him to let Ted and Sharpy give him a hand with the betting but he was having none of it.

"No, Tom, I'm doing this one myself, I want to see the look on that so called bookie's face when he's counting out the money into my hand."

"Not 'when' Charlie 'if'." I was very superstitious and I didn't like to count my chickens before they hatched, but there was no point in arguing with him about the betting. His mind was made up and to be honest I could understand his feelings.

We were all about ready to start off for the track when Peter started feeling poorly. "Mam," he wailed, "I feel sick." Jill got him to the bathroom just in time.

"I can't go now, Tom, not with Peter like this, I don't even know what's up with him. I may have to call the doctor," she went on.

"I know what's wrong with him," said Bobby smugly.

"Well ...?" we both said together, waiting to hear the reason for his sickness.

126

"He's been eating dates," said Bobby. "We told him just to have a couple but he ate the lot." Jill had been putting a few things by for Christmas and unfortunately Peter had found them.

"Well, anyway," said Jill, "I can't go with him like this. I'll stay home with the kids."

I could see the disappointment in her face, but she was right. We couldn't take a chance at upsetting the dogs by stopping and starting the car to let Peter out to be sick. Time was getting on and we had to get to the track. I kissed Jill good-bye and she wished us luck.

"We'll not need that," shouted Charlie as we drove off. Always the optimist, Charlie.

"Just the same, I'll keep my fingers crossed," she shouted.

"And me," said Bobby.

"Me, too," said Colin. Peter was just about to echo the same when he had to make a dash for the bathroom again.

As we approached the track both dogs stood up; they knew where they were. We had been making a fuss of Milly all day and all the way to the track. She was lapping it up. Pip was completely different, he was such a laid back dog, but always alert.

The handicap final was the race before Milly's. If Pip got beat we only had the £20 prize money for getting to the final to bet on Milly. It didn't bear thinking about. 'No good worrying now,' I told myself as I walked along to the paddock. Charlie was there with Pip all coated up to keep him nice and warm. Honest Jim was in the paddock with his dog, Captain. He only had his racing jacket on and the dog looked frozen stood there. I had asked Ted to take Pip on with Jill being at home. "Keep him on the move, Ted," I instructed, "and leave his coat on until the last seconds."

Honest Jim chirped in, "Thar's got that dog tu soft by half Geordie and he can't win anyhow; best thar can 'ope for is second."

"You're probably right, Jim," I replied, trying not to think of being beat.

"I know I'm right," he countered, "there's only one winner and that's my Captain."

I could see Charlie and Sharpy standing at the back, steam coming out of their ears. They were bursting to have a go at Jim. I flashed Charlie a look that told him in no uncertain terms to keep his mouth shut. I didn't dare give Sharpy the same look!

"DOGS TO THE TRAPS," came the announcement. "FOUR MINUTES TO THE OFF." Captain was clear favourite, Pip was three to one.

"Not much of a price for a dog that can't win," said Sharpy, taunting Jim.

"Too right he can't win, big feller," and with a stroke of the chalk he upped the price to four to one.

There was plenty of activity in the betting ring and a lot of money was going on a dog who had only been beaten two lengths by Captain in an earlier heat. Pip's price went out to five to one. Charlie and I looked at each other. We weren't going to get any better odds than that. "THIRTY SECONDS TO THE OFF," came the announcement.

Charlie went steaming in to Honest Jim. "Ten for Two Jim," he shouted, shoving £200 into the bookie's hand and waiting for his ticket. We wanted no mistakes over the amount of money we were having on.

"You've got that Charlie and more if thar want's it," Jim laughed sarcastically.

"Thar wain't be saying that after race," said Charlie quietly under his breath as he looked for a vantage point.

Sharpy was standing behind Charlie when he struck the bet and had intended to go on to the next bookie down but the odds there were only four to one so he backed Pip with Honest Jim as well. "£100 to £20 Jim," shouted Sharpy, thrusting the money into Jim's hand and standing there until he received his ticket.

"Thar's got that, big feller," he smirked as if winning the race was a mere formality for his dog, Captain.

Sharpy came running over to where I was standing to watch the race, he didn't have to push or shove, not at his height; you could always pick Sharpy out in a crowd as he stood head and shoulders above most of the onlookers.

"Does thar think he'll win, Tom?" asked Sharpy looking down on me with a grin from ear to ear.

"He'd best had Sharpy," I laughed, "or I won't dare go home."

The traps went up and Pip was out like a bat out of hell. Captain lost a yard or two trapping but had some good early pace. Going into the first bend it was Captain by a length from Teddy the dog he had just beaten in a heat, then came Pip hot on their heels. Coming up to the last bend Pip had moved into second place, just half a length behind Captain. As they came out of the bend Pip was just in front and when Pip hit the front there was no catching him. He flashed past the post, winning by three and a half lengths to an enormous roar from the crowd and a huge sigh of relief from me. That was the first part of the job done.

Charlie went racing round to the bookies to confront Jim. "That's £1,200 thar owes me," he grinned, as he presented the ticket to Honest Jim's clerk. Jim was still visibly shaken with disbelief that Captain had been beaten. He counted out the money into Charlie's hand without saying a word, still dumbstruck.

The attention left the books for the moment and turned to the centre or the track where Ted was receiving the trophy and the prize money. Charlie and I greeted Ted and Pip as they left the centre of the track. "Well done, Tom," said Ted smiling all over his face. "Thar said he wouldn't be far off and thar were right, he was spot on. He ran a cracker. I only hope Sharpy managed to get my bit of a bet on."

"He did that Ted and got five to one," I confirmed.

"Cor, them's Ascot prices them," said Ted rubbing his hands with glee.

Next move was to wash Pip's feet and get him coated up against the cold. There was only a couple more races before Milly's. We asked Sharpy's nephew to sit with Pip while I rubbed Milly down with an old embrocation.

Charlie was sorting out the money ready for the race. "What's thar having on, Tom?" he asked getting all excited.

"It'll not be as much as you, Charlie, that's for certain."

"How's thar mean?" he asked, sounding a bit put out.

"Well, knowing you Charlie, you'll be putting the lot on. Much though I'd like to join you, I've got responsibilities."

"Thar's got to have it on, thar's got to Tom," said Charlie, trying his best to sway me.

"Charlie, we've got £600 each. It's Christmas and there's no way I can justify risking losing the whole lot and be able to look those kids in the face on Christmas morning. We've got £60 each from the prize money, we'll both give Ted a tenner, that leaves £50 each. I'll put £200 to the fifty to make it up to £250 and that's my bet, so there's no point in saying owt else, Charlie, my mind's made up." Charlie knew I wouldn't change my mind and left it at that.

The announcement came for the dogs in the eighth race, the one before Milly's, to go to the paddock. Ted and I decided to go and check on Pip and Sharpy's nephew. On the way round we bumped into Billy Evans. "Well done, Geordie, a nice little job if ah say so myself." I tried to look innocent as if we had no idea what he was on about. "Oh, come on, lads, I was here the night Honest Jim ripped you off and I heard you say you would get your own back! Well lad, thar's done it in some style tunight, and if I were thee I'd be happy to call it a day now."

"How's thar mean, Billy," said Ted, who had just caught up with us.

"Well I'll tell thee, Ted, I've just overheard something in the car park, while I was looking for a set of papers for a dog I'd sold last week."

"And," said Ted, "get tu point lad, we haven't got a lot of time."

"All I'm goin' to say, Geordie, is have a good look at Honest Jim's dog that's in the same race as Milly." With that little bit of information he turned quickly and walked away.

That could mean only one thing. A 'Ringer'. I sent Ted round to the paddock with Milly and set off to find Charlie. After explaining to him what was going on he was more determined than ever to try and skint that twister Honest Jim. We set off for the paddock with Charlie muttering to himself about how bent Honest Jim was by running a ringer.

"He hasn't won, not yet Charlie," I said, trying to calm him down, adding, "This could work to our advantage."

"How's thar mean, Tom," he asked, stopping for a brief moment.

"Well, the bookie thinks that his ringer will win the race, right. So he'll push the price of the other dogs out. So, if Milly is lucky enough to win the race, I reckon he'll have to dig so deep into his pockets he'll think he's mining. On the other hand, the handicapper might spot the ringer and throw it out. Anyhow, there's only one way to find out, come on, Charlie," I said dragging him by the arm.

Milly was standing in the paddock all coated up after being examined. Ted was making a good old fuss of her and she was enjoying every bit it. The handicapper came to the ringer. Would he spot it or not? He looked at the dog closely, at his feet, in his ears for the markings and on his chest. "Right, lads," he said, "take the dogs on tu traps; it's way too cold to be standing about here." He had missed it and to be honest, if it was a ringer, I couldn't spot the difference either.

There was only one way to find out. The betting market would tell. Ted had left his instructions with Sharpy just to back Milly if Charlie and I backed her. I decided to increase my bet to £300. I was really wound up as tight as Charlie but I thought what the hell, I would love to put that bookie right in his place. If Milly got beat there was still enough to give the kids a good Christmas.

The bookie's dog opened at 5 - 2 and soon went out to 3 - 1. As we expected there was one mad rush and the price for his dog, Hotpot, had gone. Jim had a team of men backing his dog with every other bookie. Honest Jim was shouting at the top of his voice trying to pull money in for the other dogs. Milly went out to 4 - 1. Charlie had the money to bet. He was having £600 plus my £300.

"£3600 to £900," Charlie shouted to Jim. Jim studied for a while. "Thar's got four monkeys," meaning £500 on at 4 - 1." Charlie thrust the money into Jim's hand and stood there waiting.

"Now what's thar after, Charlie," Jim asked.

"Ticket," said Charlie very slowly, "thar's robbed us once and I'm not up for thee to pull same stunt again."

"Here's ticket, but thar waint be collecting," snapped Jim.

Sharpy, who had been watching over Charlie's back just in case he lost his rag decided to have his two penn'orth in, asked "And why not Jim?"

"Because Hotpot will win race," Jim snapped.

"Thar said same about Captain and where did he finish?" Sharpy countered quickly.

"This isn't Captain," Jim shouted back.

"Aye, and it bloody well isn't Hotpot either," Sharpy snapped. Honest Jim just stood there with his mouth open. He knew that we knew and it was too late to do anything about it. While all this was going on Charlie was busy spreading the rest of the cash amongst the other bookies and making sure he received a ticket from each one.

The hare was running. If ever we needed help from above, tonight was the night. The traps went up and Hotpot was out like a catapult. "Catch that," shouted Honest Jim as the dog flew to the first bend. Milly was four lengths behind him. As they came round the next bend Hotpot ran wide and lost two lengths. The dog was fast but he was a ringer and more likely than not he had never seen this track before. That can be suicide for some dogs. Going into the last two bends Milly was just behind him; he only had to run off at the bend again and Milly would have a great chance. Just as we had thought, the dog was track-licked. Coming round the last bend Hotpot went wide again just leaving Milly the room to come in up the inside rail. As they came to the straight they were neck and neck. Honest Jim was jumping up and down on his beer crate screaming for his dog and puffing on his cigar like a steam train. Charlie and Sharpy were shouting at the top of their voices, drowning everyone else out. As the two dogs crossed the line together, there was no separating them.

Charlie made straight down to the winning line to talk to the wide lads. These were the lads that only bet on the photo finish. "What's won?" Charlie asked hastily.

"Thar's no splitting them," said Old Tadger. He was one of the best judges on the track. "Tha'll not get a fag paper between them," he said.

The announcement came over the speakers that the Judge was calling for another print. Tadger was right, it was desperately close. The tension was unbearable. Honest Jim was pacing up and down puffing on his cigar like there was no tomorrow. Charlie had chewed his fingers down to the knuckles. It was a desperate time for all concerned.

At last there was some action from the Judge's box. You could here someone fumbling with the mike. There was a high whingeing screech before the loudspeaker was clear. A deadly hush fell over the crowd as they waited for the result, you could hear a pin drop a mile away. Then came the announcement. "AFTER HAVING TWO PRINTS, THE RESULT OF THE EIGHTH RACE IS ..." I held my breath, my stomach in knots "... FIRST, NUMBER TWO, MILLY. — SECOND, NUMBER FIVE, HOTPOT."

There was a huge roar from the crowd. Charlie and Sharpy made straight for Honest Jim, Ted and I followed close behind. I wanted to see the look on Jim's face as he paid out. I had waited a long time for this and I wasn't going to miss it now. Charlie waited until there was a big enough crowd around the bookie to rub more salt in the wound. He wanted everyone to see the revenge. Jim had already paid out some of the punters and was gathering the rest of his money from the bottom of his bag. He was ashen-white and kept fumbling the money. Charlie decided to step forward for our winnings. There was a big enough crowd to humiliate him now and Charlie was never one to miss a big chance. "Right, Jim," he boomed, "thar owes me £4,500." The crowd stood there in silence watching him count out the money into Charlie's hand. He had got to £3,500 when he stepped off his stool and went along to one of his associates. Jim had to borrow £1,000 to pay off the bet. Revenge was very, very sweet and I couldn't help but remind him about the night he had robbed Charlie and I.

"Thar's right to have a go at me, Geordie," said Jim looking very sick.. "Thar's done a right job on me and it should never have happened for the sake of a few quid, but thar promised to make me pay and thar's done that, good and proper. I've learnt one thing out of all this and that's never to cross swords with thee again, Geordie lad." With that, Honest Jim closed his bag and headed off home trudging his feet as he went. A very sorry man.

Charlie and I sorted out our money. I had won nearly £2,000 with the prize money and everything. We had ten bob notes and pound notes and tenners falling out of every pocket we had. It was the most money I had ever won, or seen. I couldn't wait to get home and tell Jill and the kids the good news.

As we pulled up at the door I could see Jill through the window sitting watching the telly. We fed the dogs before we went into the house. I had an awful habit of tossing my keys on the bench in the back kitchen if the dog had lost and that's just what I did. I told Charlie to try and keep a straight face as we went into the sitting room without a word being spoken. Jill had assumed the worst when she heard the keys on the table and went out into the kitchen to get the supper. We waited until she put the meal down in front of us on the table. Until then, not a word had been spoken, and Charlie and I were fit to burst. We couldn't contain ourselves any longer. We both stood up and started to empty our pockets, tossing the cash up into the air and jumping for joy at the same time.

There was money all over the place and Jill just stood there staring, her mouth wide open. "You pair of rotten, useless toads," she shouted, "I've sat here all night wondering what had gone on and how the dogs had done. When I heard those keys hit the bench I felt sick and to make things worse you two rotten sods have not said a word since you came in. I could bloody well kill the pair of you." When she settled down I told her how much we had won. She just sat there and cried with joy. The kids could have Christmas after all.

We decided not to tell the kids how much we had won, instead we thought we'd surprise them on Christmas morning. The next day the first thing we did was go into town and buy three bikes. It was nice to go into a shop and pay cash for a change and not ask for tick. We had the bikes delivered to Charlie's house and we collected them on Christmas Eve. We asked Charlie to join us for dinner but he said he was spending it with his folks.

He did ask if he could come down first thing Christmas morning though to see the kids' faces. The three of us were more excited than the kids.

Charlie was on the doorstep at six on Christmas morning. I was up and ready to see to the dogs and Charlie gave me a hand. Jill just had to do her best to keep the lads in bed until we came back in. The presents were on a chair each for the kids with their names on . We put all their toys, games and bits and pieces on them. There was also a pile of stuff each from Charlie. We had left the bikes in the kitchen so they couldn't see them.

The kids were just starting to stir when Charlie and I got in. It was still dark when Peter shouted down the stairs. "Has Santa been yet, Mam, has he?"

"Yes, he has, you can come down now," shouted Jill. She had barely finished speaking when they were there and through the door. Each one going for his own pile of toys.

"Thanks, Mam, thanks, Dad," they said all together as they tore at the paper, and then, as if they all suddenly remembered. "And thanks and Merry Christmas to you as well Charlie." They were surrounded by paper and toys.

I tipped Charlie the wink and he nudged Jill. It was time for the big surprise.

"Colin," I said, "do your mam a good turn son and bring in the milk from the kitchen please."

"Oh, OK Mam," he shrugged, tearing himself away from all the goodies and trudging through all the wrapping paper into the kitchen. As he got through the kitchen door his little eyes nearly popped out of his head. "Bobby, Peter," he cried excitedly, "come and have a look in here."

Bobby and Peter ran to the door. "Bikes!" they screamed. "Bikes! Look, Mam, Dad, Charlie, we've all got bikes!"

It was sheer joy to see their faces. Jill was crying. There was a sign of a tear in Charlie's eye and I had that big old turnip back in my throat again. It seemed so silly, but we were all so happy. It was the best Christmas ever.

CHAPTER TWELVE

Come the beginning of March it was time again for the sales in Ireland. Charlie and I had been looking forward to the sales since Christmas. Jill had made sure that Charlie saved some of his winnings by taking some of the money from him before he spent it all and hiding it in our house. He kept trying to beg and borrow making all sorts of excuses, but he had a better chance of winning the pools than getting a penny from Jill. His savings were as safe as if they had been in Fort Knox.

We sold Pip to the couple that bought Patch. They had seen him run in the Christmas Handicap and we knew that he'd be well looked after. That left us with Milly. She was one of the family now and there was no way on this earth we could part with her. With the money from selling Pip, the savings from the big win, minus Jill's spending spree on the kids and furniture, we had just enough to get ourselves off to Ireland to look for fresh stock.

Charlie and I had met up with another Geordie lad, Matt Cross. He was a grand lad, Matt, always trying to earn a crust, selling this, buying that, even if some of the things he did weren't exactly within the law. His wife, Rita, and Jill got on like a house on fire but I had never met a couple as queer as Matt and Rita. Rita drank like a fish and fought like a man. Her tipple was Newcastle Brown Ale straight from the bottle. I had seen her take on men at arm wrestling and beat most of them, mind you, the fact that she was five foot ten and fifteen stone meant that she didn't get a lot of takers. Matt was just the opposite. Five foot six, ten stone and as quiet as a mouse. He didn't want to fight with anyone, especially not Rita.

Matt got wind that Charlie and I were off to Ireland and was desperate to come along. He had never been before and begged me to let him come. "Please, Tom, I won't be a picking of bother and I'd love to go."

I remembered how excited I had been about my first trip and told Matt he could go on one condition. I didn't want any trouble like the last time with Paddy and Mick bouncing cheques.

Matt assured me and Charlie that he was a cash man and he wouldn't be a bit of bother. "If I'm off to Ireland then I'd better start doing some trading," said Matt, rubbing his hands.

He was a bit of a rogue, Matt, the type of bloke that if you shook his hand you checked to see if you still had all your fingers, but Matt was all right with his friends ... I hoped!

There were only three weeks to go before the sales. Matt was wheeling and dealing like it was going out of style but he was still short of cash. Matt and Rita lived about 20 miles away so we only saw them when we went to the track. One night at Lowgate track we bumped into Billy Evans. "How's thar keeping, Tom?" he asked.

"Not too bad, Billy, how's yerself?"

"Fair to middling tha knows," said Billy, "a've come wi a dog for that mate o' thine."

I was puzzled. "Who's that ... Charlie?" I asked with a puzzled look.

"Nay lad, not Charlie, t'other one, Matt what's his name, Cross," said Billy.

"I'm surprised he's buying dogs," I said. "He's supposed to be going to Ireland next week with me and Charlie."

"Well, a've got this dog here for him ... if thar can call it a dog," he went on. "It's fighting its cap off, a real villain. A've told 'im this, but he says as long as it's fawn he dun't care! To tell thee the truth, Tom, I'm well pleased to be getting shot of the old sod and for £2 it's his."

Just then someone else approached and asked if we had seen Matt; he too had a fawn dog. Then Matt and Rita came wandering into the track and were approached by another three men, all with fawn dogs!

"Right lads, take them all to the car park, I'll be with you in two shakes." He handed Billy his £2, thanked him and off he went, saying over his shoulder, "I'll see you next week, Tom." I just stood there scratching my head. There was something going on but I just couldn't work out what the hell it was and, if the truth were told, I wasn't sure I wanted to know.

Come mid week when the weekly "Greyhound Owner" came out it all became clear. Matt had put an advert in the paper which read:

"Open Race Dog for Sale. Winner of open at Lowgate, winner of open at Doncaster, winner of last five races. Genuine reason for sale, owner moving abroad. £125.00 for a quick sale. Colour - Fawn. Age 2 years."

Then the penny dropped; Matt was going to send out all of the fawn dogs to whoever sent him the £125. All he had to do was sit tight and wait for the money orders to arrive from the post office by motor cycle delivery.

Charlie and I decided that we would have a run over to see Matt. We hadn't been before but after making one or two enquiries we found out where he lived. We arrived at about 8.30 pm and found the house empty. There were two big rough-looking characters there, as big as boxers, each holding a fawn dog, standing at the gate.

"Whatever you do, Tom, keep the bleeding engine running," whispered Charlie as these two bruisers approached the car.

"Is your name, Cross?" snarled the first one.

"Cross, no not me, pal," I said, remembering Charlie's advice.

"Well you must be friends of his," he growled.

"Friends of who?" said Charlie. "I never heard of ... er what's his name, Cross. I'm just looking for Hopper Street, said Charlie quickly ... er can you tell me where it is?"

The man stared at Charlie; I was sure he didn't believe a word he had said. "No," he snapped, "I'm not from round here."

"Right then," said Charlie quickly. "Er, thanks a lot, must dash, sorry to have troubled you, we must try and find Copper ... er I mean Hopper Street!" and with that I drove off as fast as I could.

The next day Matt and Rita arrived on our doorstep. "Right, Tom, I've got me a few quid for the sales now," he smiled.

"I thought you might have managed it Matt," I laughed, "I saw the ad in the paper."

"Oh, you know then," said Matt sheepishly, his face reddening.

"Aye and I also know that you had some big nasty visitors to your place."

"I thought I might," said Matt looking very embarrassed. "That's why we did a flit. They won't find me now, I've moved into another house in the next village and changed my name. That way neither they, the tally man nor the electric man can find me," he said all in one breath.

Matt didn't care about anyone or anything. He was one of the happy-go-lucky types and you couldn't help but like him. Rita was the same, when she was sober! They had no kids of their own but they loved to make a real fuss of anyone else's, especially ours.

"I'll tell you why I've called, Tom," said Matt, "I need a bit of a favour."

"Hold up, Matt, if it's owt dodgy count me out," I said quickly.

"No, Tom," he assured me, "it's now't like that. I've bought myself a new van, well not brand new, but a different van and I need someone to give me a lift to pick it up. Then I've got to go and pick some furniture up for the new house, so's our Rita's got summit to sit on when I'm in Ireland. At the moment it's two orange boxes."

"That's OK," I laughed, "as long as the people with the furniture know your coming to pick it up."

"Oh aye, they do. Now come on Tom, you don't think that I'd do something like that, do you?" I just shook my head and laughed. "Well, yes, you probably know me better than I know myself," laughed Matt, "but it's all OK. I've got to pay for the stuff when I pick it up. That's going to put a hole in the money for Ireland. I just hope I'll still have enough to buy a dog or two."

"I hope so too, Matt, we haven't got that much time left." The time was flying by but I made sure I spent time with Jill and the kids, taking them out, watching them play football; being with my family meant a lot to me and they were sorely missed when I wasn't there.

The day arrived and we were ready for Ireland. The van was checked, water, oil and petrol. Matt arrived on time. He was as keen as mustard, there was no way he was going to miss out on this trip. He looked like a new pin. He had a new coat, new pants, new hat and new boots. The look was spoilt, however, by the cigarette burn in his green nylon shirt. The burn was right where you could see it. Now Matt was a non-smoker so it was obvious that Rita had been smoking and ironing at the same time and had dropped ash onto Matt's shirt. Not that Matt would have dared to say anything to her! Rita definitely wore the trousers in their house. Charlie and I thought it best not to ask about the burn. I kissed Jill and the kids good-bye and said if there was any problems to pop up to Sharpy's, he would sort things out, one way or another.

We made good time down to the ferry, not like the last time with Paddy and Mick. We boarded the boat and then went for a bite to eat. The boat was packed to overflowing; half of Ireland had been to Cheltenham for the Gold Cup. We had to try and get some sleep somehow as it was a long journey down to the sales in Cork. We enquired about a cabin but there wasn't one to be had, people were laying on the seats at full stretch, you couldn't even find a seat to sit on.

"It looks like it's the Flea Pit again then," said Charlie. We were shattered and had no choice. Matt didn't know what we were talking about, so while I paid our five bob and collected the blankets, Charlie explained about sleeping with one eye open and your hands in your pockets. Matt made a joke about it being like home from home as we headed down deep into the belly of the ship. Matt was just about to take off his boots and get onto his bunk when Charlie stopped him in his tracks, "Dun't tek thee boots off, Matt, sleep with them on, someone'll nick em if you dunt,"

"Don't be daft," said Matt, "I'll be right here with them." I was too tired to argue with Matt and went straight off to sleep.

The next morning I awoke to a mouth like sandpaper. "Come on Charlie, Matt, get a move on, lets get a cuppa before it gets crowded up there."

Matt put his hands under the bunk feeling for his boots moving his arm from side to side looking for them. "Some toe rag's nicked me boots," shouted Matt, as he searched frantically under his bed. "Oh no, it's OK, I've got them," he sighed, pulling out what he thought was his boots. Much to his disgust he had in his hand the scruffiest pair of sandals, all tied up with string that we had ever seen.

Charlie and I were in stitches. "There's only one thing for it," I spluttered.

"And what's that, Tom?" asked Matt huffily.

"You'll just have to pretend that you're a monk on the way to the Holy Land." We couldn't stop laughing to save our lives. Matt wasn't laughing. "I'm sorry, Matt," I said, "but we did warn you, and you have to see the funny side."

He looked from Charlie to me and burst out laughing. "Come on, lets get this tea then," he said putting on the sandals and going off up the stairs to the canteen.

Matt looked a right sight, his new outfit completely messed up with these sandals, not forgetting of course the green nylon shirt with the cigarette burn. He drew one or two curious looks wandering through Dublin looking like a posh Trappist monk.

Once the shops were open Matt bought a new pair of boots and we set off on the long journey down to Cork. The weather was great for the time of year; the sun was shining, the birds singing. It was only the second time I had been in the country but I was already falling in love with the place and especially the people, who were so friendly and helpful.

When we arrived in Cork we made enquires about the track and managed to get into a Bed and Breakfast place quite close by. It was above the baker's shop. We booked in and were shown to our rooms. We hadn't sat down before the someone was knocking at the door with tea and cakes; a typical welcome from the Irish.

"Right, me lads, said the gent in the big white apron covered in flour, get dat lot down ya necks. It'll put yer's off until dinner. It'll be me and the wife dat runs dis place and we likes to make everyone as comfy as we can. Yer can eat with us at dinner time if yer want."

"That'll be great, ..er.it's very kind of you Mr. ..."

"Oh, the name's Declan, lads, we don't stand on ceremony around dee's parts." I thanked Declan as he scurried off down the stairs.

We had our bite to eat, then went off to our own rooms to try and catch forty winks. My room was pristine clean and tidy, with the wonderful smell of hot bread drifting up into it.

We must have all been shattered as we knew no more until there was a loud banging on the door. It was Declan. "Will yer be sleeping right thru till mornin' lad, or will you be goin to the race meeting tonight?" I glanced across at the clock, it was 6.30pm. We'd slept for five hours solid. We washed and changed and went down the stairs to the most wonderful smell of home cooking you could ever imagine.

"I tort you might be a bit peckish lads an me wife's made a bit too much for the two of us, will yer be joining us then?" said Declan as he anticipated the answer and started dishing out the food.

"Well, if it's not too much trouble," I replied.

"Tis no trouble at all, lads. Sit yer selves down, tuck in and enjoy it," said Declan's wife.

We sat down at the table. It was steak and kidney pie and smelled delicious. Declan's wife must have thought we hadn't eaten for a month the amount of food she piled on our plates. She reminded me of Mrs. Moffitt in the fish and chip shop in the old days when she used to pile the salt onto your chips. Declan's wife was the same. "There's plenty on Mrs. ...?"

"Just call me, Kitty," she laughed scraping the last of the pie onto my plate. After eating such a large and wonderful meal we felt no more like going to the dogs than going to the moon. However, we wanted to see the racing and see what was in the catalogue for the following day's sale. We thanked Declan and his wife and offered to pay for the meal only to be threatened with eviction and a large broom for insulting them.

"You win, Kitty," I said, pretending to be scared, "but I can't thank you enough."

"Yer can thank me by staying here the next time yer down dis way," she laughed. "Now get on wit yer or you'll be missing the racing."

As we approached the track I caught sight of a familiar face. Unfortunately it was one I would rather not have seen. It was Dodger Smith with two of his cronies.

"Now then, Geordie, how's thar goin?" he asked, with that smug look on his face.

"No better for seeing you, Dodger," I replied.

"Now Geordie, thar doesn't mean that."

"If he dun't then I do." It was Charlie; he had to get his two penn'orth in. "Thar's now't but bother, Dodger. It's best if thar keeps as far away from us as possible."

"Dun't thee talk about trouble when thar's got him wi thee," he nodded in Matt's direction. "Thar's got half of England looking for him."

Matt just stood there, looking blank, trying to think of something to say. I butted in, "I'd rather have him wi me any day than thee, at least he won't try tu stitch his mates up." Charlie was starting to lose his rag by this time. I had to step in. "Leave it, Charlie, what's done is done."

"Thar's right, Geordie," said Dodger. "No point in falling out, let's all shek on it and start again from scratch."

"I'd rather shek hands wi a rattlesnake," said Charlie turning on his heels and walking away, Matt following behind.

"Best just forget it, Dodger; the wound's too deep with Charlie," and with that I followed Charlie and Matt into the track.

144

Matt lost a few quid on the track that night and was starting to run short of money. I had limited Charlie to £20 and he had managed to double that on the night. "Well," he said grinning like the cat that got the cream, "that's the digs and a few expenses sorted out anyway. How's thar doin', Matt?" Charlie asked.

"Not so good so far but I'm not worried. Rita's sending me a few quid over. There's a lad dropping off £50 that he owes me and she's going to send it on here." Charlie and I had a quick glance at each other, knowing what we did about Rita.

The next day we were up with the larks eager to get to the sales. Kitty had cooked the biggest breakfast I'd ever seen, I didn't know whether to climb it or eat it! "Right lads, eat your fill, cos you'll get nothing at the sales and it'll be a long day. Come on, get stuck in." We didn't have to be told twice, cleared our plates and thanked Kitty.

We walked along to the track to see the dogs arriving. I wanted to see if I could pick anything out and also see if there were any lame dogs or bitches in season. As we entered the track there was a notice up at the office saying that anyone wanting to purchase dogs should make themselves known to the auctioneer before the sale and leave a small deposit.

"This is different to what it was like in Limerick," said Charlie, "I wonder why we have to do this."

A voice came from behind us. "That'll be to save some time, sir. If the auctioneer knows who yer are and that you've left a few quid down, he's not going to be asking during the sale and it saves a bit of time, don't you see?" said the old gent as he tipped his cap and wandered off.

We thanked the old man for explaining, left our deposits and carried on into the track. Matt had left his real name, 'Cross'.

"Here," said Charlie, "I thought you'd changed your name, Matt."

"I have, only in England though, not in Ireland. No one knows me over here, anyway."

Plus, when Rita sends over me cash, I'll need some identification and I've only got me driving licence," he said, "and another thing, if

145

Dodger finds out what I've changed my name to, he'll bloody well tell everyone back at home!"

"Good point, Matt," I laughed. "You carry on doing just what you like, just don't bounce any cheques."

The dogs were arriving all the time, some in the boots of cars, some just tied to the side of an open truck and some that had walked for miles. We were looking at an old couple and were informed by the same old man that we'd spoken to before that they'd walked fifteen miles; they had six dogs between them, all from the same litter and they were rough, just like woolly bears. One dog in particular was covered in sheep tics: a parasite that sucks the blood from its host. The poor dog looked really sick of his life until the hare driver gave the hare a spin around the track to make sure that all was in working order. You should have seen that dog's ears prick up. He strained every muscle to see over the wall onto the track, nearly pulling the old boy 10 yards at the same time. I waited until the dog had his lot number tied around his neck. He was lot number 25. I put a little mark next to him in my catalogue, just small enough so I could see it, next to the dog's name. He was called Handsome Prince. The old boy must have been on the pop when he named him that because handsome he wasn't.

Matt was busy trying to buy dogs before the sale as the agent for the Spanish buyers was there and we had seen him in action in Limerick. Charlie and I were busy comparing notes on the dogs we had seen when there was an announcement. "TELEPHONE CALL FOR MR. CROSS AT THE OFFICE."

"Great," said Matt, "that'll be our Rita telling me that the cash is on its way." He was off like a shot. He had been gone about fifteen minutes when he came out of the office. We could hear him cussing and swearing like a mad man.

"You won't bloody believe this, you just will not believe it!" he raged, his face ready to explode. He was spitting every time he opened his mouth, something must be really bad.

146

"Calm down, Matt, calm down. Now what's the trouble?" asked Charlie.

"What's the trouble, what's the bleeding trouble?" curbing his swearing as a lady passed. "The trouble is that that useless so and so at home ..."

Charlie managed eventually to calm him down enough so that he could actually speak without looking like he was going to explode. We sat him down on an old seat nearby.

"Now then, Matt," said Charlie, "now start again, calmly this time. What's the trouble?"

Matt started to tell the tale "Well, you know that I told you about the bloke who wanted me to buy him a dog."

"Yes, Matt, we remember," I said. "Don't tell me he's gone and changed his mind."

"No, he hasn't. He's brought the money round and given it to our Rita; £50 quid."

"So what's the problem then?" I asked.

"Well, Rita says she was sitting in the house by herself late at night, after the chap had handed over the cash, when she thought she heard someone trying to break in. So the silly cow hides the money down her chest for safe keeping. Then, being the frail, timid little soul that she is, all 5 foot 10 of her built like a brick shi.... wall," Matt continued sarcastically, "she felt sick with fear. So she ran to the toilet to throw up, and the money fell out of her chest and down the loo, and she's only gone and flushed the bloody stuff away ... or so she says!" By this time Charlie and I were puce. We could barely breathe it was so funny. "But that's not all," Matt went on, "she managed to save herself a fiver to tide her over till I get back."

I couldn't hold it in any more, I took one look at Charlie and exploded with laughter. The tears were running down my cheeks. It was more than obvious that Rita had got the money and used it to buy her favourite tipple, Newcastle Brown Ale, and that she had invented the rest of the story as an excuse to Matt for not sending the money. Matt was in a right mess. He had very little money left

147

to buy a dog to give to the chap who had given Rita the £50. Things weren't looking good for Matt at all. The only thing he could hope for was a cheap sale and that didn't look like it was on the cards. Not with the agent for the Spanish being there.

Charlie and I had marked off a few dogs in the catalogue that we liked the look of, some of them looked like champions and some like hat racks. We had more chance of going home with hat racks than champs.

As the trials were about to start Charlie and I found a place near the winning line. The standard distance being run was 525 yards. We also calculated a distance of 450 yards, as this was the main distance we would be running at home. I would clock the 450 yards and Charlie would clock the 525 yards. I was looking for dogs that would lead to the 450 yards and then fade away. Matt was in a world of his own poor sod. He had nothing marked in his own catalogue and no clock to check the times. When you were buying a dog it was essential to have your own stopwatch because races were won and lost on your own judgement. If a time keeper gave a time off which was different to yours, you went on your own time, provided, of course, you could use the clock correctly.

The first trial was about to start. There were five runners in each trial. Charlie and I noted everything we could about the way each dog ran in each trial, what was starting fast, which were slow starters, which were the stayers and most of all which were the fighters. It didn't take long to get the trials on there way and we were soon up to the trial with one of the dogs I liked, "Handsome Prince," the dog with the sheep tics. He had been drawn in the three box, not the best of draws. The hare flashed passed the traps and to my amazement he out trapped all the other dogs. He flew to the bend and railed like a cat. By the time he got to the third bend he was starting to tire which, considering the dreadful condition he was in, wasn't at all surprising. He eventually finished last, but he wasn't beaten far. The potential was there, the only thing to do was to see if he could be bought at the right price.

The trials were soon over and Charlie and I were comparing notes. There were lots of dogs that we would like to buy and lots that we wouldn't touch with a barge pole. There were, of course, lots that we wanted but could never afford. Funnily enough the dogs I fancied seemed to be the cheap ones and no matter how much money you had, it didn't mean you would end up with the best dog. Matt had nothing written down, he looked in a sorry state. We could see Dodger in the distance, in a huddle with his cronies, a bit like the secret service, not that I was in the least bit interested in what Dodger was buying. He liked to buy his dogs ready made, he didn't want to have to do a lot of work with them to get them up to scratch.

There were only ten minutes before the sale started. Charlie and I secured a good position to see the dogs coming in. Matt had found an old wicker chair and made himself comfortable just below the stand of the auctioneer.

Dodger had placed himself in front of me and Charlie.

"Right lads, lets get dis sale on its way then," shouted the auctioneer, "let's have lot one up to the rostrum. What am I bid for dis good looking pup, turd in his trial today. Who'll be giving me 50 guineas?" There was no response. "Well then can we start at 30? I'll have to have 30 or take him down." The Spanish agent bid 10. "I've got 10, can I hear 11?" There were a dozen people in all wanting to get into the bidding. The dog was eventually sold for 60 guineas. On that basis it didn't look good for the rest of the sale. The dogs were going for good money. There was little chance of Charlie and I getting anything and no chance at all of Matt buying a 'Hot Dog' never mind a Racing Dog,

We got to lot 21. This was a good dog that had done the best time of the day. Matt had given up the ghost and was almost asleep in his chair. The auctioneer was asking for bids starting at 500 guineas. He asked for 400 guineas and then went down to 300. "Can I hear tree anywhere?" he shouted.

Matt had started to stir and opened one eye. "Three," he said jumping up out of his chair. "Yes, I'll give you three."

The auctioneer looked down at Matt, "I've got 300 guineas bid on my left."

Matt looked at the auctioneer in amazement. "No, no," he shouted, "I thought you meant three guineas," shouted Matt.

"Go back tu sleep Mr. Cross and stop wasting my time," said the auctioneer, "now let's get on with dis sale."

The crowd were in an uproar, Matt didn't know where to turn out of sheer embarrassment. Dodger and his mates went a little bit too far taking the Mickey out of Matt, pointing to him every time the auctioneer wanted a bid. Matt wasn't usually a violent man but he was also not a man to cross. There was no doubt in my mind that the tables would be turned somewhere along the line.

We were on to lot 23. A dog that had run well in his trial but not in his races.

There was a vast difference between his race times and his trial time, which meant only one thing in my eyes; the dog had been given something to make him run. The dope that I suspected was a one off thing; once the dog had received one or two doses that was it, he would never be the same dog again.

The bidding started at 100 guineas. Dodger dived straight in at 105 guineas. It was soon up to 150 and there were only two people bidding. One was Dodger, the other was a friend of the man who was selling the dog. Charlie and I had seem them together outside the track placing something in the dog's mouth. Both Charlie and I had placed a big question mark next to the lot number so that we would remember to check it when it came up for auction.

I didn't like Dodger but it was not in my nature to see someone being ripped off. I tapped Dodger on the shoulder and told him what was happening. His reply was: "What's up, Geordie, does thar want dog for thee sen," so I just sat back and told him to get on with it. The dog was knocked down to Dodger for 160 guineas. Charlie and I could see the owners of the dog smiling and rubbing their hands. Dodger had been stitched up like a kipper.

"Right lads, next lot, lot 24 to the stand." The auctioneer was looking round to see where the dog was. "If 24's not here, we haven't got all day, let's have lot 25 to the stand. Lot 25, Handsome Prince." The old man lifted the dog onto the stand with a struggle, not that the dog was heavy, the old man was weak. There was some sarcastic remarks about the name of the dog and the condition he was in. I had to ask myself if I was doing the right thing in wanting to bid for this sorry-looking animal. He looked worse by the second. Sheep tics, sores, scars and he was very under weight, but he had everything else that I was looking for in a dog, the right feet, tail and head, but most of all, his eyes.

"Right, lads, who'll start me off wit a bid for dis dog." The crowd were talking among themselves. No-one had any interest in the dog at all. I casually put my hand up and indicated 5 guineas to the auctioneer. He took my bid and asked if there were any more bids. "Can I hear 6 guineas anywhere?" he asked. I started talking to myself, 'go on, knock that bloody hammer down', "Going once, twice." He was just about to bring the hammer down when the Spanish agent put up his hand: "6 guineas." The auctioneer turned to me, I indicated with a nod that I would go to 7. "Can I hear 8 anywhere." The agent was in again. If I went another 1 guinea the agent would make it up to a round tenner.

It would sound better if I made it a tenner, so I jumped my bid up to 10 guineas. The auctioneer looked at the agent. "It's up to you sir, will you make it 12"

The agent took one more look at the dog and shook his head. The auctioneer brought down his hammer and knocked the dog down to me for 10 guineas.

"Thar's got thee sen a real open racer there, Geordie," said Dodger sarcastically.

I took no notice and followed the old gent and the dog back to the kennels.

"What's his name?" I asked him.

"Handsome Prince," he replied.

"No, I mean his pet name."

"His pet name be … Jesus, do yer know, we haven't given him a name." He turned to his wife, "Colleen, have we got a name for dis dog?" he asked.

"No, Shamus, haven't I been telling you for the past tree months we should give them names."

"Never mind," I interrupted not wanting to start world war three, "I'll just call him Prince. Not that he looks like a Prince, but you never know."

The dog had a thick brown woolly coat and looked like he had never seen a brush or a comb in his life. His shape, however, was something else. Beneath all that hair and the sheep tics, I could see the making of a good dog. I thanked the old man and woman. They looked very poor so I gave them an extra fiver. After all, I had got the dog very cheap. I went looking for the man in charge of the kennels to ask him if he knew where I could buy some dog food.

"Now wot would yer be wanting wit dog food?" he asked with a big smile on his face.

"Well, we've just bought lot 25 and he's very under weight."

He glanced down at his catalogue. "Lot 25," he said, scratching his head as he looked at me, Charlie and the dog. "You could do a lot worse dan buying dat fella. He's bred to be a champion but unfortunately Mr. and Mrs. Riley had some bad luck so they did.

"It was just over a year ago," he went on. "He'd just had de old bitch mated to a good dog. She was a champion herself, winning all over der place. Everyting in their garden was rosy until their stock started to fall like flies. Some kids had been meddling wit some tins of pesticide and it got into the animals drinking water. Just about cleaned him out so it did and dat's the only reason dem dogs is not what dey should be. Wit a bit o' luck and know-how dem pups could be anyt'ing." I was now starting to feel that my judgement might be right after all.

After feeding the dog we made our way back to the auction. Matt was still nowhere to be found. It wasn't like him to take the huff and stay away too long. Charlie assured me that Matt would be OK and that he could take care of himself. The auction was up to lot 38. We had missed the rest of the old man's litter. I made some enquires. Most of them had gone to the agent for very little money so our chances of buying something else in the sale were very slim. It wasn't that we didn't have the cash, I just had to fancy a dog no matter how good or bad he had run and to be honest I didn't fancy a lot.

It was nearing the end of the sale and it was odds on that we were not going to buy another dog, so we decided to go to the kennels to see if Prince had eaten his grub. Dodger was there. He had bought three dogs in all. Two dogs and a bitch. "Hey up, Geordie," he said, "come for thee champion. I've got a mongrel at home that could beat that thing thar's bought,"said Dodger starting to burst into laughter.

"You could be right, Dodger, but who's to say that what you've bought is any better."

"Don't talk daft, Geordie, there's no comparison." He was starting to lose his rag, he was very easily wound up.

"You're right, Dodger, there is no comparison ... in the price."

"Tha'll be laughing stock o' Yorkshire when thar gets back and tries to run that thing round t'track," said Dodger, looking at his mates for support.

"Well, Dodger, that remains to be seen." Just then Matt came into view, a brindle dog by his side. I dreaded to think where he'd got it from and I wasn't going to ask, not in front of Dodger.

We were getting Prince out of his kennel when the old man and his wife, Mr. and Mrs. Riley, came over. "Would yer be interested in dis bitch, Sir? She's a comrade of der dog yer bought from me earlier, Handsome Prince."

It was obvious that there must be something wrong with her when he couldn't even sell her to the Agent buying for Spain. I asked Charlie to trot her up and down on the hard path. She could hardly put her feet down. Dodger was still there, looking on. "It's a cripple

Geordie, get it bought, it'll match that other bag o' bones thar's got."
I ignored him, still looking at the bitch. She looked like a penny
whistle. She was that thin her backbone showed through her woolly
coat and you could have played a tune on her back, but that wasn't
the reason she was limping. I picked up one of her front feet to see
if I could find out what was making her walk so badly. I soon found
out. She had sheep tics in between every toe and on her back feet
as well. How the hell the poor bitch was walking at all was a miracle
in itself. The old man and his wife stood there, hoping to God that I
was going to buy her; if I didn't it meant a 15 mile walk for the old
couple, with a bitch that could hardly walk herself. I looked up at
Charlie.

"Dun't look at me, Tom, thar's man that's buying."

It was hard to tell who I felt the most sorry for, the bitch or the old
man and his wife. I asked the old man how much he wanted for her
knowing that, no matter how much he asked, I couldn't haggle with
him and I would still buy her. Please God, I said to myself, don't let
him ask too much.

"Will yer be giving me a fiver for her, Sir?" he said quietly and
looking as if he had asked too much at a fiver. I looked up to the sky
and thanked the Lord.

"Yes, Mr. Riley, Sir, I'll be giving you a fiver for her and I hope
that your luck changes soon."

"Thank you for your kindness, Sir," said the old man, "and I hope
dat you'll have some luck wit the pair of them." I paid the old man
his fiver and slipped another fiver into his hand.

Charlie had seen the sleight of hand and whispered, "If thar hadn't
given 'im a treat, Tom, thar would've gone down in my estimation,
but I had no doubt," said Charlie, "thar'd've seen him reet, anyway."

Dodger couldn't resist putting his spoke in, "Thar's a bigger fool
than I thought, Geordie," and walked off laughing to himself with his
mates.

"He might just be laughing on the other side of his face soon,"
chipped in Matt, who had been very quiet.

154

"How's thar mean?" asked Charlie.

"Er ... nothing, I was just talking to myself," said Matt. Matt had been up to something but he wasn't saying what, and to be honest, I didn't want to know! We asked the manager of the kennels if we could leave the dogs there with him until we went back to the digs to pick up our things.

On the way back to the digs we picked up some flowers from the little shop on the corner for Declan's wife, just to show our appreciation for looking after us so well. Matt had still not said where he had got the dog from. And I could see it eating away at Charlie's curiosity and to be honest it was killing me not knowing.

"Er, nice dog you've got yourself there, Matt, did it cost much?" I asked.

"You two think I've nicked it don't you?" Matt snapped.

"Well, you didn't have two ha'pennies to rub together when you left us," said Charlie, "and you come back with that. What are we supposed to think?" I interrupted.

"You're right, Tom, but I told you there would be no trouble and I've kept my word. I got the dog from an old chap that felt sorry for me when I made a bit of an arse of myself, on the condition that when I sell the dog I send him a tenner, so you can put your minds at rest."

"So, that's where you were all day," I said with a sigh of relief.

"Well, here, there and other places," Matt said, slyly.

I looked at Charlie, shook my head and said "Don't ask ... don't ask."

As we approached the bakery the smell of gorgeous fresh bread came down the street to meet us. We entered the shop and gave the flowers to Kitty. "There's no need for you's to go spending your money on me now," said Kitty with a tear in her eye and grasping the flowers at the same time.

"It's just to show our appreciation Missis," said Charlie, blushing up.

"That's Kitty, if you don't mind," she scolded kindly. "Now be off wit yer and get yourselves ready to eat and I won't take no for an answer."

We dashed upstairs, got washed and changed and came down for dinner.

"Right, lads," smiled Declan. " Dis is a traditional Irish dinner. We couldn't be havin' you leaving without trying Irish Bacon and Cabbage." Kitty was spoiling us as usual, large portions all round. After the meal we were all tuckered out, but we had a long way to go and thought it better we got started. We thanked Declan and Kitty for all of their kindness and hospitality. We could not have been better looked after if we had been in a five star hotel in Dublin. Kitty gave us each a parcel with 'just a bite to eat for along the way'. We took the parcels, shook hands with Declan and gave Kitty a big hug. It was like leaving your own family. I ushered the lads out before Kitty saw the tears in our eyes. We had gone over 100 yards before anyone could speak. I think we were all suffering from the same problem, that turnip in the throat again.

We arrived at the track with very little said, loaded the dogs and set off for the boat. As we came out of the track and gone a few hundred yards down the road, Dodger and his mates were pushing their van and trying to start it. We stopped and offered to help. I knew Dodger wasn't one of the best people in the world but I wasn't going to be as bad as him by not offering to help, plus he had the poor dogs in the back. We jumped out of the van and started pushing. All that is except Matt.

"You're wasting your time," said Matt. "If it won't start with all you lot pushing there must be something serious wrong with it." We all stopped for a while to get our breath back. The sweat was dripping down Dodger's face. He looked as sick as a parrot.

After he'd caught his breath he said. "Ah can't understand it," blowing like an old man, "van were running like a good un. I've checked everything on it and can't find owt wrong wi it."

"Tha'll have to find a mechanic," said Charlie, "if thar wants van back home. We can't fit another three blokes in ours but we'll tek dogs back for thee if thar likes, but we'll have to crack on if we dun't want to miss ferry."

Dodger said they would manage and for us to get on our way. To tell the truth I don't think he trusted us with his dogs, so we just set off and left them to it.

We had been on the road for about an hour when Matt said out of the blue, "I wonder if they got that van going?" He had a huge grin on his face.

"Does thar know summit that we dun't," said Charlie.

"Just a bit," laughed Matt.

"Thar's gone and done summit to that van, Matt, hasn't thar?" said Charlie.

Matt just repeated himself, "Maybe, just a bit."

"Come on," I said, "out with it Matt. What have you done?"

"Well it's his own fault," he went on, "he shouldn't have taken the Mickey out of me so much."

"So, what's thar done?" said Charlie with a snigger on his face.

"Oh, nothing serious," said Matt, trying to keep a straight face, "all I did was ram two potatoes up his exhaust pipe with a broom shank. I don't know why it stops the engine from starting, but it does! I've seen lads at the car sales do it to get the cars cheap, so it can't be that serious. Anyhow, a good mechanic will soon have it going again."

By this time, Matt and Charlie were giggling like schoolboys and, in a way, I suppose it was poetic justice for all the wrong that Dodger had done and got away with.

We arrived back home at about 7.00am. The first thing to do was to give the dogs a good bath. It was pointless feeding them, the sheep tics were taking the goodness from their bodies. We filled up the old tin bath with nice warm water and dropped a pint of sheep dip in. Charlie and I lifted Prince into the bath. We had expected him to panic and try to jump out, but he was just the opposite, calm and sensible, another sign that he was a good dog. Jill came out with more hot water and she couldn't believe the amount of tics on the dog. To look at him you would just think that they were flecks in his coat.

Sheep tics are a blood sucking parasite, the more blood they drink the bigger they grow. Some of them were the size of your little finger end. I was glad to see the sheep dip doing its job but we had to make sure that none had been missed, especially behind the ears. When we made sure there were none left, the dog was dried off with some old towels and handed over to Jill. She finished him off with a hair dryer, fussed him and made him feel welcome.

The bitch wasn't as bad with tics as the dog, except for her feet. After they were both bathed and dried we took them down to the kennels. Jill had filled their beds with nice clean, fresh oat straw. They ate their dinners and licked the bowls clean. It was pointless giving them any more it would just make them sick. The job was a little bit at a time.

We had been back about a fortnight and to look at the dogs you would hardly recognize them. There was a vast improvement. It was time to be thinking about a trial. The biggest problem with the dogs coming in from Ireland was whether or not they were going to chase the *inside* hare when all they had ever done in Ireland was chase the *outside* hare. It was always fingers crossed the first time you tried an Irish dog on an inside hare.

Charlie and I decided to take the dogs to a track that we had never been to before. The reason for that was we didn't know how the dogs would perform, good or bad, and also Dodger would be at one of the local tracks and it would be just up his street if the dogs ran badly. We arrived at the track just as the trials were starting.

Prince and the bitch, who we had decided to call Lady, were up on their hind legs looking over the wall at the other dogs chasing the hare.

"Well, Tom, at least there's an interest," said Charlie, who was starting to get excited. We decided to let them watch a couple more trials before we booked them in.

"We'll run the bitch first, Charlie, then the dog, but only solo.

We've got to give them a chance to see that hare."

As Charlie placed the bitch into the traps my heart started to pound faster and faster. Prince stood calmly at my side, watching the hare constantly, never taking his eyes from it but not worrying about it or exciting himself, again another sign of a good dog.

Stopwatch at the ready the traps went up and the bitch came out well. I wasn't too worried about the time as long as both dogs chased that hare. We had only watched a few trials but I clocked the bitch a lot faster than the others I'd seen already.

Charlie came off the track full of the joys of spring and looking all excited, "Dus thar know what time that bitch has done, Tom?"

"Well I clocked her at 27-10," I replied, "but I don't know what sort of time that is around here."

"I'll bloody tell thee what sort of time it is," Charlie said, hardly able to contain himself. "It's six yards off clock, that's what sort of time it is."

For a bitch in her condition and the first time running after an inside hare it was an incredible run.

Already one or two of the local lads had made it their business to come and have a closer look at her as she stood there with hardly a pant in her. To say that I was over the moon was an understatement.

It was time for Prince's trial: if he could run anywhere near the bitch's time that would be a real bonus. Because of Lady's time we had caused quite a stir with the locals and the focus was now on Prince.

Charlie placed him into the traps. He walked in like an old lamb; for a pup so inexperienced it was frightening. The hare started to move. He was so cool, he just stood there still until the last second then he was down at the box and out like a bullet. The hare driver had to speed up the hare to stop the dog from catching it. At the end of the trial Charlie had a job to prise the dummy hare away from Prince. He had his feet wrapped around it like a pair of pliers.

There was plenty of activity amongst the locals, all chattering amongst themselves and looking at their stop watches. I knew myself that Prince had done a fancy time, but little had I realised how fancy; he was just one and a half lengths off the track record.

"It's a good long time since a dog went round this track in a time like that," said one of the locals, gazing down at his clock. "Is he for sale?" he asked. Before I could answer him another two chaps approached and said that they would like a chance to bid if the dog was for sale.

"I'll top owt these two fellas want to give thee," chipped in a little stout red-faced chap. "I'm the local butcher and I'll outbid any man here," he boasted.

If there is one thing in life I don't like it's a boaster and a big-head. I turned to the man and said, "The dog is definitely not for sale and even if he was he wouldn't necessarily go to the highest bidder."

"Thar's talking daft, young man," he said, looking even redder for being rebuffed.

I repeated myself. "The dog is not for sale."

He wasn't going to be easily put off. "I'll give thee £200 for dog." Charlie and I started to walk away. "I'll mek it £250," he shouted. Charlie and I kept on walking, showing not the least bit interest. "My final offer," he yelled, "£300."

We got into the van, without saying a word, and drove away. We'd got about two miles down the road when Charlie said, "Does thar think we did right thing, Tom? It's a lot of cash to turn down."

"It is a lot of money, Charlie," I said, "but I've got a gut feeling about these two dogs, and, yes, I think we did the right thing." When we arrived home we washed the dogs' feet and gave them a good rub down and a drink. I couldn't wait to tell Jill how the dogs had done, my mind ticking over like a clock on overtime. I hadn't felt like this since I had my first dog, Sandy, when he was in the final of the Easter Handicap. Good memories and sad ones, but the same feeling was there.

All that week, Charlie and I increased the dog's exercise. As they got stronger we planned to give them another trial to prove that the first wasn't a flash in the pan, not that I had any doubt in my mind. The only problem was, where could we take them without drawing too much attention? There was only one thing for it, we had to go back to the track were they were last time. Only this time we would take Ted and Sharpy with us, let those two take the dogs on and Charlie and I could find a discreet place to watch from and clock their times. That way we could see if there was any improvement and not cause the locals to get suspicious. After all, they were only two black dogs, weren't they, and if I've learned one thing in the dog game, it's that people associate dogs with people! I knew that if Charlie or I were to take any of the dogs on ourselves you would always get the wise lads to connect the dogs to us, hence Sharpy and Ted.

Lady ran first and this time she lowered her time to just two lengths off the track record. Sharpy had instructions to bring the bitch out as soon as she had run and four or five of the locals followed him out to the car park. This was Ted's chance to give Prince his trial. The hare flew passed, the traps went up and Prince was out like a shot. This dog could start. He started in Ireland and he was doing the same here. He was what you called 'A Natural Trapper' and their weren't too many of them kicking around.

I knew that the dog was doing a fast time by the sound of the hare, but what I didn't expect was for Prince to break the track record by three lengths. Ted must have clocked him as well, he couldn't get the dog's coat on quick enough and get him out of the track. We thought if the dogs ran well they might cause a bit of a stir so we had arranged for Ted and Sharpy to leave the track with the dogs and meet us two streets away. Charlie and I sneaked out without anyone taking any notice and caught up with the lads further down the road.

"No the wonder you wanted the secret service with you today," said Ted, trying to get his breath back, "I know tha said that these dogs were good, but I never thought they would be that good!" an expression of sheer delight on his face.

"Aye, and them's nowhere near being reet, yet," laughed Charlie.

"We'll clean up with these dogs, Tom, or else I'll stop gambling."

"For once in thee life, Charlie, tha could be reet!" laughed Sharpy. My mind boggled with the thought of what these dogs could turn into just so long as we could keep them sound.

Ted was telling Charlie and I about the up and coming opens at the Doncaster track. It was in two weeks time. "There are sure to be some big guns there, fancying there chances from the licensed tracks," Ted was saying, "and from what I've seen of these two, they can bring whatever they want, because them their dogs will take all the beating," he boasted.

"Well, Ted, I value your opinion, but I'm not counting my chickens just yet," I said. Deep down in my thoughts, I would be bitterly disappointed if these two dogs didn't fulfil all my dreams.

Meanwhile, we had heard on the grapevine that one of the dogs Dodger had brought back from Ireland was fighting as good as Cassius Clay. It was the dog that I had tried to stop him from buying. It was fighting to the inside hare and was very moderate to the outside hare. It would be a grand opportunity to ram it down Dodger's throat for all the stick he had given us in Ireland, but a better way would be to let him see how good Prince and Lady had turned out and that would be at the big Donny meeting where Dodger would be sure to have a runner of his own, or he would at least be sneaking one in for the well known licensed trainers who were barred from running on the flaps, or unlicensed tracks as they were called.

Not that that ever stopped them, of course. They would come down to the flaps with their big money dogs, send them in with one of the locals and try to hide from the public and the NGRC, but somehow there was always someone who could spot the big trainer and in no time at all it would be round the track in a flash. I was hoping that at this meeting, Dodger, or one of the top trainers he was connected to, would be tempted by the amount of good prize money that was on offer, as it was often a lot better than what was on offer at the licensed tracks.

All that week Charlie and I were increasing the exercise and training. Both Prince and Lady were thriving on it, their coats and general condition unrecognisable from the flea bags that came over from Ireland a few weeks ago. Everyone was doing their bit to try and have the dogs ready for the big day. Jill would cook the meat and veg and try to vary their diets as much as possible with fish, chicken and meat. Ted would pop down when my back was bad and take the dogs for a walk; even the kids would do their bit by cleaning out the kennels and putting fresh sawdust down when the dogs were out for their walk.

I hadn't felt this way about a dog in a long time. Every time I looked at Prince I got goose bumps up and down my spine. I would sit looking out of the window and daydream of what might be with a bit of luck and then I would get a flashback of the old man and woman in Ireland, Mr. and Mrs. Riley, from who we had bought the dogs. I couldn't stop my conscience pricking me, thinking about how poor they were and how we got the dogs for next to nothing. On the other hand, if I hadn't bought the dogs they would probably have ended up in Spain, racing twice a day in temperatures that would cook a chicken. It was small consolation to the old gent and his wife, but I was certain they would prefer the dogs to have at least a chance to show that everything the old man and woman did was not in vain.

There was a week to go before the races at Donny. I had decided to take Jill and the kids to the local track at Lowgate. Matt and his wife Rita were there. She was pleased to see Jill and I, but she was extra pleased to see the kids. Rita and Matt had no kids of their own and they always made a fuss of ours. If she got the chance Rita would take them all straight off to the shop on the track and buy them sweets. She was telling the kids that she had her favourite dog running in a later race and that she fancied it to win. She had had the bitch a long time and it was more like a pet than anything else. Matt was telling me about the dog he brought back from Ireland when he went with me and Charlie.

Apparently the dog turned out OK and Matt had kept his word

and sent the chap over his tenner. In return, the Irishman had sent him over another dog on the same basis, but the dog arrived with the cough and Matt hadn't had a chance to run it.

Our old friend Dodger was there and of course he couldn't stop himself having a go at Matt and myself. "Now then, Matt, had any more burglars lately. They tell me it cost thee a few quid," said Dodger, sniggering through that big, fat, red face of his.

Matt turned around slowly and looked at Dodger, "Aye," he said quietly, "but they tell me it wasn't as much as it cost you for your van to be repaired."

Dodgers face was fit to burst. "I knew it was thee," Dodger shouted at Matt. "We were stuck in Ireland for four hours trying to find out what were wrong wi van before that useless mechanic found out that some silly bugger had stuffed tattie's up the exhaust!" He ranted on, " I know it was thee, Matt Cross, and it's not forgot, not by a long chalk." Rita was standing a few yards away with the kids, taking it all in but saying nothing. If there was going to be any trouble, Rita would be the one to sort it out. Matt wasn't the fighting type.

The dogs were called to the next race. It was Rita's little bitch, Poppy's race. It had come at the right time to diffuse the situation with Matt and Dodger, or so I thought, but to my disbelief Dodger had a dog in the same race. It was one of the dogs that he had bought in Ireland. Dodger's dog was off scratch, Rita's was off six yards. No matter who won, there was bound to be trouble afterwards. Rita was parading her little bitch and for some reason Dodger was parading his own dog, which was very unusual. Dodger had to be up to something. I decided to walk down to the traps to watch the dogs being loaded into the traps. They were all in but Dodger's. Everyone else had gone from the traps except him. The starter was standing in front of the six traps ready to indicate to the hare driver to start the hare. Dodger was still having trouble placing his dog into the trap, or so it had seemed. The starter asked if he wanted any help and he replied that everything was under control, but what the starter hadn't realised was that Dodger had moved the trap up half a yard whilst pretending to be struggling with his dog. It was too late to stop the race, the hare was approaching the traps, the lids went up and the dogs were away. Dodger's dog was not too fast away, but Rita's little bitch was on her way home. There were 200 yards to go when Dodger's dog started to catch up with Rita's little Poppy.

The kids were screaming at the top of their voices, Peter, the youngest, seemed to be leading the chorus and there was method in his madness. He knew that if Poppy were to win, Rita would treat them all to sweets from the shop. Coming to the line, Dodger's dog made one final effort to catch Rita's but just failed by a neck. Jill and the kids were jumping for joy. Matt was quite pleased because he had had £20 on her and got a good price with Dodger backing his dog.

The dogs were at the trip and the owners were making their way over the track to collect them. Then the trouble started, there was screaming and shouting at the trip.

Dodger's dog had got hold of Rita's little bitch and had started to fight. By that time all of the owners had made it over there. Dodger was trying to kick little Poppy but he hadn't seen Rita right behind him. She always carried her dog lead around her neck as did all of the other owners. As she approached Dodger the dogs had been parted and someone was holding Poppy waiting for Rita to come and collect her. She walked straight passed the bitch and stood right in front of Dodger. She slowly placed her hands on either end of her dog lead and with one swift move she had looped it over Dodger's neck, pulling him in towards her. She landed him with one almighty head butt, much to the amusement of the crowd. As Dodger fell to the ground bleeding profusely from his nose, Rita turned to her little bitch, gave her a quick pat and checked that she was all right, placed the lead around the dog's neck and walked off the track feeling ten feet tall and as if nothing had happened.

It was the day of the open races at the Doncaster track. I had been looking forward to this day since we had given Prince and

Lady one more trial and found out that they were a little bit special. They were both entered and paid for by one of the locals, a mate of Ted's who fortunately had a couple of black dogs that looked similar (if you had one eye closed and were ten feet or so away, with the sun in your eyes). We had to do this, because there is one thing I have learnt through years in dog racing, people connect the dog to you, not you to the dog. If they see you at Lowgate with a good black dog and then they see you at Donny with a black dog, to them it's the same dog. We weren't doing anything wrong exactly, just trying to beat the wise boys and the bookies.

The chap who had entered our dogs had a couple of fair dogs himself, but they were not in the same class as Prince and Lady. If my intuition was right the punters would be thinking that the dogs he had on the track were his and that they would not have the greatest of chances. He had called the dog Midnight and the bitch Miss Black, after his own two who were regular runners at the track and wouldn't cause much interest. The prize money for winning the final was £400, a tidy sum which was badly needed. The only chance we had of winning anything from the bookies was if they were betting ante-post and hoped our little ploy had deceived the books and the wise lads. We couldn't win if we were to bet the dogs on each race, because after the first heat, if they ran as good as I expected them to, the odds would be very short indeed.

Ted had already taken the dogs to his mates, with strict instructions not to let them out of his sight.

He might be a friend of Ted's but I didn't know this man and in this game you had to be very careful. We were drawn in heats five and seven. The track was full of strangers and the news soon got round that there were some handy dogs on the card from the licensed tracks. Jill and the kids were talking to Rita, while Charlie and I were looking for the bookie who was betting ante-post; ante-post being the price the bookmaker gave every dog before the heats had started. There were two of them and both had Midnight and Miss Black at the same price, 33-1. Things were not that good in the cash flow department so I had £10 on each of them to win the final. Charlie had Ted's and Sharpy's money, together with his, which made up £75 between them. He had £60 on Midnight and £15 on Lady, after all, they both couldn't win, so we had to plump for the one we fancied most and that was Prince, plus there was always the chance of Lady coming into season. We struck the bets at the same time with each bookie and the odds immediately fell to 15-1. That was our job done, it was up to Prince and Lady now.

Just as we were walking away Dodger and his mates were backing a dog called Sweet William at 20-1. They must have had a few quid on, as the odds dropped sharply to 4-1 and to top it off, the dog was in the same race as Prince. I started to get butterflies again. Was Prince as good as I thought he was? Only time would tell but deep down I knew that he was something special and that they all had him to beat. The first four heats were won by good dogs and at least two of them were from the licensed tracks.

The times of the heats were quite fast with the suspected licensed dogs winning. One of them, Starlight, ran four lengths off the track record. Another, Big Red, was six lengths off. It was time for Prince/Midnight's race. The old stomach started to churn. Prince looked a picture, but so did the dog that Dodger backed ante-post, Sweet William.

He was a fine looking brindle dog and was rumoured to be from the Nott's area, trained by a man with the nickname of 'The Chameleon' because of the many disguises he used when raiding the flapping tracks. Prince/Midnight was 3-1 with Sweet William favourite at even money. The punters soon took the even money, leaving the favourite odds on. Ted was standing by my side, "He must be some kind of dog for that sort of money to be going on him" said Ted looking a bit uneasy.

Charlie retorted in his usual way, "Thar must be barmy, Ted. There's only one winner in this race and that's ours." Never one for being a pessimist was our Charlie!

"Thar could be right," said Ted. " Hare's running and we'll soon find out."

The traps went up but Prince/Midnight missed by a mile. Sweet William was soon in the lead with Prince trying to pick his way through the field, when all of a sudden he was down. My stomach fell to my feet. Charlie and the rest of the lads just stood there, open mouthed and white as a sheet. "Well at least he's OK," said Jill, as he picked himself up and started chasing the others again. All my hopes and dreams had gone at the first bend. There was just 100 yards to go when somebody up there must have been smiling down on us. The hare had broken down just before the race was complete.

"SORRY LADIES AND GENTS, THAT WILL BE A VOID RACE. IT WILL BE RE-RUN AT THE WEEKEND," they announced over the system.

You would think that Charlie and Ted had won the pools the way they were jumping up and down, and to be honest I felt like joining them.

Dodger walked past looking as sick as a parrot and was heard to say, "Well at least we've still got our bet on at ante-post."

"Yer might as well toss that away, Dodger," laughed Charlie.

Dodger turned on him, "If thar thinks that thing thar's backed has any chance of beating Sweet William, thar's dafter than thar looks." I grabbed Charlie by the arm and dragged him off to cool his temper.

"Look, Charlie, we've still got a good chance with Prince. He hasn't shown any running at all and nobody's the wiser. This is the first time he has missed the break and I don't think he will do it again. We've been lucky, it hasn't cost us a penny, our ante-post bet is still on and we still have another bite at the cherry."

"Oh, can I have a cherry please, Mam," piped up little Peter. Charlie and I just looked at each other and laughed. It seemed to take the edge off Charlie's temper.

It was nearly time for the bitch's race, so we sneaked outside to check on her and the dog. Prince seemed to be fine. No visible injuries except for a little nick on the top of his toe. It was fingers crossed for Lady as she walked onto the track.

She looked full of herself as she trotted off with Ted's mate. His wife had stayed with her in the car to keep her company and she looked the better for it. The dogs were in the parade ring and a good set of animals they looked, although I must confess that Lady looked like a real champion. Her black coat was shining like shot silk, not like the brown woolly coat she had in Ireland. The betting had started and Lady was just 3-1. I turned to Charlie, "I hope no one has got wind that this bitch is not the one it is supposed to be. Still, we've got ante-post and there's not a lot they can do about it," I said shrugging my shoulders. I had barely got the words out of my mouth when there was a mad rush. It was Dodger's team, they were backing a dog in the race called Half Pint. Lady's price went from 3-1 to 6-1. It didn't make a deal of difference to us though, we were all skint after betting the dogs ante post.

Dodger and his men steamed in again, making their dog, Half Pint, big odds on. Dodger still didn't know that Midnight and Miss Black were the same two dogs that I had bought in Ireland for a few pounds. I'm sure if he knew that Miss Black was that scrawny little thing that could hardly walk he would be making his dog even bigger odds on. The dogs were being placed in the traps. I looked up to the sky, "Please God don't let Lady miss the break as bad as Prince." The words just left my lips when the traps opened and she was out like a shot. She was soon well clear of the field with Dodger's dog a good three lengths behind her in second place. She eventually crossed the line a good six lengths in front, with no excuses for the other runners. Then came the winners time: 26-90. It was just half a yard off the track record. I turned to Charlie and the rest of the team, "Well, we might not have won on the race, but at least we beat that dipstick, Dodger."

Jill chipped in, "You lot might not have won, but I've done all-right." She had just won £38 on the forecast, and took great delight in counting the money in front of myself and the lads.

As the dogs came off the track there were a few from Dodger's team and the locals, scratching their heads with bewildered looks . Dodger couldn't understand how their dog had been beaten and the locals couldn't understand how Miss Black had run so fast. Dodger's luck was right out. First the void race when their dog should have won and now being beaten by an unknown dog! It was just not their day. Maybe someone up there was giving us a helping hand. God knows we needed it?

There were three days to go before the next round and the re-run. Ted had waited for the card to be printed on the night of the heats. Both Prince and Lady were jumping out of their skins, they seemed to be getting better after every run. I was looking forward to watching both Lady and Prince run again. Lady had drawn trap two in the fourth heat against a dog called Starlight who had won his heat in good time. He was one of the dogs from the licensed tracks, or so the rumour was. If the rumour was true, he was in the care of one of the top trainers in the country, a man who would be recognized no matter what disguise he decided to use. At six foot four with a four inch scar down his left cheek he wasn't that difficult to notice. If he wasn't in the track, he wouldn't be far away that's for sure. Prince was in the first heat, the re-run of the void race, surely he couldn't trap as badly as he did in his heat or could he?

With a couple of days to go before the heats, Jill and I were very glad when Colin and Bobby came home from school with the news that they had been picked to play in a football match for the school. At least it would take our minds away from the dogs. We loved to watch the lads play football. Both were very good, but Bobby had that little bit of something special. It wasn't long before people watching his matches started to take note of the little Geordie genius. The lads won their match 3 - 0. Bobby got two and Colin the other one. After the match Mr. Jones, the PE teacher, came over to have a word. He was genuinely pleased with how well they had done and told us that if they kept up that kind of performance he was going to put their names forward for the County trials. Bobby and Colin were thrilled to bits and Jill and I were as pleased as punch. That night, all we heard was football, football, football; the kids were so excited at the prospect of being in the county team that the dogs were not even mentioned.

It was Saturday and time for the heats. Everyone was excited, including the kids, they were up with the larks making themselves busy doing bits of odd jobs around the house and cleaning out the kennels, changing the dogs beds. Jill and I had just finished grooming the dogs and you would just think they knew it was race day, they were clawing at the ground to show their fitness.

Charlie and Ted were at our house to finalise the arrangements for the night. Charlie was more excited than anyone, plus he'd won a few quid on the horses. "Does thar think Prince will miss lids again, Tom?" asked Charlie with a worried look on his face.

"If I knew that, Charlie, I wouldn't be trying to make a few bob at the dog game, I'd be mind reading," I replied.

"Thar knows what I mean, Tom."

"Yes, Charlie, I know, and I've got that gut feeling that Prince won't miss out this time...." I hope!

"Tha'll do for me, Tom" said Charlie rubbing his hands. "I've got £50 and lot's going on Prince."

I knew arguing with him was a waste of time, I'd tried it before. Charlie had a mind of his own and nobody could change it for him. The only thing we could do was hope and pray that Prince hit the lids.

All that day my stomach was in knots. It was the same feeling I'd had when Sandy, my first dog, was in the final of the Easter Handicap all those years ago. Tears started to well up in my eyes when I remembered how I had sat on the track with Sandy's head in my lap. I couldn't go through that again, not for anyone, but it was always there in the back of my mind. I must have been standing a few minutes, just thinking about Sandy and the old times. It seemed like I was in another wold.

"Tom! ... Tom!" my thoughts were interrupted by Jill.

"Sorry, love, I was just thinking back." My eyes were still full.

"What's up, Tom?" she asked, concern in her voice.

"Nothing, it's just a fly in my eye, love," I said as I wiped my eyes and blew my nose at the same time. "Right, lads" I said, giving my eyes a final rub, let's get things sorted for tonight."

We made arrangements to meet Ted and his mate, confirming the place and the time and left it at that. Both Prince and Lady had their pre-race meal, just something light to take the wind off their stomach. A lot of trainers didn't give their dogs anything before a race, but I'd always found that you have a more contented dog if he's had a little bit of something to settle him down.

It was time to set off for the track. Prince and Lady knew they were going racing as soon as they came out of the kennel, jumping up and down and wagging their tails. Jill and the kids piled into the van with the dogs and off we went to meet up with Ted and his mate. They were spot on time as we transferred the dogs to their van quickly. We then set off for the track. There was a good crowd when we got there, lots of old familiar faces and lots of strangers. Matt and Rita were there, Dodger and his cronies looking as devious as ever and, of course, Charlie who had rushed through the turnstile having just finished work.

Charlie spotted us and came straight over. "I'm starving, Tom. Has thar got owt tu eat? Asked Charlie. "I could eat a rusty can, I'm that hungry." Rita pointed Charlie in the direction of the cafe and off he went. Time time for the first race. Ted's mate was in the paddock with Prince. One of Dodger's mates had Sweet William looking better than ever. My mind started racing again. 'Was Prince good enough? After all, this was his first race, if you didn't count the void race.' It was too late to have second thoughts: the dogs were leaving the paddock. Charlie came running out from the Cafe clutching two pies in one hand and a mug of tea in the other. "Here kids, hold me pies till I get a bet on," he said, handing the mug of tea to Jill and the pies to young Peter to hold on to. He should have known better, it was suicide giving anything edible to Peter to hold and to expect him not too eat it. Although he was the youngest, Peter had an appetite like a horse and, as the saying goes, he could eat a buttered brick and ask for seconds!

There was plenty of activity with the bookies. It was mainly on Sweet William who was big odds on favourite after showing such speed in the void race. Prince was 6-1, after all no one had seen him show anything in his heat, sleeping in his box and falling down, hardly a recommendation for a gamble. The hare started to move and Jill and I ran towards the finish line. Rita, bless her heart, took the kids off to a less crowded part of the track.

The lids went up and out shot Prince like a bat out of hell. "Go on, my son," I shouted as he went two lengths clear of the field, forgetting that I shouldn't be shouting at all!

A tall chap standing next to me with a scarf around his face and his coat collar turned up high muttered to himself, "What the hell is that?" As he got more and more restless watching the race the scarf fell down from around his face revealing the large scar on his left cheek. This was the trainer from one of the best tracks in England and by the look on his face he couldn't believe that his dog was being beaten by a dog from a flapping track.

Prince was a good seven lengths clear coming round to the winning line and increasing his lead round to the trip. Jill was jumping up and down, screaming for the dog and hugging me all at the same time. I just stood there letting it all sink in, waiting for the time of the race to be given off.

"LADIES AND GENTLEMEN, THE WINNER OF THE VOID RACE WAS TRAP THREE, MIDNIGHT (Prince's alias), SECOND OUT OF TRAP TWO, SWEET WILLIAM. THE DISTANCE WAS SEVEN AND A HALF LENGTHS, THE TIME 26-60, A NEW TRACK RECORD AND CONGRATULATIONS TO THE WINNING CONNECTIONS. I couldn't believe it, Prince had run four and a half lengths faster than any dog that had ever been around that track. The man with the scar just stood there with his mouth wide open, absolutely gobsmacked at the record time that Prince had recorded. Meanwhile, Charlie and the rest of the lads were off.

They waited especially until Dodger had paid his money on, then they went to collect their winnings. Dodger and his crew just stood there, wondering, and for once he had nothing to say. The chap with the scar had gone as mysteriously as he had arrived and all eyes were on Charlie and the lads. They were all wondering why they had backed Midnight with such a hotpot in the race as Sweet William. It wasn't long before the local lads realised that this Midnight was not the Midnight they thought it was!

Charlie came over counting his money and asking Peter where his pies were. Peter looked up at Charlie sheepishly, gravy from the pies dripping off his chin, but said nothing. Charlie just laughed. "Never mind, lad, thar can have as many pies as thar wants tonight and if they have all gone we can call in tu chippie for more!" Charlie was never more happy than when he was winning.

Ted's mate, who had taken the dog back to the car where his wife was waiting with Lady, came running back into the track. I feared the worst. "What's up?" asked Ted. "Is dog all right?"

"Aye, dog's fine," he said as he caught his breath and wiped his nose at the same time.

"Well, what's the problem then?" I asked with a bit concern.

"There's a chap out there wanting to buy dog and he say's thar can name thee price."

I had a feeling that this might happen. It was always the same. If you were lucky enough to have a good dog there was always someone with plenty of money who wanted to deprive you of it. I turned to Ted's mate and said, "You go back to the mysterious man and tell him that the dog is not for sale, at any price."

"Right you are, Geordie, I'll tell him it's not for sale. Not for sale. Not for sale," he repeated.

"At any price," I reminded him.

By this time another two races had gone by. It was time for Lady's race. She had run such a good race in her heat that we expected her to be favourite and she was. I was still a bit uneasy about Prince and went outside to make sure that Ted's mate's wife was still with him. After all, it wouldn't be the first time a dog had been stolen from a track.

As I walked towards the car I turned quickly to see a slight figure following me in the shadows. I knew immediately who it was. He was known as "Walter the Weasel"; one of Dodger's mates, a pathetic little man who was about seven stone wet through. He had a sharp pointed face and a lit cigarette seemed to be permanently stuck to his bottom lip. I had a quick glance into the car where Prince was; he seemed fine. So as not to disturb him and draw too much attention to the car, I walked quickly off into the shadows only to be followed by Walter the Weasel. I hid behind a big van and waited. "Got you, you little shit," I said, as I grabbed him by the scruff of the neck. "What's your game, then?" I said, shaking him like a rag doll. He stood there looking like a scared rabbit. You can bet if he had underpants on they'd have skid marks on them by now. I had never seen anyone so frightened in all of my life.

"Ah... ah didn't mean any harm, Geordie, honest. It was Dodger, he asked me to follow thee tu see if the black dog was thine." His voice shaking with fear.

"You can stop snivelling now you little snot and go back and tell Dodger that you are no wiser now than when you started following me." With that, I turned him round, shoved him forward and with a kick up the backside sent him off into the night. He scurried off only stopping to light up a fag, his hands still shaking.

I made my way back to the track only to be met by Charlie. "Where's thar been Tom, Jill's looking all over for thee?"

"Well I'm here now, Charlie, what's the problem?"

"Lady's in next race and I wanted to see if thar wanted a bet."

"Not for me, Charlie, but thanks just the same."

"Well, it's there if thar wants it," shaking his head as he walked away.

I should have taken it, because knowing Charlie it would be all or nothing and although I really fancied Lady to win, anything could go wrong. It was soon time for her race. Jill and the kids were getting excited. By this time most of the locals had realised that she was our dog and they were coming up to wish us good luck. Lady, who had been entered in the race as Miss Black, was even money with Starlight at 3-1. Dodger and his mates still backed their fancy, Starlight, hoping that Lady's win had been a flash in the pan. The hare was running, up went the traps. Lady came out better than she had ever trapped before and it wasn't long before she had gone well clear with Starlight taking up the second spot. Jill and the kids were screaming their heads off when she passed the winning line a good four lengths in front.

"FIRST NUMBER TWO, MISS BLACK. SECOND NUMBER ONE, STARLIGHT —WINNING TIME 26-82." Lady had broken the old track record, but not the new one set by Prince. It was still a good run and I was just as pleased with Lady as I was with Prince. We had two dogs going through to the next round.

Dodger was standing in the background talking to a stranger and looking over in my direction. I knew what the next move would be and I wasn't wrong. Dodger came straight over and asked straight out if the bitch was for sale. By that time Charlie had drawn his money and made his way back to us. He was standing behind me counting out his money in full view of Dodger. "What's thar want Dodger," sharp enough to take Dodger's head off.

"How much does thar want for that bitch?" he asked.

Charlie rounded on Dodger again. "I wouldn't sell a caterpillar tu thee 'cos thar run it till all its legs dropped off," said Charlie, "plus fatty, thar wouldn't want tu buy a pathetic thing like that would thar?" There he was again, you could guarantee that in a temper Charlie would let his mouth run off with his brain. He was a great one for opening that great gob of his before he had time to think.

Dodger stood there, silent, his bottom jaw resting on his double chin, his words forming slowly and spilling out of his mouth, "That's ... that's never bitch thar bought in Ireland," said Dodger, looking quite dazed. "It ... it can't be," he shook his head, "and if it is, "don't be telling me that Midnight is that flee-bitten dog?"

"Thar's reet on both counts," snarled Charlie. Dodger looked directly at me.

"Well, Geordie, is he coding me or not?"

"Looks like not," I said with a big, big smirk on my face. I was nearly getting as much pleasure out of this discussion as I was getting from Prince winning and breaking the track record.

"I have to hand it tu thee, Geordie, I wouldn't have brought them two dogs home if that old bloke had paid me to."

"Just goes to show what sort of judge thar really is," said Charlie, who had to have the last word.

I had to intervene before blood was spilt. "Look, lads," I said, "to save any more hassle, neither the bitch nor the dog are for sale — at any price."

With that Dodger walked off to relay the message to his heavily disguised friend who was standing in the shadows. You could see an animated discussion going on. Lots of pointing the finger and shaking the head. It wasn't long before we had another representation from the shadows. This time they sent the Weasel. "Er, no offence, Geordie," his voice quivering as he spoke, "if thar wai'nt sell bitch, will thar tek £700 for dog."

There was no way I wanted to sell the dog, but if they had bid £700, they would be prepared to go a lot higher. I turned to Walter and said, very slowly, so that he understood my meaning, "Neither the dog nor the bitch are for sale."

Before I could send him on his way he'd upped the bid to "£800?"

There was no doubt that Dodger had filled the trainer in on the background of both myself and the dogs. The dogs had only cost a small amount of what they were worth and Dodger knew that I was still out of work with back trouble. Charlie, Jill and I stood looking at each other. It was a lot of money for a dog that had only cost a few quid and, to be quite honest, I could have done with the cash.

I looked at the Weasel and said, "Go back to your man and tell him …" there was a deep silence, the anticipation from Charlie and Jill hanging in the air, Ted and Sharpy holding their breath, "… tell him the same as I told Dodger. The dogs are NOT for sale."

You could see the delight in Jill's eyes. Weasel just stood there with his mouth wide open, his fag stuck to his bottom lip, dangling there. "And if thar doesn't move and move quick," said Sharpy, "I'll use thee as a pipe cleaner, you little weed," he snarled. It was a rotten thing to say, but no one I knew had a good word to say for the Weasel.

We said our goodbyes to Matt and Rita, picked up the dogs and made our way home. After washing their feet and giving them a good massage we bedded them down to a well deserved supper.

The following day I received a letter from my doctor saying I had to see a specialist in Sheffield in two days time. That would be just four days before the next round. The dogs had come out of their races well and the next couple of days seemed to fly over.

I made arrangements with Charlie and Ted to see to the dogs while Jill and I went off to see the specialist. It was a morning appointment so it gave us plenty of time to get back home before the kids got in from school. We found the hospital without any trouble and were pleased to find out that there was only one patient to go before it was my turn.

The doctor's name was Mr. Raymond. He was a nice man with a down to earth attitude. "Right then, Mr. Watson, let's have a look at this problem back of yours." After a good examination he proceeded to examine all of my x-rays. "I'm afraid that it's not going to be good news," he said quietly. "You have at least two damaged discs and probably three. I had a feeling that there was disc trouble there, but not to that extent."

I drew in a deep breath. Jill, who was sitting there waiting for the worst asked, "What does that mean then, Doctor?"

"It means that Mr. Watson will require surgery and the sooner the better." That was the last thing I wanted to hear, surgery!

"And what if I don't have surgery?" I asked, a worried look forming on my face.

"It will never get any better," said the doctor, "and most certainly get worse."

"And if he does have surgery, Mr. Raymond, will it cure his back?" asked Jill.

"There are no guarantees, Mr. and Mrs. Watson, it's a catch 22 situation I'm afraid. The best thing you can do is to go home, have a long think about it all and let your doctor know what you want to do; he in turn will contact me."

All the way home there wasn't a word spoken between us, both of us lost in thought, wondering what the other was thinking. I had no fancy for an operation myself, but I had to think of the future. At the moment it wasn't too bad, a bit like when you go to the dentist, the pain seems to go away, but deep down I knew that it would only get worse. I could see in Jill's face that she was worried and I tried to take her mind off the situation by starting to talk about the dogs, the kids, football anything. Although she was joining in the conversation I could tell that her mind was elsewhere.

As soon as we arrived home Jill ran into the house and broke down in tears. I followed, putting my arms around her to comfort her. "Why the tears?" I asked.

"Tom," she sobbed, "what if anything happened to you on that operating table, I just ... just don't know what I would do." The tears becoming worse.

"I'll tell you what you can do," I said, grinning.

"And what's that, Tom?" she sobbed.

"Get the kids' teas ready, they'll be in from school shortly."

"You, you can't be serious for one moment, Tom Watson, you make my blood boil," she screamed. We didn't have a lot, but we had each other, we had the kids, a sense of humor when we needed it and that meant the world to me.

Saturday was the day of the semi-final. Luckily, Prince and Lady had missed each other in the heats. If they had been drawn together, which one would we shout for? It didn't bear thinking about. Lady was more active than usual and Prince was paying more attention to her than normal. This could only mean one thing; Lady was starting to come into season. I had feared that from the first day she arrived from Ireland. It was quite common for a bitch to come into season with the journey and the strange surroundings and to be quite honest I had expected it. At least she had won a couple of races. If we could get her through the semi that would be her last race for three months, the full length of her seasonal rest. Some trainers ran their bitches right through their season, but not me. I was a great believer in letting nature take its course. I decided to take Prince through to the track in my van and let Ted's mate take Lady, just in case she did come into season and upset Prince.

We arrived at the track at about 7.30pm. The car park was filling up quicker than usual. It looked like being another big crowd. "Is somebody giving summit away?" Charlie asked one of the locals. "No, they've all come to see track record go," said an old gent.

"Oh aye, and who's going to brek that?" laughed Charlie.

"Thar knows, Charlie, thar knows," said the old man as he walked off towards the turnstile.

Charlie turned to Ted and Sharpy, "Does thar think I'll get a bet on with one of the books that Prince will brek clock?" That was Charlie, always looking to make a few bob somewhere.

I had taken Prince out to stretch his legs and give him a quick rub down, then brought him back to the van. Jill was in the van with her knitting. There was no way she was going to leave Prince by himself. The track was filling up with all sorts of strangers with queer accents and the car park was full of posh cars. Matt and Rita were just pulling into the car park. Matt was trying desperately to squeeze his big van in a place hardly big enough for a mini. Ted was watching in anticipation. "He'll never meck it," said Ted.

"Bet thee five bob he does," said Charlie.

"Thar's on," said Ted. Both Charlie and Ted were shouting instructions to Matt; he didn't know what to do. Go forward, no, go back, they were shouting, no, to the left. In the end, he squeezed the van into the middle, locked the doors from the inside and him and Rita climbed out through the back, to rapturous applause from all of those who had stopped to watch the performance. Charlie, of course, was cheering the loudest.

"Right, Ted, thar owes me five bob," he laughed. "My luck's right in, I can feel it in me watter," he shouted at the top of his voice.

Ted gave Charlie the five bob with some reluctance. Sharpy just stood there sniggering. "Thar should know better, Ted, than to bet wi Charlie when he's carrying the luck he's carrying. Let's hope it carries on to the semi's."

Ted and Charlie were still arguing when the announcement came over the loud speakers "CAN WE HAVE THE DOGS IN THE FIRST SEMI FINAL TO THE PADDOCK PLEASE." That was Lady's cue. I only hoped that she hadn't come into season.

We had to push and squeeze to get close to the paddock, I'd never seen as many people at a dog track before.

As I got closer I could see that Lady had not come into season, but one or two of the dogs were starting to sniff about her. It was just a matter of time, but at least we were safe for the time being.

As Lady left the parade ring she was attracting a lot of attention from the strangers. In the betting ring she was still favourite at even money, but then the money started to drift. One or two of the other trainers started to bet their own dogs. Someone had heard that a couple of the trainers thought that their dogs would run better races now they had been round the track a couple of times. They could be right, but it didn't alter mine, or Charlie's opinion that she was the best dog in the race.

Lady had drawn trap six. It was the first time she had been drawn wide. The hare was running and I was looking for a good vantage point to watch the race, but the crowd was too big. The traps were up and there was a loud "OH!" Lady had missed the break.

By the time I'd got near enough to see, she was five lengths behind. Charlie was shouting at the top of his voice. I couldn't see him in the crowd, but I could certainly hear him, "Go on, Lady, thar can do it." You'd think she could hear and understand him. She started to move through the wall of dogs in front of her, picking them off one by one. With one dog to pass there was a huge roar as she sailed by him and went on to win by three lengths. Lady had run a cracker of a race and I was immediately approached by a well dressed couple.

"I'm so sorry to interrupt you in your moment of triumph, but would you be interested in selling your bitch? I have never seen anything as exciting as that for a long time," the chap said.

"I'm sorry," I said, as I started to get my breath back, "but she's not for sale, and if you'll excuse me I must dash, I've got another dog in the next semi." I could still hear him shouting as I ran off to fetch Prince. I was stopped no less than four times before I could get outside the track. Jill had heard the news and the time 26-78. It was a cracking run for a dog that had been left in the traps. Jill had Prince all ready and coated up for the race. Ted's mate had left his wife with Lady so that Jill could see Prince run. The heartbeats started to get faster as we forced our way into the Paddock.

All eyes were on Prince. After all, you don't see a track record holder every week. Prince looked fantastic as his walking out coat was removed to reveal the look of a real champion.

As I left the Paddock, I grabbed Jill's arm. "Let's find a good spot to see the race or we'll end up looking at a row of heads again."

Rita and Matt had the kids sitting next to the Judge's box, the best view on the track. Charlie and the lads were busy trying to get a decent price on Prince.

"PLACE THE DOGS IN THE TRAPS," the starter announced.

The butterflies in my stomach were doing somersaults. Jill gripped my arm as the hare started running. "Come on, Prince, come on, my son," she was whispering to herself, "please don't miss those lids." Prince was drawn in trap four. It wasn't the best of draws, but as the hare went past and the lids went up, Prince flew out and was on his way to the first bend. There was a sudden roar from the crowd. Some joker had jumped onto the track at the other end and was waving his coat to try and stop the race. It was an old ploy if you had backed a dog and it wasn't in the lead at the first or second bend; you would try and stop the race. I had a gut feeling that Dodger was behind this, when all of a sudden the man waving the coat was rugby tackled and thrown back over the wall. Luckily, Sharpy had seen the man jump onto the track and had been close enough to do something about it to avoid it being a no race, and also to prevent the dogs being injured. There was a loud cheer as the man was grappled to the floor and sat on until the police came.

It was all over in a split second, as was the race. Prince had won by a convincing margin. "THE RESULT OF THE SECOND SEMI FINAL — FIRST, NUMBER FOUR, MIDNIGHT. SECOND, NUMBER TWO, GOLD LABEL — THE WINNERS TIME, ANOTHER NEW TRACK RECORD: 26-48 AND FOR THE INTEREST OF THE LARGE CROWD TONIGHT, THE IDIOT WHO TRIED TO STOP THE RACE HAS BEEN ARRESTED AND WILL FACE CHARGES. HE IS ALSO BARRED FROM THIS TRACK FOR LIFE." The incident had taken some shine off the night, but it didn't stop Prince breaking the track record again, thanks to Sharpy.

There were still lots of people interested in buying the dog and the bitch, including the couple I'd been talking to earlier on, and of course, Dodger's team.

By the time Sharpy made his way round to where we were standing he was fuming. He had given the chap who had tried to stop the race a little bit of a persuader to find out who had paid him and Sharpy wasn't happy. He made straight for Dodger. "You, you bloody fat tub of lard, it was thee who put that low life up ter jumping onto track!" Dodger's face drained white.

Walter the Weasel started to shake at the knees, his cigarette sticking to his bottom lip as his mouth gaped open. "It weren't me Sharpy," the Weasel cried, looking up at Dodger as if to say 'it was him'. The Weasel was not the best man to have in your corner when push came to shove.

Sharpy stood staring at Dodger with a look that could kill. I knew that if I didn't do something there would be a lot of trouble. I pulled

Sharpy to one side. "I know how you feel, Sharpy, I feel the same way, but if there is any trouble about this and it comes back to us, we might end up being barred, and so will Prince!"

That seemed to bring Sharpy to his senses. His fixed look on Dodger seemed to relax a bit, much to the relief of Dodger and Weasel. It was quite plain that both Dodger and Weasel had seen Sharpy in action before. Like I said earlier, if Sharpy said it was Christmas in July you would sing carols. Charlie turned to Dodger, "If thar wants to enjoy a healthy life, thar best walk away now, and tek thee stick insect with thee," meaning the Weasel. They didn't need a second invitation. Dodger and Weasel scurried off into the crowd.

That was enough excitement for one night. We said our goodbyes to everyone, including those that were interested in buying the dogs. All I wanted to do now was to get home, see to the dogs and take the weight off my feet.

The following day my expectations were right. Lady was in season. The first thing I had to do was get her away from Prince. There was nothing that could distract a dog more and make him lose all form than a bitch in season. With just a week to the final there was no time to waste. I walked up to Ted's house with Lady. I knew he had a spare kennel and one old bitch he kept as a pet. I knocked at the door, there was no answer. That was all I needed; perhaps he was round the back garden in the kennel. I opened the gate, but there was no sign of Ted or his bitch. I had to find a good kennel for Lady and quick.

It was a good forty minutes walk from our house to Ted's and with standing so long the night before my back was starting to play up. I sat down on a seat that Ted had in the garden and decided to wait.

Lady and I had been there about twenty minutes when Ted's gate opened. It was Sharpy. "Hey up, Tom, I'm glad I've seen thee. I want to apologise for losing me rag last night."

"No need, Sharpy, I wanted to do the same as you, but I think we did the right thing in the end."

Just then Ted came through the gate. I was just about to speak when he said, "Don't ask where's thar been?" smiling all over his face. "I've been down to your place. We must have missed each other on the way. I'd a feeling that thar would be needing a kennel so I thought I'd walk down and bring bitch up."

"I wish I'd known that before I set off Ted, my back's bloody killing me!"

"Dun't worry, Tom," said Sharpy, "after thar's got bitch settled I'll run thee home."

When I got home Jill was in a right state. Prince had been going mad, barking, howling and trying to get out. I had never seen him like that before. I went straight down to the kennel to see what the problem was. I stroked him, talked to him and fussed him. He looked OK physically, but there had to be something wrong somewhere. I decided to take him for a walk to see if it would make him any better. It was like dragging a wheelbarrow without any wheels. Prince was just not himself. I decided to take him back home, he went back a lot better than he set off.

"How is he?" asked Jill, who was waiting at the gate when I got back.

"Not himself by a long way," I replied. Jill gave him a drink and put him in his kennel. My back was starting to get worse after doing too much walking so I decided to lie down when Prince started to bark, howl and create a right racket. Jill and I decided to feed him early to see if that would settle him down. Beef stew and veg. If Prince could do one thing better than run, it was eat.

Jill opened the kennel door and placed his food on the floor, I could have eaten it myself it smelled that good. Prince just sat there looking at Jill and me. That wasn't like him at all, usually he would have half of his dinner gone before the dish was on the floor.

By this time the kids were coming in from school. Colin came straight down to the kennel. "What's up with Prince, Mam, his dinner's still there?"

He too was used to seeing Prince devour his food. "And where's Lady? You haven't sold her to that horrible Dodger man, have you? Have you, Mam?"

"No son, no we haven't sold her to anyone. Lady's not well so we've sent her up to Ted's for a rest."

"Is Lady, Prince's girlfriend, Mam?" young Peter chipped in.

"Why do you ask?" I said with a smile.

"Well, if she's gone up to Ted's, will he not be missing her? I missed Mary Crookshank when she went into Mrs. Smith's class."

Out of the mouths of babes! Jill and I just looked at each other. That was it, Prince was missing Lady, but what could we do about it, Lady was in season. By this time, Charlie had arrived and after telling him what was going on it was decided that he should go back up to Ted's and ask if he would bring his pet bitch, Sooty, down. It was a long shot but we had to try something. In the meantime, Prince had still not touched his food. If Ted's bitch didn't do the trick, it looked like all of our dreams of winning the final were out of the window. From being on cloud nine one week ago, to wondering if we would even have a runner in the final, didn't bear thinking about.

It was a good hour before Charlie got back. He tried to catch his breath as he came down the path to the kennel. "Ted weren't in and I've been all over place looking for him."

"Did you find him?" I asked hurriedly.

"Aye, but tha's not going to like what I've got to tell thee, Tom."

"Come on then, Charlie, spit it out!" I wasn't in the mood for guessing games.

"Top and bottom of it is, Tom, that Sooty has come into season as well." There was a stunned silence. Things were starting to look bleak. Prince had still not eaten his food and there were only five days to the final. We had to find a bitch from somewhere, but where!

It was real bad luck that Ted's bitch had broken down as well, but it was not the first time I had heard of one bitch bringing another into season.

"Well," I asked, "anyone got any suggestions?"

"What about Matt and Rita," suggested Jill. "I know Rita has at least two bitches and it would be bad luck if both of those were in season as well."

"It's worth a try, Jill," I said, "after all, we've got now't to lose now, have we." I jumped into the van with Charlie and we set off for Matt's place, hoping to God that he would be in and that his bitches weren't in season too.

We pulled up at Matt's house just as he was about to pull away in his van. "Caught me just in time, Tom, I was just off to the station, what can I do for you?"

"You can tell me that none of your bitches are in season for a start." Matt looked at me as if I was daft.

"You've got me beat there, Tom. What difference would it make to you if any of my bitches were in season, anyway?" After explaining the situation to him he shook his head. "I'm sorry, Tom, but you still have a problem."

"Why, you said they weren't in season!"

"They aren't, but one of them is a replacement for a dog that is being sent back. In fact I was just on me way out to Donny Station to pick the dog up and the other is in the second round of the handicap at Lowgate track tonight."

"Shit," said Charlie, kicking the tyre on the van. "That's it, now, all the ante-post bets on Prince are lost and the best dog in the heats won't be running."

"I'm sorry Tom, but what can I do?" said Matt.

"Oh, it's not your fault, Matt, but if we can't get Prince to eat he'll have to be withdrawn from the final."

"Wait there just one minute," said Rita scratching her head, "what about the one you have to pick up from the station?"

"A dog's no good, Rita," snapped Matt.

"It's not a ruddy dog you dipstick, it's a bitch." She was talking to Matt, who sometimes didn't know what day it was.

"That's right, my little cherub, it is a bitch," he said, very nicely.

"Don't you try taking the Mickey out of me, Matt Cross, or it won't be cherubs you'll be seeing, it'll be stars."

"Point taken, my little dewdrop," said Matt, laughing, but hiding behind Charlie at the same time and keeping well out of reach of Rita's left hook.

"Right," I said, "no time to waste. Let's get off to the station and pick up this bitch."

"There's no need for me and Rita to go now, Tom," said Matt. "I'll just give you a letter of authorisation and that should do the trick." Matt gave us the letter and we were just about to leave when Charlie asked him why the bitch was being sent back. "Er ... er, some geezer said she was fighting on the track, but I don't believe him for a moment, she's as straight as a die that little bitch." Rita looked at him, raised her eyes heavenwards in amazement and shook her head.

"Come on, Charlie," I said, laughing at Rita and Matt, "let's be off. No time for chit chat, the quicker we get home the better."

We got to the station and asked about the bitch, handed the station porter the letter and he showed us to the parcels office with a big grin on his face; something was amusing the porter? Was it me or Charlie? Were our flaps open, or did he just feel in one of those moods? As we approached the building where the bitch was being held, the porter burst into laughter once more and with good reason. There stood the bitch with a big pair of boxing gloves tied around her neck.

I think someone was trying to tell Matt that his bitch was a real fighter, and from what the porter was telling me, this was the third time in six weeks that the bitch had been sent back. It was another one of Matt's little games. If he got someone who complained about a dog he had sold them, he would send them anything to keep them quiet until he could get something suitable to replace it. She was a friendly little thing, wagging her tail as we removed the boxing gloves from her neck.

As we drew up outside our house we could hear Prince howling his head off. "Thank the lord you're back, Tom," Jill sighed, looking exhausted. "Prince has not shut up since you left and he still hasn't eaten."

We took the bitch from the van and checked her for fleas, walked her down to the paddock and let her off. Prince jumped straight off his bed and started smelling around her, his tail wagging with joy, until she went across to his food. The hairs on the back of his neck stood up and his tail stopped wagging. She was just about to tuck into his dinner when his top lip started to quiver as he barred his teeth. The bitch looked up at him timidly and slowly walked away. Prince immediately started to eat his dinner. At least he was eating. We thought it best to leave them together, but to watch from the kitchen window, just in case. Prince seemed to be back to his old self. He cleaned his dish and started playing with the bitch. Jill made some more food for Boxer, as we had christened her for obvious reasons!

The next few days were like nothing had ever been wrong. Boxer had settled in and Prince was on cloud nine. We were back on target for the final. We informed the track that Lady was a non-runner because of her condition and they expressed disappointment that she wouldn't be running, but wished us luck with Prince.

On the day of the final Jill seemed more fidgety and on edge more than usual. Something else was on her mind. There was only one thing for it, I asked her outright, "Is there a problem love?"

"Not really," she replied quietly.

"Well, there's something wrong. What the hell's the matter with you?" I asked.

She busied herself polishing the furniture and fussing. She took a deep breath and said, "Well, if you call being pregnant a problem." She stopped work for a moment and looked me straight in the eye. "Well say something, Tom Watson, instead of standing there with your mouth wide open." I was dumbfounded. We had been trying for a little girl, for Jill's sake, as we already had three boys. Jill wasn't sure whether to laugh or cry. "I didn't want to tell you, Tom, until after the final, so now what have you got to say?" she sniffed.

"There's only one thing to say. Let's hope it's a girl this time!"

Just then Colin, Bobby and Peter walked in, covered in mud. They'd been playing football. Jill looked at me and shook her head. "I hope you're right, Tom Watson, I hope you're right," she sighed and then turned to the boys. "Right then, you scruffy lot, up them stairs and into the bath. You don't want to be going to see Prince running in the final looking like a set of urchins. Last one up the stairs is last in the bath and we all know what that means, don't we?"

"Yes, Mam," said Peter, "last one in gets stuck in the middle with legs coming from all over and it's always me," he said as he started to cry.

"Tell you what," I said. "Why not let Colin and Bobby have the bath and you can have the sink?"

"Great, Mam," he said, a big smile breaking out. "I hate it when them two get in the bath first and I'm stuck in the middle."

"Well not tonight, my son," I laughed. "Tonight you've got the kitchen sink all to yourself, but make sure your mum hasn't left any forks in there," I said with a wink and a smile.

We all arrived at the track looking spick and span. Everyone wishing us the best of luck. It was a great feeling to have a dog in the final and an even better feeling to know that you had a great chance of winning. I decided to stay outside the track with Prince, you were never sure of what might happen with the likes of Dodger and his mates about.

I was standing outside the van when I was approached by a couple inquiring about the bitch and asking if she was for sale. I turned him down, politely, as he seemed like a genuine chap. "Best of luck tonight young man. Not that you'll need it if I'm any judge of things."

"You always need luck in this game," I replied. "Anything could happen; he could fall down or miss the break, anything."

The man looked at me and smiled. "Aye, you're right, young man, but I reckon it would take all of those things put together to beat that dog tonight."

Deep down, I knew he was right. Prince was something special and I would be the most disappointed man on earth if he were beaten in the final. As the man bid farewell he reminded me that if I were to change my mind about selling the dogs, would I give him first chance. He and his wife seemed like nice people, so I nodded my head in agreement that I would give him first chance.

Only one race, then the final. I started to give Prince a good rub down when Ted came out of the track. "Tom," he said, catching his breath, "it's Mickey, the kid who's been taking dog on; he's gone and broken his leg and can't tek dog on track. I thought I'd better come and let thee know so's thar can get someone else tu tek him in."

"Ask Jill," I said. "Prince gets on best with her and she knows how I like him to be looked after." Ted nodded and went back off into the track in search of Jill.

I was just finishing off Prince when Jill came out. "What on earth is your game Tom Watson," she said. "I've got all my best clothes on and my best shoes. If Prince wins I'm going to look a right mess with mud all over my shoes!"

"If he wins, sweetheart," I laughed, hugging her, "you can buy as many shoes as you like."

"I'll keep you to that, Tom Watson, you see if I don't," and with that she started to get Prince ready for the track.

Jill knew how strict I was about leaving the walking out coat on as long as possible. Let the public see him in the paddock, but as soon as he's out of the paddock, back on with the big coat. You had to keep your dog as warm as possible. As the dogs left the paddock there were only two with big coats on, the rest were standing around shivering. I had to give Prince as much help as possible.

Charlie, Ted and Sharpy were trying to sniff out a price for Prince but the bookies were having none of it. Prince was big odds on and that was the way it was going to be. I made my way to a good

191

vantage point. I could see the whole of the track from where I was standing. Jill was keeping Prince on the move, stopping every now and again to pat him on the head and make him feel at home.

"PLACE THE DOGS IN THE TRAPS, MR. STARTER," crackled the announcement. Prince had drawn trap two.

My heart started to race and the hare started to move. 'Please, oh please, don't miss the break, Prince,' I prayed to myself. I crossed my fingers and held my breath. The hare flashed by, the lids went up and he was out like a rocket on his way to the first bend. Jill was in the middle of the track running nearly as hard as the dogs around the inside of the circuit and shouting for Prince at the same time.

I could hear Charlie and the lads screaming over the noise of the crowd. "Go on, my son, thar's won from there," Charlie was screaming. Prince was increasing his lead hand over fist when the hare started to slow down. Either the hare was breaking down or, more likely, there was more dirty work afoot. It seemed to be the latter and I would put money on Dodger being behind it. Prince had got within half a yard of the hare and was starting to snatch at it, slowing himself right down and allowing the other dogs to catch up with him. Suddenly, someone from the crowd ran up to the hare driver's box and in a split second the hare was speeding up.

It was none other than the big stranger with the scar on his face; I'd recognized him from the clothes he was wearing. He was taking a big risk that someone might recognize him and realise that he was a licensed trainer. If he was recognized and reported to the NGRC, his governing body, he would more than likely lose his trainer's licence.

As soon as the hare crossed the winning line and Prince had won, the stranger disappeared into the shadows as mysteriously as he had arrived. There was a loud cheer from the crowd and much celebration, but I knew that I had the tall stranger to thank for Prince winning the race.

Jill stayed on the track to receive the trophy and the prize money, to the cheers of the crowd. As the photographer arrived to take some shots, I sent the kids on. I could see Jill looking down at her shoes and I laughed to myself as she placed one of the kids conveniently in front of her.

The prize money was £400 for the winner, plus the ante-post bet I had at £10 at 33-1. Not a bad days work, but there was something wrong, an emptiness I couldn't quite put my finger on. I was standing there wondering what it was when there was a tap on my shoulder. It seemed to bring me back to what was happening on the night we had just won the Big final!! The tap on the shoulder was from the old man and his wife who I was talking to before the race.

"Congratulations, young man, there was never any real danger, even if the hare driver did try to get your dog beat. You see, son, when you've been racing as long as I have you'll find that class will always tell, even if there is the odd shady character in the game and your dog is a character in his own right. You had the man jumping on the track in the semi final who was waving his coat, that didn't break the dog's concentration, nor did the hare slowing down tonight. Believe me, young man, you have a dog and a half in that fellow and if you ever want to sell him at any time, you just let me know."

Before he could say any more I put my hand up to stop him and asked how much he would pay for the dog. Jill, Charlie, Ted and Sharpy turned and looked at me with their mouths wide open.

The old gent asked, very politely, "I'm sorry, what did you say?"

I turned and repeated myself. "How much will you give me for the dog?"

"Are you serious?" he asked with a slight grin on his face.

"Why don't you try me?" I encouraged.

"All right then, I will," he smiled. Jill and company still looked gobsmacked. "I won't mess you about," he continued. "He's the best dog I've seen in a lot of years and if I buy him at the end of his racing days he will be used as a stud dog." By this time, quite a crowd had gathered, Dodger included.

I pulled Charlie and Jill to one side and told them to trust me. Charlie just shrugged his shoulders and said, "If thar knows what thar's doing Tom, it's up to thee."

193

The old gent came closer. "I'll give you £1,200." There was a large gasp from the crowd. Dodger was coughing and spluttering on a pie he was eating. It was a lot of money for a dog, no matter how much he had cost and there was an old saying in the dog game, 'if you turn down good money for a dog, something will always go wrong with it'. I stuck out my hand to seal the deal. The old gent grabbed it before I changed my mind.

The deal was struck. I instructed the old couple to follow me back home. I was insistent that Prince was washed down and fed before he went on his journey. There was hardly a word said on the way home in the van, but I knew that I had done the right thing. The emptiness I was feeling before wasn't there anymore and I felt a whole lot better inside. I knew what had to be done and I did it. It was the old gent and his wife that had filled the emptiness I was missing.

Prince was given a good wash down and his dinner in his kennel while the old gent and his wife had a cup of tea and sorted out the money. He must have had an idea that he would come away with the dog or the bitch because of the amount of cash he was carrying. He counted it all out in £20 notes. I gave him some luck money back and Prince was on his way. The thought of losing him was a strain on my heart, he was the best dog I had ever had and maybe the best I would ever own. I couldn't compare him to Sandy as that was different; Sandy was the first, maybe not the fastest, but there was always a lump in my throat when his name was mentioned.

The old gent and his wife assured me that Prince would have a good home for life and that I could see him whenever I wanted. Jill and Charlie had faces that would turn milk sour and to be honest you couldn't blame them.

We bid the couple farewell and came back into the house. I took a deep breath and said: "Please hear me out before you go jumping to conclusions. Is £1,200 a good price for a dog that only cost a few quid?" Charlie just shrugged his shoulders. "Good answer, Charlie," I said, giving Charlie a shrug of my shoulders.

"Well, what's thar want me tu say," he replied.

"I want you to give me an answer," I said.

"OK," he shrugged, "It's a fair price."

"Right then, I'll carry on. Have we still got the bitch, who's not that far behind Prince on times?"

"Thar's got chair Tom, carry on" Charlie shrugged.

"And," I went on, "have we not won a fair bit of money on him?" It was a wall of silence all the way. Jill and Charlie sat stone-faced. I shrugged my shoulders. "I'll come straight to the point then. When the old couple approached me to sell the dog, they reminded me of the couple in Ireland that I bought the dogs from, only the couple in Ireland didn't have two pennies to rub together. I just thought that it might be nice if we sold Prince and gave the money to them. God knows they need it."

There was still a silence from both Jill and Charlie for a few seconds. Then Jill came over and hugged me, tears welling up in her eyes. "You great big soft lump," she said, as she wiped her tears on my clean white shirt. "I thought there must be a good reason for selling Prince," she sobbed. "There just had to be."

"Thar's right, Tom," nodded Charlie in agreement, and nearly breaking into a smile. "It'll do the old man and woman more good than me and thee," then off he went shouting over his shoulder, "I'm off tu Fish shop before there's now't left," whistling his head off as he went.

The next day Jill was up bright and early, it was a nice sunny Sunday morning, "Right, you lot," she shouted, "downstairs in two minutes or there's no breakfast."

"But Mam it's Sunday and we always have a lay in on Sunday," said Colin, still sounding half asleep.

"Sunday or no Sunday, you've got one minute left to get down those stairs or there's no football next week." There was a thunder of feet jumping from their beds and down the stairs.

"There you are, Mam, all up and ready for breakfast," said Bobby, terrified he was going to miss a football match.

"Well now that you're all downstairs, you can all go back up and get yourselves washed and ready." Peter was always last at everything and today was no exception, trying to keep up with the other boys and tripping over his pajama bottoms and complaining the boys wouldn't let him in the bathroom.

"What's all the racket about, Jill," I asked. "The kids are running up and down stairs as if the house was on fire?"

"Well, Tom Watson, for your information we are all going out for the day; Lady is in season, Prince is with his new owners, that only leaves Boxer and I have arranged for Charlie to see to her, so there is NO excuse for not going out." I was just about to say where are we going, when Jill jumped in, "And before you ask where we are going, we are going to the seaside and that's that! The kids and I just stood there, not saying a word, as Jill busied herself making the breakfast. I don't know whether it was Jill's forthcoming pregnancy that had put her in that mood, but whatever it was, it was good enough for me and the kids. We had a super day.

CHAPTER THIRTEEN

The next few weeks were used to sort out things for the journey over to Ireland. Jill had made sure that all the bills had been paid and the kids had some new clothes. Things were looking a bit rosy for a change, after all, I'd been off work for a good few weeks and we had to do without so many things. Charlie had booked a few rest days from work and had, somehow, managed to keep hold of most of his money, which was a small miracle in itself. It seemed strange going all the way over to Ireland and not to buy dogs, but I was sure that the old man and his wife were in much greater need that we were. The only thing that troubled me was that something might have happened to one, or both of them. Their health had been so poor the last time we saw them at the sale.

We arrived in Ireland without any problems. The van was as smooth as silk and the crossing was good, which was just as well as I was the worst sea traveller God had put on this earth. I had copied the old chap's name and address from Prince's identity book. It was Main Stream Farm, County Cork. The scenery on the way down was out of this world, as were the people. We stopped every now and again to ask directions and we couldn't have had more help than these people gave us. It didn't help a lot that both Charlie and I were useless at finding our way.

We stopped at a little cafe on the road side as Charlie was feeling hungry, as usual, and I decided to ask in there if anyone knew where Main Stream Farm was. An old man sitting in the corner heard me asking the cafe owner. He took his pipe from his mouth and banged the contents into his hand, "Wud dat be der Riley's place you'd be seeking lads?"

"That's right, Sir," I replied.

"Ah well den, you'll be wantin' to be on the Ballymorn Road, dat will be taking you right up to Main Stream Farm."

"And how far are we from the farm now?"

"Well, let me be seein'. You'd be eight miles from Cork. I'd be saying you want another seven miles."

We finished our meal, thanked the old man and got on our way. We soon found a sign for Ballymorn, a narrow road with lots of twists and turns, hardly room for a car and a bike to pass, never mind two cars. We followed the road running alongside the stream and I felt more at home here than I did in England. There was just something mystic and peaceful about the place. The old man in the cafe was right, we were half a mile from Main Stream Farm.

As we drove through the gates we could see how good the farm must have been in its prime with lots of buildings and the stream running along beside the house. It was plain to see, however, that the old pair had fallen on really hard times. The doors were falling off the outbuildings, fences were down and there was very little livestock. A couple of cows, a few hens and an old donkey. We parked the van in the yard and shouted to see if anyone was at home. There was no reply, when all of a sudden this dog came flying out of one of the buildings, barking, snarling and snapping at Charlie's ankles. Charlie immediately grabbed me by the shoulders to put me in front to protect himself. We were just going to make a run for the van when we heard a voice shout, "DOG, behave yerself." It was the old man.

"Am I glad to see thee," Charlie sighed, wiping the sweat from his brow and checking the bottoms of his trousers. I was just glad to see the old man was still alive.

"Can I be helpin' you, Sir," asked the old gent. It was obvious that he hadn't recognised us. As he got closer, he took off his cap and scratched his head. "Be Jesus, if it's not der lads from England dat bought the dogs." I was glad that he had recognised us, it made me feel a lot happier. "Come on into the house lads, come in, come in." He ushered us into the house. It was in desperate need of repair. There was damp running down the walls and a couple of broken windows with cardboard stuck in to keep out the wind. "You would just be in time for a cup of tea and a bite to eat," said the old man. "Sit yerselves down till I make the tea. I won't be a moment."

Charlie and I sat down, looking round the house as we did. There were trophies, cups and photographs all over the place. It was quite obvious that Mr. and Mrs. Riley had seen better times. I was glad to see his wife enter from the kitchen, that they were *both* still alive. The old lady poured four big mugs of tea. "Here you are lads, a nice mug of tea to warm you up," said the old lady and hurried back into the kitchen.

Mr. Riley was asking what he could do for us and before we could answer he was explaining that there were no more dogs. Handsome Prince and his comrades had been the last litter they had bred. They couldn't afford the stud fee never mind the cost of bringing them up. "Yer see lads, tings is not too good at the moment, what wit the wife's health and all, it would be just too much to be taken on." He was trying to hide the fact that they had no money and made the excuse that it was down to his wife's health. He was a proud man and we didn't want to hurt his feelings. I just hoped that he wouldn't be offended when we gave him the money.

We assured the old gent that we weren't looking for dogs and were just about to tell him about the money when his wife came out with something to eat. I had seen Mrs Riley making something in a small basin as she went back into the kitchen.

"You'll be stayin' for a bite to eat," said the old man. "It's soup and it'll be warming you up." We tried not to offend the couple by saying that we had just eaten, but they insisted, and if I wanted to give them the money I couldn't afford to offend them. Mrs. Riley placed three bowls on the table, one each for Charlie, myself, and Mr. Riley, insisting that she wasn't hungry. These people had nothing and yet they were willing to share their only meal with us. I couldn't help but feel guilty, depriving them of their meal, but what could I do? We either refused the meal and offend them, or eat the meal and feel guilty. I looked over to Charlie for guidance but all I got was a shrug of the shoulders. It didn't look all that appetising, mainly potato, with one or two veg. The old man had soon finished his off, wiping the bowl clean with his bread. Charlie and I ate ours and thanked the Rileys for their kindness. We then went on to tell them about Prince and his sister.

He was so glad to hear that the dogs had turned out well, pleased as punch that all of his work and effort had not been in vain. We weren't sure how he would react when we told him that Prince had been sold. I was amazed at the next words out of his mouth. "Well lads, now'll be the time to be sellin' the dogs on. They'll be bringing a good price and that's the time to sell." I could feel the tension leaving my body and I could see the look of relief on Charlie's face.

"Well Mr. Riley, that's why we've come to see you. We sold Prince, and we did get a good price for him."

"Good fer you, young feller, dat's what dis game is all about."

"Well," I went on, "the point is, Mr. Riley ..."

"Oh for God's sake, be calling me Shamus and the Missis is Colleen."

He wasn't making this any easier by interrupting all the time. "Right then, Shamus," I pressed. "The thing is, we sold the dog and we've come over to give you the money." I took the cash from my coat pocket and put it onto the table. Colleen nearly dropped her soup bowls when she saw how much money there was lying on her table.

"There's £1,200 on there, Shamus, and it's all yours."

"Jesus Christ," he said crossing himself at the same time, "'tis a long time since I seen that kind of money, but I can't be takin' that from you lads. It'll not be mine to take."

"It is yours, Shamus," Charlie and I insisted together. I went on to say, "It's for you and Colleen. Charlie and I have won a lot of money off the backs of your two dogs and if it wasn't for you, we would have nothing."

"But it's such a lot of money, lads," he said, choking back the tears. Colleen was already crying. She flung her arms around me and then Charlie, sobbing like a baby.

"Dun't be doing that Missis," said Charlie, swallowing hard, "tha'll be having me at it in a minute."

The old man grasped my hand. "God bless you, Tom. God bless you both." By this time it was almost impossible to keep the tears away. Best thing Charlie and I could do was to be on our way. We bid Shamus and Colleen Riley good-bye and got into the van. Colleen was still crying as she ran behind the van waving her hand until we were out of sight. It was a very, very emotional time for all, and I don't think I will ever forget the look on the faces of that old couple as I placed the money on the table. As Charlie and I left the house, we promised to keep in touch. All in all, it was both a sad day and a happy day, sad to see how far the old couple had fallen from what once looked like a very prosperous farm, to a shadow of what it must have been, and happy to see the expression on the faces of two very grateful old people.

CHAPTER FOURTEEN

Four months had passed since Charlie and I had been to Ireland. Lady was just coming out of season and things weren't going too well financially, or on the health side. My back was starting to play up something rotten and the money we had won on Prince had all but gone. Still, there was always Lady to look forward to. The only problem was where on earth we were going to run her and how on earth we were going to find the money to have a bet when she did run! After her great runs in the open races it would be hard to get a decent price anywhere local; the only thing to do would be to travel. I had talked it over with Jill and decided to take her and the kids up North, for a long weekend. Jill hadn't seen her family for some months and with her being seven months pregnant it would be nice to see them before the happy event.

Plans were made and Charlie decided to join us. Lady had only had three trials since her season's rest but she showed some great speed in her last run. It looked like she would be coming to hand early, which would be good, especially as it took some bitches five or six months to come to hand. The biggest problem was how to slow her down for her grading trial up North. I had thought about feeding her, but sometimes that didn't work. Giving her a pill was out of the question. If we just let her run she would grade in too fast and would have very little chance of winning the race. It was a catch 22 situation, so I decided to leave it at the back of my mind and cross that bridge when I came to it.

We arrived in Durham without any problems. The van was OK and Peter wasn't sick. I dropped Jill and the kids off at her parents and proceeded to try to find a kennel for Lady. This proved to be no easy task. I had tried four different people, but got the same answer from them all: 'No room at the inn'. Time was running out with only a few hours to go to the trials. Charlie and I had just about resigned ourselves to leaving Lady in the van when who should come waltzing down the street but Fancy Fred. He was called this by all that knew him because of his dancing. He loved to go ballroom dancing. I stopped the van and took Lady from the back. I knew that she would catch Fred's eye, because of his love for gambling on the dogs.

"Hello there, Tom," said Fred, a broad grin on his face. "Long time no see." I had worked with Fred at the pit before we had moved away.

"Nice to see you again, Fred. How's it going?"

"Fine Tom, fine. Mind, that's a nice looking bitch you've got there Tom, is she any good?"

"She's a little cracker, Fred, and I mean that."

"Is she running tonight?" he asked with a gleam in his eye, hoping to get some information that he might be onto a winner.

"Well Fred, she is running in a way, that is to say she's up here to try and grade in, but there's a problem."

"What's the problem, Tom, you know you can trust me," he said, looking over his shoulder at the same time to make sure that no-one was listening or watching.

"Well, Fred, I've got the wife and kids up for a few days and I need a kennel for the bitch."

"No problem," replied Fred. "That's sorted."

"Second problem is, I need to find a good jockey (meaning someone trustworthy) to take this bitch for her grading trial."

"No problem on both accounts," said Fred. "I've got an empty kennel and I'll take the bitch on myself."

"That's just the job, Fred," I said, rubbing my hands with glee. "I knew I could rely on you. I'll see you back at your allotment in two hours." With that, Fred was on his way.

Charlie looked puzzled. "I thought thar were wantin to get 'bitch kenneled up?"

"I do, Charlie, I do, but I also need to find a way to steady her down."

"Aye, thar's reet, Tom, but how's thar gunner do that?" I looked at Charlie with a glint in my eye, patting the side of my nose with my finger. We lifted Lady into the back of the van and headed back up the road. "Where's thar goin' then?" asked Charlie, looking a bit puzzled.

"Just up the road a way; if I'm not mistaken there should be a big pond."

Charlie gave me a sly look. "Things ain't that bad, Tom, are they? Just joking Tom, just joking," he laughed.

"Well, if things don't start to get better soon, Charlie, it might not be a joke." Charlie looked at me with a serious face. I paused for a moment before saying: "Now who's joking Charlie?"

"You bloody toad," he shouted, before starting to laugh.

We found the pond all right. The plan was to swim Lady for as long as possible, just to tire her out. I thought I might have a problem getting her into the water, but she took to it like a duck. In fact, I had a job getting her out. She must have been in there for at least an hour on and off. After getting her home and dried off, we made our way to Fred's allotment. He was there as keen as ever and ready to go. The big problem was Lady. Had she done enough swimming to slow herself down for the trial? We would know very shortly, it was only a couple of miles to the track.

Charlie and I followed Fred down in our van, so as not to cause any suspicion. We needn't have worried, the track was full of people wanting trials. Lady was in the fifth trial. The handicapper wasn't hanging about, no sooner was one trial finished than they were in the boxes for the next one. Fred was next with Lady, she had drawn the six jacket. "Hurry along with those dogs," shouted the handicapper. "We haven't got all night."

Fred placed Lady in the traps. They all came to the bend together and lo and behold Lady ran straight out of the little gate from which she came; this gate led straight onto the running track about 80 yards from the traps. Lady just stood there sniffing the ground as if looking for something. Both Charlie and I looked at each other in amazement. "Now what the hell made her do that?" I said, shaking my head in disbelief.

"All dogs grade in that trial," was the announcement. I looked at Charlie, Charlie looked at me. Lady should not be among the dogs that qualified, but what the hell, we had to take the chance.

"It's worth a go, Charlie," I said. "Try to catch Fred's eye and tell him to take her in to mark her up." With the handicapper in such a hurry it was quite possible that he hadn't seen Lady run out of the gate.

Fred was in the line waiting his turn, looking nervously back to where Charlie and I were standing for some assurance. I had an awful feeling that Fred was going to blow it, not that the chap who was doing the marking up was taking much notice, but Fred was becoming more and more nervous by the minute and when Fred got nervous, he started to stutter. "Next," shouted the man who was doing the marking. There were two people before Fred. The marker wanted to know what trial you were in, what jacket you were out of and your finishing position in the trial. I decided to take a chance. I walked over to Fred and told him he was wanted at the main gate. The look of sheer relief on his face was a picture. You'd think he had backed a winner. I was just in time. It was his turn next. "What trial?" asked the man.

"Five," I replied, "out of trap six."

"And where did she finish?" This was the tricky bit. "Fifth or sixth," I said rather hesitantly. He looked up at me and I thought, 'oh oh, he's twigged.'

"That bloody handicapper," said the man. "He's always the bloody same on trial night, as long as he's got the trials off, he couldn't care less. We'll put her down as sixth." A sigh of relief came over my face and I could see a relieved Charlie out of the corner of my eye.

I gave the man Fred's name and address and quickly left the track. Charlie was waiting outside.

"Thar's cracked it, Tom, that were a good bit of thinking. Now all we have to do is get our hands on some money."

Fred was waiting in his car round the corner. We gave him a nod for him to set off home and we would follow. We arrived a few minutes after him. He was full of apologies. "I'm so sorry, Tom, I just losssst me nerve." He stuttered with excitement.

"Calm down, Fred, it's not a problem," I assured him. We washed Lady's feet, and were about to take some grub out of the van when Fred came out with a big bowl of boiled veg and meat. It smelled good enough to eat.

"Right, Tom," he said. "Let the bitch get stuck into this and I'll settle her down for the night." We arranged to pick her up early the next day and left her in the capable hands of Fred.

"Right, Charlie, now there's just one thing left I have to do before I go back to Yorkshire."

"And what's that, Tom," he asked, curiously.

"Something I haven't done in a long time. Pay a visit to an old friend. We jumped into the van and drove a few miles up the road to a row of colliery houses where I had lived with my gran and grandad, a place full of so many happy and sad memories. Gran and Grandad had long passed on, but whoever had taken over the house had kept it nice and they had also kept Sandy's grave as it was, there at the bottom of the garden, in the middle of the flower bed. I just stood there, filling up with tears. The memories of that night flooding back ... the night Sandy gave his life for me to win that trophy. Charlie didn't need to ask what I was doing there, he knew. I stood at the bottom of the garden just looking at the grave when someone came out from the house and up to the gate. I had to look twice. It was Mr. Grainger. He had been an old mate of grandad's.

"Is that you, Tom Watson?" he asked, the tears rolling down his cheeks.

"It is Mr. Grainger, it most certainly is." I could hardly believe that he was still alive.

He opened the gate and flung his arms around me. "By God, Tom, it's good to see you after all these years."

"The feelings mutual, Mr. Grainger, I can tell you that. Where's Mrs. Grainger?" I asked.

"I'm afraid I lost her about the same time as your gran passed away," he said, wiping the tears from his face.

"I'm so sorry to hear that, Mr. Grainger," I consoled.

"Well, young Tom, that's just the way life is, isn't it. There isn't a lot you can do about it Tom," he went on.

"When I lost the wife, I was up in Scotland you know, and I got to thinking that when it comes to my turn I want to be among the friends I have lived with all of my life, so I came back and was lucky enough to fall in for your grandad's house and that's why Sandy's grave is still here. You see, Tom, I was at the track that night and I know how you must have felt when you lost that dog. But have no fear, Tom, as long as I have a breath in my body, that grave will be here, and when I go, I will leave a letter telling the story of Sandy, and I'm sure whoever takes over from me will respect that."

"That's nice to hear, Mr. Grainger, and I'm so very grateful," I said, choking back the tears. I could see from the corner of my eye that Charlie was in difficulties too, wiping a tear from his face with his sleeve.

"You will come in for a pot of tea before you go, Tom, won't you?" asked Mr. Grainger.

"I'm sorry," I shook my head. "I have to get off. I've got the wife and kids with me and they'll be wondering where on earth I've got to."

Mr. Grainger looked up at me and laughed through his tears. "Who'd have believed it, little Tommy Watson with a wife and kids."

"It happens, Mr. Grainger, it happens," I said. He gave me a huge hug and shook my hand. It was time to get back to Jill and the kids. I took one last look at Sandy's grave and bid Mr. Grainger good bye.

"God bless you, Tom," he shouted as we walked down the garden path.

As we sat in the van silence was all about us. I tried to hide the tears from Charlie as I fumbled with the keys and when I looked up Charlie was as full as I was. There wasn't a word spoken on the way to Jill's parents' house, both overcome with emotion. In fact there was very little said all the way back to Yorkshire.

Next day we had a few words with Fred on the phone to confirm the arrangements; he was to phone down if the bitch was on the card and tell us the mark she had in the race. That would give us a few days to try and rake up some money, which was going to be a feat in itself.

It was midweek and Charlie and I still hadn't managed to rake in any cash. Things were starting to look grim. We were half hoping that Lady wouldn't be on the card to race, but it would be just our luck that she would be and that she would have a good chance of winning.

We were out for a walk with Lady when we bumped into Gypsy John, a local travelling lad who liked a flutter on the dogs himself. "Hey up, Tom, Charlie, how's it going?" he asked, a piece of straw stuck in his mouth.

"Not too good, John, I'm afraid. Same old story though, short of the green stuff."

"What's thar wanting money for Tom?" he asked putting his hand into his pocket. "If it's a few quid for Jill and the kids thar can have what I've got," said John, and he meant it.

"Thanks, but no thanks, John; Jill and the kids are fine and the bills can wait a while." John looked puzzled as he chewed on his straw.

"Well, if it's not the kids or the bills, you must have a gamble on and no money to gamble with? Am I right Tom?"

"Pretty close, John," said Charlie

"When's dog on card?" asked John anxiously.

208

"Weekend, we hope, if we can get our hands on any money," I replied.

"Tell thee what, Tom. I've got some rugs coming in today; there's plenty of profit to be had from them, for all of us." Things were starting to look better already. "I'll drop them off when I get them," said John and with that he was off down the lane, still chewing on his piece of straw.

Gypsy John was true to his word. He arrived at our house about an hour after Charlie and I got back with Lady. He pipped the horn outside the house and shouted, "Come on then you two, if yer want tu make any brass, tha'll not be doing it sitting in there on yer backsides." Charlie, me and the kids set to and carried the rugs into the house.

"Reet," said John, the straw still hanging from his mouth, "there's sixty rugs there and I want twenty-five bob apiece for them. Yer can knock them out at thirty bob each, no bother." He was just about to leave when the phone rang. It was Fred to say that the bitch was on the card in a level break. That was great news, she had to have a great chance especially as she had won a couple of opens.

"Good news," said Gypsy John as he saw the expression on mine and Charlie's faces. "Would there be the smallest chance of a bet, Tom?" he asked shrewdly, smiling at me.

"Why not," I laughed. " There's plenty of betting for all of us if we can sell these rugs."

"Don't you worry about them rugs," John said. "They'll sell themselves at that price. There's only one condition," he went on, still chewing on that piece of straw.

"And what will that be then?" asked Charlie.

"Thar can't sell the rugs local."

"Why not," I asked, wondering if I really wanted to know the answer.

"Dun't worry, Tom, there's now't wrong with them," said John. "It's just that if thar sells them round here it'll spoil job for next lot."

A sigh of relief swept over Jill's face. She had been sitting quietly listening and taking it all in, but saying nothing. If Jill had a dislike for anything it was dodgy deals and dodgy people, and in this game there was an abundance of both.

"Reet, John," said Charlie, "thar's got thee sen a deal." With that, Gypsy John spat on his hand and smacked it onto Charlie's hand. The kids found this most amusing and all started spitting into their hands and shaking hands with each other.

I talked it over with Jill that Charlie and I would be setting off early on the day of the race. I didn't like leaving her when she was seven months pregnant, but I had to do something to earn a few bob and racing the dogs seemed to be my best option. The dogs had pulled us out of the fire on more than one occasion and I had to stick to what I thought I knew best.

Charlie and I loaded the rugs into the van at 6.00 am on the day of the race and Lady made herself quite at home in the centre of them. We had set off early for two reasons. One to get Lady into Fred's kennel as soon as possible so she could rest up from the journey, the other was to try and sell the bleeding rugs. If we didn't manage to sell the rugs we were in real trouble. All we had in the cash line was £9 and that was for petrol and entry into the track. I didn't want to let it enter my mind.

We pulled into a garage just a few miles from the village I was born in. As Charlie walked Lady round on the grass verge to stretch her legs, someone came out of the office. He looked at me rather curiously. "It's ... Tom, Tom Watson, isn't it?" said the man.

"Aye, that's right," I replied, "but I'm afraid you've got me beat."

"Harry Bell," he replied.

I looked at him again. "Tubby, Tubby Bell, well I never, I would never have recognised you in a million years," I said, shaking my head in disbelief. Tubby wasn't Tubby any more. He was a six footer with not an ounce of fat to be seen.

He was pleased to see me, shaking my hand vigorously. "What's your game?" he asked, still shaking my hand.

"After all these years, not much," I replied. "After moving from one coal field to another and then having my accident, things could be a lot better."

"Tom," he said, "if there is ever anything I can do for you, you just let me know. After all, we were good pals at school and I have done quite well for myself. It's not a big garage," he continued, "but it is mine." He was obviously very proud. By this time Charlie was on his way back with Lady.

"We'll have to get cracking Tom if thar wants to sell them rugs," shouted Charlie.

"I had no idea you were in the rug game, Tom."

"I'm not, Tubby, I'm selling the rugs for a friend of mine and at the same time trying to get a few bob together to bet this bitch."

"Still at the dog game, I see," said Tubby with a smile on his face. "Let's have a look at these rugs, then, I might just be your first customer." He asked the price and picked out four, two for his wife and two for his mother. He handed me the £6 and I thought to myself, we still had a long way to go before we could get a decent bet on Lady, but at least it was a start.

We were just about to pull away when a thought came into my head. "Tubby," I shouted across the forecourt as he was just about to enter his office. He turned and came back towards the van. "You said if you could ever do anything for me I only had to ask!"

"That's right, Tom," ask away.

"Well you can buy this van from me."

Charlie nearly choked on the bottle of pop he had bought from the garage; he looked at me as if I had lost all of my marbles at once. He tried hard to get some words out of his mouth as he screwed the top back onto the pop, "Thar's gone stark staring mad, Tom," he raved. "They say all dog men end up on the funny farm in the end and it looks like thar's just bought a first class ticket straight tu nut house. If thar sells this van, how are we going to get dog tu track?"

Tubby turned to look at me, "He has got a point you know, Tom."

"Will you both just wait a minute and listen to what I have to say,"

211

I shouted. "Hear me out. What I have to say might not sound too stupid." I turned to Tubby. "How much is this van worth?"

"At first glance Tom, not a lot."

"How much is not a lot?" I asked.

"'Bout £70 or £80 at the most."

"I would say a little more, Tubby," I laughed, "but that's not the point. What if I asked you for £30?"

Charlie turned and looked in amazement. "Now I know thar's gone bleedin' barmy," he said.

I turned and looked up at Tubby. "As I was saying, if you give me £30 and let me keep the van until after the race, if the bitch wins we give you £35 back, if she gets beat you get to keep the van."

"That's bloody great thinking, Tom," snapped Charlie sarcastically, "how's thar goin to get home wi no van?"

I turned to Charlie and said, "And how are we going to get home without any money, without any petrol and without any money for Gypsy John?"

Charlie scratched his head for a minute and then looked at me and said. "Thar's right again, Tom, sell van!" We did the deal with Tubby and set off to Fred's. We left Lady in Fred's care and went about the task of selling the rugs. At least we had £30 to bet Lady even if we never sold a rug. Gypsy John had been right, the rugs sold themselves; no sooner had we knocked at one door and sold a rug, then the lady of the house would pop next door to tell her neighbour and that's the way it went all up and down the streets until the van was empty. Our main problem was Lady. Would she do the same as she did in her trial? It was still in the back of my mind that Lady had stopped at that little gate going out of the track for a reason, but why?

When we added up the money for the rugs and the money that we had for the van, it was a nice little sum: £120 in all; £90 all told for the rugs and £30 for the van. Out of this, £75 was Gypsy John's. I looked at Charlie, Charlie looked at me, and we both thought 'oh, what the hell, it's only money.' It was sink or swim time, all or nothing.

We made our way back to Fred's to check on Lady. Everything was OK. Fred had some news on the other dogs in the race. By pure coincidence, one of the chaps who refused to kennel Lady had a dog running in the same race.

The dog was unknown to Fred, but this lad had a reputation for keeping a good class animal. But that wasn't our only problem, Charlie and I still couldn't work out why Lady had run out of the gate in her trial.

She was too genuine a dog just to pack it in and not chase the dummy hare. There had to be another reason, but for the life of me I couldn't work out what! We decided to take a chance anyway, we weren't going to change our minds at this stage. Fred was still a bit apprehensive as he hadn't seen Lady race. No matter how much Charlie and I tried to persuade him to change his mind he was having none of it, £5 was going to be his maximum bet.

We had been sat on the allotment for about an hour when an old mate of Fred's came down the path. "How's things, Fred," the old chap asked.

"Not bad at all, Bert, not bad, and how's things with you?" asked Fred.

"Fair to middling," was his reply.

"How's the dog game?" Fred asked, knowing Bert liked a bet on the dogs.

"Dog game, dog bloody game. I couldn't win a summons, never mind win at the dogs," said the old man starting to get frustrated. "I was there on Thursday night and should have backed two winners," he moaned.

"Change your mind then, did you?" asked Fred.

"No," said the old man, starting to curse and swear, "backed both of the bloody winners and never got paid."

"Why not?" prompted Fred; we were all curious by now.

"Both bloody void races," he fumed, banging his walking stick on the side of Fred's leek trench.

"Did hare brek down?" asked Charlie.

"Nope," said the old man.

"Traps not open?" asked Fred!

"Nope."

"Well, are you going to bloody tell us or not?" Fred was starting to get impatient by now.

"Well, first void race was a dog that ran straight out of the gate that leads onto the track for no apparent reason and then back onto the track, stopping the race." Charlie and I looked at each other in unison. The old man continued. "Then stone me if the second race was almost the same thing. Two dogs ran off the track at the track entrance, one of them then jumped back onto the track and ran towards the other dogs, so the hare driver had to stop the race. After the meeting, the groundsman and the handicapper had a good look round and found a nest of rats behind the entrance gate to the track. They reckon that they've dug them out now, but it's a bit bloody late if you ask me," said the old man, starting to curse all over again. This, however, was just the news that Charlie and I wanted to hear. There had to be a reason for Lady to stop chasing that dummy hare and that was it.

We were growing more and more confident by the minute and decided to stick to our original plan of letting Fred take Lady in for the race and for Charlie and I to do the betting. We followed Fred down to the track travelling at a safe distance so as not to draw too much attention. Tommy Swift was standing in the car park with the dog Fred had told us about. It was a nice big brindle dog, very well put together. We watched as Fred walked to the kennels and out of sight before we left the van. Swifty made a point to shout over, "Did you get that old bitch a kennel, Tom?" with a smirk on his face.

"Yeah, Swifty, we managed in the end," I said, while thinking 'no thanks to you'.

"Nice dog you've got there," Charlie said to Swifty, trying to make conversation.

"Oh, he's just an old rubbing rag I picked up for a few quid," said Swifty, trying to make out that the dog was no good.

"Not worth having a couple of quid on then?" asked Charlie.

"Couple of quid on this fella, he couldn't run if his arse was on fire," said Swifty, doing his best to try and look serious. Charlie and I were letting all of this go right over our heads. We'd heard it all before; when someone was trying to put you off backing their dog, beware!

"Oh well," said Charlie, "best of luck, anyway."

"He'll need more than that," said Swifty as Charlie and I walked through the turnstile.

Three races had gone by without a hitch. The rat problem seemed to have gone. Lady was in the next race. All the dogs in her race were new dogs, none of them had raced on the track before. I had named Lady, Jill's Girl, for luck. The betting seemed quite good, ten books in all. We decided to split the bet. We had £120 for the rugs and the van, £10 for Gypsy John and £5 for Fred, making a total of £135. That was every penny we had. If Lady didn't win we had now't. Charlie had £70 and I had £65.

There were lots of people milling about, waiting for odds to change and to see what was trying in the race and what wasn't wanted. You would always get two or three people in a race who wouldn't try with their dogs because they were unsure of the opposition. This usually left two or three triers per race. If I was any judge, I knew that Tommy Swift's dog was a definite trier. I instructed Charlie to wait until there was a move in the market and then not to move until I told him to. Sure enough, Swifty and one or two of his mates went diving into his dog, Mr. Big. That was all that the bookies and the punters were waiting for, someone to make the market. Swifty brushed past me and Charlie looking a bit embarrassed after telling both Charlie and I that his dog wasn't much better than a mongrel.

It didn't take long after that for the prices to change. Lady's price shot out to 5-1. Now was the time to strike; "Five Seventies," said Charlie, "on Jill's Girl."

"You've got that young man," the bookie said, handing Charlie his ticket.

I went in at the same time. "Five seventies on Jill's Girl," I said. The bookmaker was taking money hand over fist and hadn't noticed that there was only £65. It was too late to start to get a conscience now, the race was about to start. Lady was in the six trap, the same trap as for her trial.

Charlie and I stood together. As the hare flashed past Lady came out well, but Swifty's dog was right behind her. She was just going to take the bend in front when she altered her stride and looked towards the gate, "Shit," said Charlie, "that's done it now." Two dogs had passed her before she straightened herself up. It was quite obvious that Lady still had that rat on her mind when she went passed that gate and now she had a race on her hands. Three hundred yards to go and she was still third dog. I had visions of me, Charlie and Lady hitching a lift down the A1 and then having to explain to Gypsy John that we had lost all his money.

All was not lost though. Lady had passed one of the dogs and was just two lengths behind Swifty's dog. You could hear Swifty shouting: "Nothing will catch that feller when he leads". On the face of it I was inclined to agree with him, then all of a sudden Lady found another gear. You could see Fred running round the inner track, screaming and shouting for her. As they crossed the line you couldn't part them. They were locked together.

"PHOTO FINISH," called the Judge.

No-one on the line could split them, half saying Lady had just got it, half saying Swifty's dog had just kept a whisker in front. If it was a dead heat, Charlie and I would still win because Lady's price was so high. The tension was unbearable and Charlie was half-way to his knuckles, having chewed off all of his nails.

The loud speaker crackled. "Here it is Charlie," I whispered. My heart was beating like a drum.

The crowd were deadly silent, waiting to hear the result. "FIRST, NUMBER SIX, JILL'S GIRL."

Charlie and I grabbed each other and started jumping for joy at the same time. "She's done it," we screamed, "she's done it." What a great bitch. To come from where she was in the race, to get up and then win, was some feat. We were far too busy celebrating to hear the time and the distance. Also, by this time, Swifty had realised that Lady was the bitch we had wanted him to kennel. He didn't half look soft standing there with egg on his face.

He had condemned Lady as an old bitch and his own dog as a rubbing rag and there he was, Tommy Swift, standing at the books waiting to pay his money on and there was Charlie and I standing waiting to be paid out. What a great feeling. It reminded me of a certain Dodger Smith.

Charlie drew his money right in front of Swifty and stood there, counting it over and over again, just to annoy him. To make matters worse, the bookmaker I had my bet with was calling me over to collect my money. "Don't you want this young man?" he asked. I held out my hand as he started to count the cash into it. "Right, young fella, that's £350, plus your £70 stake." I hesitated for a second, should I tell him there was a mistake or should I take the money and say nothing! I stood there as if I was in a dream. "Is there something wrong," asked the bookie. "Have I paid you short?"

"No, not really," I replied. "Actually, you've given me too much. I only had £65 on, not £70. I made a mistake when I called the bet on."

The old man took off his cap and scratched his bald head. "Well, I've been pulled for paying out short, but never in my life have I been pulled for paying too much! Tell you what, lad," said the bookie, "I've had a good result on this race. If the favourite had won I would have gone down for a lot more, so as a reward for being honest, keep the extra few quid." He laughed, slapped me on the back and sent me on my way.

I felt a whole lot better about myself now and Swifty was looking a lot worse. He looked as sick as a man who had lost a £100 and found a sixpence. It didn't help matters as he watched Charlie and me stuff our winnings into our pockets and head off to meet Fred at his allotment.

Fred was already there when we arrived, washing Lady's feet and giving her some supper. "She ran a cracker, didn't she?" said Fred. "What price did you get, lads?" he asked with a big grin on his face.

"Five's," replied Charlie, taking some money out of his pocket.

"Just the job," smiled Fred. "I'll bet Swifty was a bit sick to say the least." Fred held out his hand as Charlie started to count.

When it got to £30, which was what Fred had won, he kept going. £35, £40, £45 and so on, right up to £100. Fred's hand was shaking, "Wwhat's, wwhat's all that for?" he asked, stuttering with excitement.

"Well Fred, that's your £30 winnings, £30 Tom got from the bookie for being honest and the rest is from us both for looking after us and the dog."

"I can understand about the winnings and I appreciate the treat from you two lads, but a present from a bookie for being honest? Now that has got me beat."

"It's a long story, Fred," I laughed. "Let's just say it's from a very happy bookmaker and leave it at that."

Fred wasn't the type to look a gift horse in the mouth. He thanked Charlie and me once more and neatly folded the money and placed it in his pocket. I don't think he had ever had that much money before in his life. Fred was a miner earning no more than £15 a week. He shook our hands and was close to tears as he wished us a safe journey and assured us that Lady, Charlie, myself and any other dog we cared to bring, were welcome at any time.

We bid our farewells to Jill's parents and set off for Tubby's garage. Tubby was standing on the forecourt with his mechanic when we got out of the van.

"Well," he asked, "is it mine ... or is it yours?"

"What do you think Tubby?" I said with a smile as wide as the Tyne Bridge.

"Looking at the expression on your face, Tom Watson, I'd say you still had a van."

"There was never any danger," I smiled, thinking 'if only you knew Tubby, if only you knew'.

We thanked Tubby, handed him his £35 and set off for the long journey home.

We hadn't been home a couple of minutes when Gypsy John arrived. "Good timing, Tom," he said, as he pulled up alongside our van.

"I hope thar doesn't think I'm pestering thee for money, Tom," he said quietly, "but I was just passing when I saw the van, so I thought I might as well call in."

"It's all right, John," I assured him. "You couldn't have timed it better, Jill's just put the kettle on." John made himself comfortable in the easy chair still chewing on a piece of straw, Charlie and I just sat there talking about anything, the weather, the news, anything but dog racing. Every time John tried to ask about the rugs or the race, Charlie and I would change the subject. You could see John getting more and more frustrated. Jill could see what we were doing and didn't take to it at all; we often did the same thing to her. Again, every time John tried to open his mouth, Charlie or I would stop him in his tracks.

"That's it," shouted Jill, "you two big kids have had your fun; now tell the man what he wants to hear!"

"OK," smiled Charlie, "what's thar after knowing, John?"

"Well, how did the rugs go for a start?"

"So, so," replied Charlie

"And what about the bitch?" Charlie looked across the room at me and was just going to kid John on again when he saw Jill giving him the evil eye. That was enough for Charlie. "The bitch did thar say, John? Oh, she won." He was looking up at Jill innocently as if to say all the jokes are over now. John rubbed his hands with glee. If there was anything he loved it was having a few quid on a winner.

I looked up at John's face, "There's only one thing wrong, John," I said.

"And what's that, Tom?" he asked, his smile turning into a blank expression.

"We got all of the money on, except yours."

Jill looked at me through the corner of her eye, she knew that I was still trying to kid poor John.

She picked up a cushion and made as if to throw it, aiming straight for my head. "If you don't stop this silly game, Tom Watson, you'll have me to answer to!" That was enough for me. When Jill lost her temper, you knew about it.

Charlie, who was keen to stay in Jill's good books, was quick to respond. "Aye, thee money was on John, no sweat, you didn't think that we'd put ours on and not yours," Charlie smiled at Jill, looking at the cushion at the same time.

"What about the rugs," asked John, knowing that with Jill in charge he would at least get some straight answers now.

Quick as a flash Charlie answered back, "All sold John, all sold." The smile was now all over John's face again.

"You've done well the two of you, that's £75 for the rugs and me few quid off the bitch," said John.

I started to count the money into his hand, a total of £135 in all. John was more than pleased and pressed £10 into Jill's hand. "That's for the kids Missis and I won't take no for an answer," he smiled.

"Thanks, John," I said, "but there's no need." John looked at his hand, spat on it and shook mine and Charlie's hand. Jill quickly gathered up the teacups, filling her hands before John could get to her and then making sure that her hands were in the kitchen sink up to her elbows as he left.

"Thanks for t'tea Missis," said John as he left still chewing on the same piece of straw.

"And thanks for the present," said Jill, still keeping her hands in the water. He hadn't got out of the gate when a new piece of straw came out of his pocket and into his mouth. That was the trademark of Gypsy John.

I never did get round to telling Jill the full story of the day out at the races, selling all the rugs and putting it all on Lady, selling the van and the nail-biting photo finish, after all she was seven months pregnant. Would you have told her?

CHAPTER FIFTEEN

Jill was in hospital when a nurse friend of Charlie's phoned down to say that she had gone into labour. I rushed next door to Mrs. Slones and asked if they could keep an eye on the kids until I came back, then sped off to the hospital. By the time I arrived it was all over. "Congratulations, Mr. Watson," was the greeting as I burst through the door and into the ward.

"Is ... is Jill all right?" I stammered as I tried to catch my breath.

"Yes, Mr. Watson, Jill is fine and you have a fine healthy ..." I waited with anticipation, was it a boy or a girl? "... son," continued the nurse.

I made straight for Jill's bed and gave her a big hug, because I could see there was a slight disappointment in her face. She had hoped that this time it would be a little girl, but her words were, "If the man upstairs wanted us to have a boy, who are we to ask questions."

After a few days in hospital Jill was glad to be home and the kids were glad to see her, after all I had been feeding them for a week on Blue Ribbands and baked beans, so no wonder they were glad to see their mam. The first words out of Peter's mouth as Jill walked through the door were, "What's for dinner, Mam?" not 'How are you, Mam?' or 'How's the baby?' But that was Peter for you. He loved his grub. We decided to call the new addition to the family, Tom, after me. It wasn't my choice, but it was what Jill wanted and nine times out of ten, Jill got her own way.

The baby was only a couple of months old, but that didn't stop Jill wanting to watch the older boys playing football. It was a cup round and both Colin and Bobby were playing. Peter was just that bit too young to get into a team, but that didn't stop him cheering his brothers on. It was a cracking game, with both boys playing well but not scoring. The game went into extra time with our lads winning by the odd goal. Colin had to be carried off with a very badly bruised ankle and had to hobble into the van with Peter showing great concern letting Colin use his shoulder as a crutch. When we arrived home Colin had to hop from the van to the house.

"Lay down on the settee, our Colin," said Peter, fussing around him like a mother hen. Jill was busy with the baby.

"I'll make the tea," I said. "You just carry on with what you're doing love."

Colin, Bobby and Peter looked from one to the other and then to me and in unison said, "I hope we're not getting baked beans and Blue Ribbands again, Mam, are we?"

"No, you are not," Jill shouted down from the bathroom. "I made a nice stew before we went out to the match." That put the smile back onto their little faces. Peter started jumping up and down and even Colin was hopping on one leg.

"What's up with you lot? You would think you'd won the cup not just got through to the next round," I laughed.

"But, Mam," laughed Bobby, "it's better than winning the cup, not having to eat those beans again."

"Three cheers for Mam," shouted Peter. "Hip, hip hooray!"

"OK, lads, point taken, just settle down," I said, thinking to myself, 'cheeky little sods,' but I loved them.

Jill dished out the stew and I must admit it was a long way better than any tin of baked beans I had ever tasted.

"Why don't you see what's on the telly Colin," Jill suggested. "You can't go out to play with an ankle like that."

"I'll see what's on," said Peter looking around the house for the paper. "This should be good, I think," said Peter.

"Come on then," said Colin, "what is it?"

"Taza, son of Choc-ice."

"What?" said Bobby, looking very confused. "Taza, son of Choc-ice," repeated Peter.

"Give me the paper and let me look," said Bobby, snatching the paper away from Peter. "You thick head, Peter," he laughed. "I thought you could read."

"I can read," said Peter indignantly.

"Oh, yes?" said Bobby, who was hardly able to speak for laughing. "What it says in the paper is 'Taza, son of Cochise' the Indian fighter, not an ice cream bar, you thick head."

"Well it looked like choc-ice to me," said Peter, huffily, "and it sounds better anyway!"

Jill and I were in stitches by this time, laughing at their antics. We didn't have a lot but what we had was better than money. We had a great family and we were very, very happy.

CHAPTER SIXTEEN

The bad luck had started to set in with the dogs. Lady had cracked a hock in a race and was going to be out for some considerable time. Charlie and I had bought another dog, a nice type but not in the class of Prince, or Lady. Old Mr. Riley in Ireland had picked himself up, which was good news, and we were glad to hear he had started breeding again after our last visit and was sending one or two dogs over for us to sell.

The dog we were racing was one of Mr. Riley's. We had planned to win a race at Middle Town track where there was a good betting market and a nice track to run on. Charlie had been doing well on the horses and wanted to bet the new dog, Poppy, first time in. I didn't think that the dog was ready and normally Charlie would listen, but on this occasion he was digging his heels in; the dog was bought between us and neither one of us had the divine right to say the dog was trying or not trying, and in true gambler's tradition we tossed a coin to see who had the final say. I lost. It was OK for Charlie, he had no ties and he had a good job. On the other hand I had a wife, no job, and four hungry kids to feed. We were just struggling to keep our heads above water. If it wasn't for winning a few bob on the dogs, I sometimes don't know how the hell we managed.

I was just about to leave the house when the phone rang. It was Donney Station. There were two more dogs to collect from Mr. Riley. That was Mr. Riley's only fault, he hated the telephone, so he would send over two or three dogs and wait a week to contact us to see if they had arrived. That's the way it was done in Ireland, because in a small community where Mr. Riley lived, everyone knew each other, and it was obvious, but only to Mr. Riley, that he thought it was the same here! Fortunately, Charlie and I had been to Donney Station that many times we were well known and were on good terms with the stationmaster.

After I'd picked up the dogs from the station the first thing I had to do before they were allowed in the kennel was de-louse them. No matter what dog you got from Mr. Riley they always had fleas, but after a good bath and a brush up they looked OK. A nice black dog and a good looking fawn bitch. Both had won races in Ireland, but nothing to write home about.

I then had the task of selling them on. They had to be advertised in the 'Greyhound Owner,' a paper with news of dogs for sale up and down the country.

Sometimes you could hit on lucky and sell the dogs straight away and other times you could have them in the kennel for weeks. And you always got the time wasters; they would phone, say they wanted the dog for definite and then never send the money or let you know that they had changed their minds. In the meantime other genuine people would ring up and you had to tell them the dog was sold.

Charlie arrived at our house, straight from work, to inform me that he had entered Poppy for that weekend. No matter how hard I tried to persuade him to wait another week he wouldn't listen. It was like talking to a stuffed dummy talking to Charlie. Once his mind was made up, that was it.

I did my best with Poppy all that week. The dog was well, but he was not 100%, just a bit short and in my book if it wasn't 100% it didn't run. Charlie wouldn't budge and to make matters worse he was betting £400. I could barely scrape £20 together. The dog still had a good chance of winning if there was nothing too fancy in the race.

We arrived at the track and found someone to take in the dog and left it in the lap of the gods. The gut feeling I normally had wasn't there. Charlie had given half the money to me to make it easier to place on the books. I was to start at one end and Charlie at the other.

There were only two dogs in the race being backed, that meant that we had a better chance than I thought. Things were starting to brighten up. Charlie and I stood back, looked at the prices on the boards and decided to step in and bet the dog as planned. The price for Poppy was different at all the books and it was difficult to remember how much and what price we had on each book. As there were only seconds to go there was no time to wait for a ticket, the hare was running. The time to sort out the betting was after the race and only if Poppy won!

The traps came up and Poppy came out well, neck and neck with one of the other dogs that had been gambled on in the race. Poppy was doing quite well, matching the other dog stride for stride. It looked like I might be eating my words later, but as long as Poppy won, I could handle that. I started to try and sort out the prices in my head. There was sure to be trouble after the race, trying to sort out the bets, but I could deal with that.

50 yards to go and the dogs were still locked together. They crossed the line in another one of those heart-stopping photo finishes. There were four lads on the line. One said Poppy had won it, the other three were for Tiger. If Poppy was beaten it was down to the fact that he was not 100%. If he had won, I would have to eat humble pie, and I would be glad to do so.

"THE RESULT OF THE PHOTO FINISH IS FIRST, NUMBER ONE, TIGER. SECOND, NUMBER TWO, POPPY."

I was bitterly disappointed. Not in the way that Poppy had run, but in Charlie, and he knew it as he came towards me kicking the ground with his hands in his pockets. That would be about all that was in his pockets; once again Charlie was skint. If he had had £400 and one penny, he would have bet the lot, that was his nature.

"Thar were reet, Tom," said Charlie as he shrugged his shoulders. "If dog had had another week it would have made all the difference. From now on tha'll say when dog's ready or not." I stood there saying not a word. "Well say summat then," he encouraged, "even if it's to say told thee so."

"No point, Charlie. As long as you've learned by your mistake, it's history now. I've got a few bob left in my pocket for fish and chips for Jill and the kids and us. Poppy's dinner will be ready when we get back and we still have the two dogs from Mr. Riley to sell, so we might make a few bob yet. I've advertised them, but we can still give them a run out at the weekend, see how they go. You never know?"

Charlie still looked down in the dumps. There were only two things that made him happy, that was winning and eating. The first was out of the question now, but I knew he would be smiling again by the time we came out of the chippy, and he was.

CHAPTER SEVENTEEN

The two dogs Mr. Riley had sent over were starting to look something like the shape they should be in. The fawn bitch was a right character. She would set herself and then all of a sudden start flying round the paddock, having a quick nibble at the other dog who just stood there acting as if the bitch didn't exist. It was time to see what they were made of. A trial was arranged at Lowgate Track.

Matt and Rita Cross were there trialing a couple of their dogs. "How's things, Matt?" I asked.

"Only so, so," he replied, with a quick glance at Rita.

"Don't you be looking at me like that, Matt Cross," scowled Rita. "I've told you, from now on if you want owt doing, you do it yourself."

Charlie was standing at my side itching to find out what Rita had done this time, because in the past she had dropped some right clangers. "What's up, Matt?" asked Charlie casually.

"I'll tell you what's up, Charlie; that stupid mare!" As he said this, he moved behind a small wall, putting enough distance between him and Rita, just in case. "I was a bit short of cash," he went on, "so I decided to sell some of the hens that weren't laying."

"There's none of them laying," whispered Rita out of the side of her mouth. Matt threw her a look to shut her up, but still kept a safe distance behind the wall.

"As I was saying, I wanted to sell some hens at the local market, so I sent broken brains there down to the shops to get half a dozen eggs to put in the bottom of the cages, you know, to kid the punters that they were good layers."

"Well, what's wrong with that?" asked Charlie.

"I'll tell you what's wrong with that, Charlie, me old son. The first cage sold well, but when they looked into the bottom of the cage to take out the eggs, the eggs were all nicely stamped and it's a bloody good hen that lays ready stamped eggs, isn't it! Needless to say all the hens had to be taken back and I got a ticking off from the auctioneer as well!"

By this time Charlie was doubled up and in kinks of laughter. That was just what we needed to cheer us up. There was one thing about Matt and Rita, there was always a good tale to tell when you met those two and it always cheered us up.

It was time for the two new dogs to trial. We had decided to run them together, after all, their times in Ireland were very similar. The dog looked very keen but the bitch seemed to have other things on her mind. The traps went up and the dog flew out, leaving the bitch a good ten lengths behind. When she decided to join in, the dog was a good fifteen lengths clear, but in no time she had caught up to him and went half a length clear. Instead of going away from him though, she was quite content to stay that half a length in front. There was no doubt she could run, but she could also dodge and with a dodger you never knew which way they were going to go. I was glad that the advert was in the paper. The sooner she went the better, she was no good to me or Charlie, but whoever bought her would have to be told that she wasn't 100% genuine. That left us with a problem because not a lot of people would be interested in a dodgy dog or bitch. We had already valued the dogs on their Irish form and asked £80 each. £50 each dog for Mr. Riley and the rest for Charlie and myself.

All that weekend I waited for that phone call that would sell the pair of them, but it wasn't until Tuesday that anyone showed any interest. A chap from London called. He wanted to know it all, where the bitch was bred, how many were in the litter, did she have papers, had she been injured, the full SP. I told him all that I knew, that she had just come over from Ireland. I also told him that she was a bit dodgy. He didn't seem to mind that she wasn't 100% and that he would get back to me the next day.

The next day came and went; it looked like he was another time waster. I was just moaning on about this to Charlie when the phone rang and lo and behold it was our Cockney friend from London. He made all the excuses that he could think of. He then asked for my address and the post office that the money was to be sent to. I told him what he wanted to know and thought that that would be the last I heard of him. However, I was wrong, he was as good as his word and the money arrived the following day.

The problem was I had forgotten to write down the name of the station he wanted the bitch sending to. The only thing to do was to wait until he rang back to ask where she was. It was well into the evening before I heard from him and he was none too pleased, I might add. Apparently, I told him the bitch would be on the midday train and he had been waiting from midday until now. After he had stopped shouting and I could get a word in to explain, he ended up apologising to me, which in my book made him an OK sort of fella. After all, it was my fault. The next day the fawn bitch was on her way to London.

Meanwhile, I had received a letter from the hospital informing me that I needed to be fitted with another plaster jacket. I wasn't too pleased as the other two had done nothing at all to ease the pain in my back, but I had no choice but to go along with what they wanted to do.

I could see that it was all starting to get on top of Jill. Me not working, no money coming in. I had even asked my own GP to sign me off so that I could look for light work, but because I was under the treatment of a hospital specialist I had to abide by their rules. At times I thought they were only using me as a guinea pig, with all that traction and plaster jackets, but who am I to query the word of a specialist! The only thing to do was make the best of what I had and try to keep my head above water. As my old grandad used to say 'there's always someone worse off than you.'

Five weeks had come and gone and so had the jacket. We had

sold the black dog and were just about getting by. Jill and I were spending most of our time watching the lads playing football for the school. It became a bit awkward when Peter made the second team. I would have to drop Jill off at one game and dash off to the other, but it was great fun watching the kids enjoying themselves.

We had been to a match one Saturday morning and had just got back for lunch when the phone rang. I recognised the voice as soon as I picked it up. It was the Londoner who had bought the fawn bitch. 'Oh, no,' I thought, 'here comes trouble.' I was sure he was going to complain about her not being 100%, but to my surprise he was over the moon with her and wanted to know if we had anything else for sale in the same class as her. I explained to him that I was waiting for some dogs coming over from Ireland.

As it happens I wasn't, but with Mr. Riley this wasn't a problem, he could have a dog on your doorstep the next morning. The Cockney also wanted to know if there were any open races going on up here. Open races are for dogs from anywhere in the country and as a friend of his had a handy dog there might be a chance of making a few bob.

I was all for that and so was Charlie, who had been having a bad run on the horses again. I told the man, who I knew now was called Johnny, that I would be in touch as soon as I heard about any opens. At least things were starting to look a bit brighter.

I was soon in touch with Mr. Riley who said that he would send off a couple of dogs as soon as he could. Meanwhile, Charlie was trying to find out about any open races. He came back with just the job, a one off race at Donney over 500 yards and to make things a bit sweeter, it was rumoured that Dodger had an entry. It was a long time since Dodger and I had crossed swords. I only hoped that the dog Johnny was bringing up from London was good enough to win both his team and mine a few quid.

We made arrangements to meet Johnny and his friends just outside the track at a certain time. Coming from London we had no idea what to expect; someone posh, rich or what! When Charlie and I met them we had mixed feelings. There was Johnny, a jovial chap about six foot with a nose spread all over his face. We weren't too surprised when he said he was an ex-boxer. Then there was his friend and his friend's father. We didn't know what to make of them at all in the first instance. Then there was the fourth man. A tall chap who didn't have a lot to say and seemed to keep himself to himself. Little did I know then that he and his wife would turn out to be the best friends that I would make in all the years I'd been dog racing.

Ron, the owner of the dog, and his father seemed to be running the show with plenty to say and everyone to hear them. If he wanted to keep it a secret that a dog from London was running at Doncaster, we had no chance. Every man Jack and his mother knew there was a Londoner racing and Dodger delighted in telling those that had not heard. He was telling everyone that would listen that this dog had won this and that, so that the price of the London dog would be short and the price of his would increase.

The race, as it happened, was a formality, with the London dog winning by a long way.

Ron and his father were shouting about the short price on their dog, so I ended up telling them, in no uncertain terms, that if they had kept their big mouths shut the price would have been a lot better. It was plain to see that Ron and his father weren't used to someone telling them what they thought of them. If there was anything I disliked it was someone mouthing off and blaming everyone but themselves.

Johnny stood back in amazement, a little pipsqueak like me telling his mates what I thought of them. It was plain to see that Ron and his father had some clout down in London, but they weren't in London now and I had to speak my mind, huff or please. The fourth chap, Jack, just looked at me as if to say 'good for you lad'. Ron and his father stomped off, leaving Johnny and Jack to see to the dog.

Johnny was full of apologies. He knew that Charlie and I hadn't had a bet, with the dog being odds on it was pointless; 4/5 was the best price, and there was no way I was betting £20 to win £16. Johnny promised that things would be better next time. I felt compelled to tell him that there was very little chance of there being a next time. Jack interrupted and assured me that things *would* be better next time and that this wouldn't happen again. For some reason, I was inclined to believe Jack, and as we shook hands and parted company we promised to keep in touch. I had a good feeling about Jack which would prove right in years to come.

True to his word Jack and his wife Jenny kept in touch and were often coming up to visit for weekends. They had a family of three girls and in no time at all we were all like one big happy family. There was something special about Jack and Jenny, a certain chemistry that seemed to gel our two families together. It was as if we had known them all our lives and not just met a few months ago. There was no brag about them, they were very down to earth.

Jack had just bought a derelict old pub, but unfortunately hadn't been able to buy it outright on his own and had needed to find someone to share the expense. That someone had been Ron, the chap with the big mouth who had come up for the open race with his father and Johnny. It was a massive pub with Jack having one half, and Ron the other. In order for Jack to get his hands on some extra cash he had to rely on the dogs, the same way as I had to. Fortunately Jack had access to some very handy animals. Unfortunately, most of them were connected to Ron and that meant if one of Ron's dogs came up to race, it was accompanied by Ron.

By this time, Ron had realised that the clout he had in London meant nothing in Yorkshire and especially to me.

This meant he was very subdued every time he visited. I had phoned Jack about an open that was due to come off at the Donny track, the track where Ron and his father had let everyone know where they were from, so I decided to turn that to my advantage.

I asked Jack to telephone Doncaster track with an entry for the open race knowing fine well that within a short time everyone would know that there was a dog up from London for the race. Ron couldn't understand what the plan was and I could hear him in the background shouting and ranting about the poor price and going on to Jack that we must all be thick up north. I didn't want to get into a slanging match on the phone so I left Jack with instructions not to go directly to the track. He had to meet me at home and all would be explained there.

Even Charlie was looking a bit curious as I put down the phone. "Dun't say owt, Tom, if thar's got a plan, that's good enough for me. I only hope that dipstick cockney, Ron, can see plan, whatever it might be," said Charlie shrugging shoulders.

I had managed to win a few bob on the horses with three five bob doubles and a five bob treble, winning £28 in all. Half of that went to Jill, so at least I would have a few bob for a bet. As Charlie left the house I asked him to enter me a dog in the same Donny open as Jack's

"Thar's gone barmy again, Tom," said Charlie, with a worried look on his face "but if thar wants a dog in open, I'll get thee an entry," he said shaking his head in disbelief.

"Oh, one more thing, Charlie, call into Sharpy's and ask if he'll pop down in the morning. I'd like a word with him." Charlie stood there, shrugged his shoulders and shook his head once more. He was mumbling something about losing my marbles as he closed the door behind him. I just looked at him with a sly grin on my face and bid him good-bye.

The following day, Sharpy was down at the crack of dawn. "Charlie called in and said thar had finally gone round the bend and could I tek some of me dad's pills down to stop thee goin loopy," he laughed. "What's to do, Tom?" he asked.

"Oh, take no notice of Charlie," I said, "if he doesn't understand what's going on, then everyone's barmy," I smiled.

"Well then, what's the job?" asked Sharpy, trying not to seem as confused as Charlie.

"Have you still got that good looking bitch you bought a few months ago?" I asked.

"Dun't remind me, Tom," said Sharpy, looking despondent. "That's the worse bleeding dog I have ever bought!"

"Good," I replied, "that's just the dog I want." Sharpy looked at me out of the corner of his eye.

"Ah think Charlie may have a point, Tom. Thar's on way tu funny farm."

"Just tell me one thing, Sharpy, is she available for this weekend?"

"That bitch is available at any time, any day and to go anywhere," he emphasized.

"OK Sharpy, I get the point, she's available."

"That bitch, Tom, couldn't run to keep herself warm, if thar's thinking of showing it thar's got a reet good chance. If thar's thinking of running it ... forget it."

"No, Sharpy, I'm not going to show it, I'm going to race it."

Quick as lightning, Sharpy replied, "And thar has a good chance of beating it, Tom," he said sniggering to himself. "But dun't say no more, Tom, ah dun't want to know. When's thar want her for?"

"Bring her down about 6 o'clock on Saturday night if you will, Sharpy, and make sure she's had a good brush down and looks good."

Sharpy went out of the door, muttering just like Charlie had the night before and if things didn't go right on the night, both Charlie and Sharpy could be right. I might end up on the funny farm!

The following day I received a letter from the hospital explaining that due to the failure of the plaster jackets and the traction there was no alternative to surgery and, if I was agreeable, a date had been set for a month's time. Jill was both pleased and frightened.

We both knew it would have to end in an operation, but it was still a shock when it came. Jill hadn't been herself since the baby was born and this didn't help matters.

The kids were off school for half-term, so I suggested that we all had a week back in Durham. If there was anything Jill loved it was going back home to see her family. Her face would light up as soon as you mentioned a visit home and to be quite honest I had been thinking that if it had to come to an operation and things didn't turn out the way they should, then maybe we should move back north anyway. But there was no point in looking on the black side; there was a race to be won and hopefully a few quid to be earned.

Jack had been on the phone to say he had received word back from Doncaster track confirming his entry and that the dog he was bringing was a real handy tool and to make sure that I had plenty of cash to bet with. That was my main problem, lack of funds, and with the prospect of going into hospital, things weren't going to be made easier.

It was Saturday afternoon and Jill and I had just came back from watching the kids play football. I was looking at the horse racing in the morning paper, trying to find a winner or two when young Peter asked what I was doing. "Trying to find a winner, son," I replied.

"I'll find you one, Mam," he said, confidently looking down the race card. He stopped when he came to a name he liked, "that's it, Mam," he said, getting all excited. He had stopped at a horse called 'Peter's Gift'. "That's my name, Dad," he shouted, "that's sure to win."

Colin and Bobby wanted to join in then. "Let me pick one, Dad."

"And me," shouted Bobby. There was going to be no pleasing them until they had all picked a horse.

"I'm having that one," said Bobby. It was 'Bob's Delight'.

"And I'll have this one," said Colin, pointing to 'Inside Out'.

I could understand Peter and Bobby's choices, but Colin had me beat. "Why that one, son?" I asked.

"That's easy, Dad. When I got ready for school yesterday I put my jumper on inside out."

I pondered for a while and then said to myself, 'oh, what the hell. If I don't put them on and they win, I'll kick myself, and if I do put them on and they get beat I'll have a quid less to bet tonight'. I wrote them out and popped up to the betting shop.

Charlie was in there as usual; it was his second home. "What's thar backing, Tom?" he asked.

"Just three horses that the kids have picked out Charlie," I laughed.

"Let's have a look, then," said Charlie, taking the slip from my hand. "That's got no chance," he said pointing to 'Peters Gift', "and that thing," he said pointing to 'Bobs Delight', "it'll be pulling a milk cart in morning."

"You've missed one out Charlie. You might as well give me your expert opinion on all three."

"Ah, well, thar's got a reet chance wi 'Inside Out'."

"So you think I'm wasting my time with the other two!"

"Might as well tear up betting slip now," he laughed.

It was too late though, I had made up my mind, anyway, as I handed over the betting slip to the man behind the counter. "Take that sir and thank you very much," I said. As I turned to walk out the door I said over my shoulder to Charlie, "See you tonight and don't be late."

He nodded and as I left I smiled to myself as I heard him telling one of his mates, "That Tom, if thar tells him not to do summat he does it, and if thar tells him tu do it, he waint - barmy, completely barmy he is." That was one of Charlie's favourite sayings. If anyone did something he couldn't understand straight away, they were barmy.

By the time I'd got home Jack had been on the phone to say that he was setting off. That was the thing about Jack, there was always plenty of communication and if he said that he'd be there for a certain time, then he would be there.

It was 2.30pm and Jack was due at 6.00pm. By that time, all the horses the kids had picked would have run. Five o'clock; I would soon find out my fate. I picked up my coat and headed out to the betting shop.

As I entered the shop, Charlie was marching up and down like a soldier on guard duty, "I dun't know how thar does it, Tom," he raved. "Here's me, up at crack o' dawn studying form and can't back a bleeding winner," he raged, "and there's your young 'uns picks out three winners 'cos of their names! The game's gone barmy." he went on. "Two of them horses had no chance, no chance," he said shaking his head and still marching.

"Thar's wrong, Charlie," said one of the blokes sitting in the shop.

"How's thar mean I'm wrong," said Charlie starting to lose his cool.

"Well, 'cos they've all won," said the man.

"Ah, but they shouldn't hev," said Charlie, "it meks nonsense of form. A man can't pick winners out wi form like that," he said, rolling his betting slip up and kicking it in the air.

"You're right, Charlie, but the kids can," I said with a smirk on my face, "and that's what I'm getting paid out on." I handed over my slip. Charlie stood right behind me.

"Right, sir," said the man behind the counter, "that's £104."

Quick as a flash, "Thar's wrong," said Charlie. Charlie must have worked the bet out well before I'd came into the betting shop.

"No," said the man, indignantly, "I can assure you it is spot on."

"Spot on or not, it's wrong," Charlie insisted, "thar should have £114 Tom."

There was one thing you could guarantee about Charlie, he could reckon a bet in an instance and didn't need the help of a reckoning book. The man sat back and started to work out the bet out again. "Before thar starts," said Charlie, stopping the man in his tracks, "I'll bet thee a fiver thar's wrong."

"This book is never wrong," said the man, looking quite smug.

"Well, if thar's reet, thar's got nowt to lose," said Charlie looking quite confident.

"Right, your on," said the man as he started to work the bet out again. "There ... there must be something wrong with the figures," he said, as he started to work it out again for the third time, Charlie watching him like a hawk.

"Thar can fiddle all thar likes, but tha'll still get £114," said Charlie. In the end the man had to give in. Charlie was right. He paid out the bet and gave Charlie his fiver. It was a good day for all. The fiver Charlie had won was all he had. He couldn't even have paid the man if he had lost the bet. "I wasn't worried about paying the man anyway," said Charlie smiling.

"Why not," I asked. "Were you that confident that you were right?"

"Well put it this way, Tom, if I'd been wrong you were still collecting £104, so I could have borrowed £5 from you!"

I gave Charlie £20 from my winnings, but insisted he keep it for Jack's dog on the night, after all he had saved me £10 and I could now have a decent bet. £115 with my stake from the bet, less the money I'd given to Charlie, left me with £95.

I walked down from the bookies to the corner shop. Mr. Mossop, the owner, was behind the counter. He was a right old scrooge and I loved to wind him up. He was the sort of man that turned off the gas while he turned over the bacon.

"Two pound of spring cabbage, five pound of potatoes and half a pound of that nice bacon, please. On second thoughts make that a pound of bacon, please."

"Yer feed them young'uns too well," he grunted. "It were jam and bread and a bit of dripping from someone else's meat when I was a lad," he moaned. "We never had luxuries like bacon and what not, we had to wait until somebody killed a pig and we were lucky to get the trotters." Mr. Mossop was like this every time you went into the shop. You'd think he would be encouraging people to spend their money instead of grumbling about how much they were spending. I always made a point of going right over the top when I had a win. You could see him thinking to himself, 'how the hell can he afford all this stuff when he's not working.'

It used to drive him mad when I always finished off the order with a load of sweets for the kids and a box of chocolates for Jill. You could see his face getting redder and redder by the second and the nervous twitch from the corner of his mouth to his eye would get worse.

"I think that's all, Mr. Mossop," I said, "but if I've forgotten anything, I'll send one of the kids down."

He took the money, slammed the till drawer shut and shouted, "Close that door on your way out." Jill and I didn't have a lot of cash, but we were much happier than Mr. Mossop, who had loads of brass but a miserable life.

I walked into the house laden with all of the goodies. Jill and the kids knew then that the horses must have won and were eager to find out how much. I looked at Jill and winked. "Right lads first one who guesses gets a prize." It didn't make any difference who guessed right, they would all get a prize. Peter guessed £50, Bobby £70 and Colin £200.

Jill said, "And what about me?" She had her guess and I shook my head, higher than that. She had another guess. I shook my head again, Jill and the kids were getting all excited and shouting figures out all at the same time, when all of a sudden Jill gave out a scream. "The oven," she cried. "I've got fresh bread in there for Jack coming up." She opened the oven door. "Phew!" she sighed as the smell of home made bread filled the house. There wasn't a better smell anywhere in the world than home-made bread. Jack used to kid on that the only reason he visited was for Jill's home-made bread.

In the end I couldn't keep it any longer from Jill and the kids, so I told them how much I had won. "£114 is what the bet came to and I have Colin, Bobby, and Peter to thank for that."

"Can we pick some more, tomorrow?" asked Peter, jumping up and down.

"I don't think so, son, it's Sunday and they don't race on a Sunday, but we'll see about next Saturday."

"Do we still get a prize, Dad?" said Peter hopefully.

"There's a big bag of sweets each in that bag, but don't eat them all before tea." If the kids loved anything as much as football, it was a bag of sweets.

Time was getting on and it wouldn't be long before Jack and Ron were knocking at the door. Jill had baked apple pie and home-made bread. She had also made a big bowl of home-made custard to go with the pie. She then started on the dinner, spring cabbage, bacon, new potatoes and Yorkshire puddings. With that and the smell of fresh bread all through the house, who could wish for anything better!

It wasn't long before Sharpy arrived with his bitch. She was a real beauty even if she couldn't run. She looked every inch like an open race winner, which is just what I had wanted. Sharpy was still baffled as to what I intended doing with her and kept emphasizing about her not being a good runner.

"Don't worry, Sharpy," I said. "All she has to do is look the part and from what I can see she looks a proper picture." We left her in my spare kennel and arranged to meet up with Sharpy later on at the track.

"Ah hope thar doesn't want me to tek that bitch on in an open, Tom, not an open," he said as we left the kennel.

"Don't worry, Sharpy, everything will turn out for the best."

"I've heard that before," he shrugged. "Every time Charlie tells me that, it never turns out right."

I shook my head. "Just do me a favour, Sharpy, just go to the track. All will become clear when the dogs are paraded for the open race."

Sharpy took some convincing, but I think I got the message through in the end. Just as he was leaving, Jack and Ron arrived. They opened up the back of their van and a very handsome fawn dog climbed out. A real good looking animal.

"I'll have to do something about that, Jack," I said. "He looks too good."

"He's a bleeding picture," said Ron, "one of the best dogs in London."

"That's the problem," I said, "he looks too good. We have to make him look not so good so he doesn't look like an open race dog."

"You bloody northerners," snarled Ron. "I'll never understand the way you race up this part of the country."

I sighed and tried to explain. "Put it this way, Ron. If you were at a dog track and you saw a dog that looked a picture against a dog that looked like it had slept in the coal house, which one would you bet on? Not the one that looked rough, I'll bet. You would bet a good looking dog every day and don't say that you wouldn't."

By this time Charlie had arrived. He took one look at the dog Jack had brought up and said, "Bloody good looking dog that Tom; bet he can run a bit."

Ron looked at me and said, grudgingly, "Point taken Geordie, you're in charge. What do you want to do with the dog?" He sighed, "Thank goodness that lot's sorted out, I might get my tea in peace now."

Jack walked the dog onto the field to give him a bit of exercise and to make sure he had a good empty and then placed him back into the van. As soon as Jack came through the door he could smell the home made bread, "If that dog gets beat tonight, it would still have been worth coming up just for this bread," he said, giving Jill a hug, "but I don't think that he will get beat! With a bit of luck, I could be getting two bites of the cherry today, home-made bread and a winner as well!"

Jack and Ron cleaned their plates and finished off with apple pie and custard. Jack looked at Jill and said, "That was worth coming up here for even if there wasn't a dog to run."

"You're quite welcome, Jack, any time. As I've told you before, we don't have a lot, but we try to keep a good grub house," Jill said.

"Thar's right there, lass," chipped in Charlie, scraping the last bit of custard from his bowl and nearly taking the pattern off at the same time. Charlie would eat a scabby horse if it was between two slices of bread.

After the dishes were cleared away it was time to sort out the money for the bet. It was no good going to the track and handling money in front of everyone unless, of course, you wanted to and that was just what I wanted to do to a certain extent. I wanted to let a certain section of the crowd see Jack handing over some cash to me. Ron was still confused and Charlie had never not been confused, so I thought it was about time I put everyone in the picture.

"Right lads, here's the plan."

"Thank God for that," said Ron, "I've been wondering since I arrived what the hell is going on."

"Well you're about to find out," I said. "Charlie, do me a favour and bring that bitch of Sharpy's in from the kennel."

"Reet, Tom," said Charlie and off he went. Ron and Jack just sat there looking at each other. When Charlie came in with Sharpy's bitch the penny had dropped with Jack, but Ron still looked as puzzled as ever.

"Right, Ronald," I said, "I am going to put you out of your misery once and for all. This is the bitch that Jack will be taking on the track. No doubt everyone in the track will think that this is the dog you have brought up from London. Right." Ron thought for a while and nodded his head in agreement, so I went on. "You have to admit that she looks the part for the job." Both Jack and Ron agreed. I continued, "Meanwhile, I have arranged for someone to take your dog in and by sheer coincidence the dog that this chap owns is also a fawn dog, and will be any price. The dog you take on, Jack, will be favourite. Take my word for it."

A smile spread over Ron's face, at last the penny had dropped. There were just two things to see to now; the money and to make Jack's dog look like he'd been sleeping in a coal house. The best way to do that was to brush his coat the wrong way and sprinkle coal dust into it. Another thing to do was to take off his good collar and lead. I could see that Jack didn't like what we were doing to his immaculate dog, but we had no choice if the plan was to work.

Then came the shock. Ron pulled out of his pocket this wad of notes; all fivers, but they were old, and I hadn't seen the like for a very long time. Charlie's eyes nearly fell right out of his head. "Thar can't use them," said Charlie. "We'll get locked up." The fivers were big blue ones that I thought had gone out of circulation. I asked Jack in a whisper if he thought the money was all right?

"It might have come from a shady deal," he whispered, "but I think it's still legal tender."

I had to be careful what I said; I knew that Ron had a bit of a reputation down in the smoke and who was to know where the money had come from? One thing was for sure, it was very old. There was only one way to save our embarrassment with the money and that was for the dog to win. As Charlie and I were well known at the track and didn't have to pay on until after the race, and that was only if the dog got beat, there would be no problem. I just had to cross my fingers and pray that the dog won.

Charlie, Sharpy and me were doing the betting. We could have done with Ron giving us a hand, but then he would have had to pay his money on to the bookie and we couldn't take the risk, so we had to share out the money between us. All told there was £520; £70 for me, £50 between Charlie and Sharpy and £400 for Jack and Ron. Everything was sorted out. All we had to do was meet up with the chap that was taking Jack's dog on. The rest was up to us.

We met the man, dropped off the dog and set off for the track. Sharpy was at the gate waiting. "I'm glad to see thee, Tom," he said, looking anxious. "That fat toad, Dodger, has sold his entry in the open race and plans to bet the dog up from London."

"Is that right, Sharpy," I smiled thinking. 'So there is a God after all!'

"It's now't to be smiling about, Tom. Thar can bet that fat toad's goin' to pinch market." I calmed Sharpy down, slowly explaining to him what the game plan was. He was so pleased that he could hardly wait to get on with the job. "Right, lads, this changes things a bit, but not a lot. All we have to do now is see which jackets we have drawn and work it from there."

The announcement came over the speakers for the dog owners in the open race to draw for traps. Jack wanted a wide draw for the good dog and it didn't really matter where Sharpy's dog was drawn, she was only there for show, but a very important part of the plan. Jack came down from the Judge's box with the two jacket; our friend with Jack's dog had the number six. It couldn't have been better if we had fiddled it ourselves. I walked over to Jack, pretending to be helping him to saddle up the bitch. All eyes were on us. This was the best opportunity for the crowd to see Jack and I exchanging

244

money. Jack shoved a great roll of notes into my hand, trying to be a bit discreet, and then turning to the bitch proceeded to give her a good rubbing down. Dodger and his mates were watching every move and that was just the way I wanted it. Walter the Weasel was standing not three yards away from me when I was counting the money to Charlie and Sharpy for the bets, after giving them further instructions as where to stand and to which bookmaker they had to bet with. I made it quite clear to both of them not to move until I gave them the nod. Weasel was off like a shot to report this to his lord and master, Dodger. I just hoped that he hadn't missed anything out. Then I changed the plan. I told Sharpy and Charlie that when I nodded they should move forward as if they were going to bet the dog Jack had on, but not to bet anything, because if I was right, Dodger and his crew would fall for the set up hook, line and sinker, and bet the wrong dog. We then had to re-group and look disappointed and hopefully the price on the other dog would have drifted out and Dodger would think that he had stolen the market.

It was all going as planned. Dodger's lads were all lined up like soldiers and as soon as I gave the signal to Charlie and Sharpy they were in like a shot. Charlie, Sharpy and I were all standing there looking as confused as we could. Punters were saying that we had only got half the money on, some were saying that we had got none of it on. If they thought we were confused, they should have seen Dodger's face when he saw us casually bet the six dog.

"Five for one," shouted Charlie and moved on to the next book. We all had two bookies each and had managed to get the best price from each. By now, total confusion reigned with the punters not knowing what was going on. Had we bet the two dog? Had we bet the six? There were arguments starting up all over the place, especially among Dodger and his mates (and I was loving every minute of it). All of the money was on and, thank the Lord, none of the bookies had asked for the money at the time of the bets. It was all up to the dog now.

I stood at the wall next to Ron and waited for the hare to pass the boxes. "He's got to start," I commented to Ron as the hare got closer, "the first bend on this track is lethal if you don't lead."

Ron turned slightly and said, "He can't start to save his life."

I could feel the colour drain from my face. I must have looked ill because Ron asked if I was OK. "You're not worried because I said the dog couldn't start are you?"

"That could have something to do with it," I gulped

"Don't worry," said Ron turning to the track, "just watch the race." Ron was right, the dog couldn't start to save his life, but he had great early pace, and before the other dogs had got anywhere near the first bend he was in the lead and on his way to the winning line.

Dodger and his mates could only watch in HORROR. Dodger had been the victim of his own greed; Jack's dog won by six lengths. We had to send out a search party for Sharpy's dog she was so far back. Dodger and his cronies were there at the books, paying on. I was so glad it wasn't me and Charlie paying on. I was sure those fivers were no good. But that's something we will never know. One thing I did know, Ron was going home with the Funny Fivers he came up with.

Dodger was standing there while we collected our winnings. As we turned to leave, he said to me, "I have to put my hand up to thee Geordie." He was half grinning as he said it, "I might have got thee when thar first came down here, but I think thar's got thee own back many times since. Thar's cost me a fair few quid in past and ar think I'll have tu think long and hard before I hev a bet against thee again." Off he went, a poorer but wiser man.

We collected our winnings and the prize money, picked up the dog from our friend, gave him a good treat and set off home. Jack and Ron had won £2,000, plus their stake, making £2,400. I had won £350, plus my stake, making £420 and Charlie and Sharpy both had the same, £125 plus their stake, £150. Now that's what I call a good night I thought. Jack had wanted to come back and thank Jill, but it would have meant doubling back on himself and it was far enough to

London without making the journey any longer.

Jack handed over the bitch to Sharpy. "I'm not holding that thing," said Sharpy. "What's people goin tu think."

I laughed. "That bitch made our job possible, Sharpy. Without her you wouldn't be standing there with a pocket full of money."

"Thar's reet, Tom," said Sharpy, "but it still can't run for toffee," and with that he gave it to a kid standing by a car waiting for his father. "Here young'un hold on to this bitch and I'll give thee a quid, I'll only be 10 minutes."

The young boy grabbed the lead and said, "Tha'll do for me, mister, thar can stand there all night if tha likes, for a quid."

Ron was talking to Jack and then came over and shoved something into my hand. "We might not have seen eye to eye, Tom," said Ron, "but I have to admit you've done a real good job and that few quid I have put in your hand is appreciation for that. We've had a right good result and it's all down to you; that's just a little thank you". I held my breath for a moment and hoped he hadn't given me a treat with those Funny Fivers! I had a quick glance down at the money in my hand; it was all right. I shook Ron's hand and thanked him.

"I'm sure Jill will find something to do with it," I assured him.

We bid Jack and Ron farewell and said we would keep in touch. Charlie and Sharpy were already planning what to do with their money. My first stop was the fish shop. Whenever I had a win, especially on a weekend when the kids didn't have to be in bed early, I would always call into the fishy on the way home. It wasn't until I got into the fish shop that I realised how much money Ron and Jack had put into my hand. It was £200! I was gobsmacked, but very grateful, and knew that Jill would find a good use for it, especially as I was due to go into hospital.

When I arrived home I held up the fish and chips as an indication that I'd won. Only the kids were pleased. Jill looked troubled. I asked what was wrong. She said that it was nothing really and that she was pleased the dog had won. I decided to wait until the kids were in bed before pursuing the issue further.

Sure enough, as soon as the kids were up to bed and settled, the tears rolled down Jill's face. I knew there was something wrong. "Come on, sweetheart," I said, giving her a big hug, "what's the problem?"

"I'm so worried about you and that operation," she blurted out. "You mean the world to me, Tom Watson, and if anything was to happen to you I would be on my own down here."

"There's nothing going to happen to me, you know what they always say don't you?"

She stopped me short. "Don't you make light of this, Tom Watson, by saying something like, only the good die young."

"I'm sure I'll be all right," I assured her. "There's no good worrying about it!" I placed my arm's around her, looked her straight in the eyes and said, "Now look here, Jill Watson. I have the best wife on this earth and four of the best kids - sometimes! I have a gut feeling that it's not my turn yet. Besides, if the man up above was to draw my number out of the hat, it would probably say six and seven eighths." Jill couldn't see the funny side and started to lose her temper. "Only joking, sweetheart, only joking." This operation had really got to her and I suppose she was right in a way. What would happen to her and the kids if anything did go wrong?

That weekend I decided to take Jill and the kids up North to see her parents and whilst I was there I'd made up my mind to try and find a house. It would mean uplifting the kids but if it made Jill happy that was all that mattered. I was still in the Miners' Union and decided to seek help from them. After telling them of my accident and about having to retire they were more than willing to help. The Coal Board had lots of houses that were empty for one reason or another and they gave me keys to houses in three different areas. I had been away so long that I had forgotten how rough some of the places were. They were good people, mostly mining stock, but the Coal Board had let some of the properties go to wreck and ruin.

I finally came to a row of terraced houses in a place called New Herrington. There were only about three families living in the street and most of the houses had been vandalised. The majority looked the same, windows broke, tiles missing from the roof, but there was one I couldn't get into, right in the middle of the street.

I was fiddling with the lock when one of the neighbours came out. "Can ah help yer, bonny lad," he said in his broad Geordie accent. It was a long time since I had heard anyone speak to me like that. "Jimmy's the name, Jimmy Robson. If thar wants ta get inta that house, that's nee bother, bonny lad. I've got keys for the lot," said Jimmy fumbling about with a huge bunch of keys.

"Just this one will do, Jimmy, thanks." He opened the door and we went in. It was nowhere near as bad as some of the houses I had seen that day and to sway things in the kids' favour, there was a football field right outside the front door. This was it; sink or swim. I asked Jimmy if I could borrow the key until I went over to pick up Jill and the kids. "Nee bother, bonny lad, help thee sel. It'll be nice to see another family in the street."

I was straight into the van and headed off to Jill's parents' home, the only fear was that Jill might not want to take on a house that needed a hell of a lot of work doing on it. But why was I worrying! Jill thrived on hard work. I was still trying to convince myself when I pulled up outside in the van.

I loaded up Jill and the kids without telling them where I was taking them. When we entered the street, Jill asked, "Who do we know who lives down here?"

"Nobody," I replied.

"So what are we doing down here then?" a puzzled look on her face.

"I just want to show you something." We stopped outside the door of Number 10. "Just have a look in," I said. She was giving me one of her looks and I thought, 'Tom, she's going to scream her head off any minute.' "Well," I pressed, "what do you think?"

"What do I think about what?" asked Jill

"The house," I said. "It's yours, if you want it."

Jill just stood there, not saying a word. I thought, 'This is it, she's going to explode any minute.'

"You mean, this is ours?"

"Only if you want it, love; the decision is yours."

"Well," she said, "it's no palace, but with a bit of hard graft, who knows what we could do to a place like this. we certainly can't make it any worse than what it is!"

"So you like it then?" I asked eagerly.

"Tom Watson, you couldn't have made me more happy if you had won the pools." The only problem now was telling the kids, but looking out of the front window I didn't think that would be too hard. They were all playing football with Mr. Robson's boys. Jill was wandering around the house making notes. "No bathroom, light fittings missing, no inside loo." To put things bluntly, the house was a right mess, but it was nothing that couldn't be put right with a bit of hard work.

That was it then. We had made up our minds, we were taking the house. All that I had to do now was to inform the NCB and give notice to the council in Yorkshire that we would be leaving in the next few weeks. It was going to be a big upheaval. We had made a lot of good friends in Yorkshire and we were going to miss them badly. Then there was the kids' school, their friends and most of all their football. They were doing so well, playing for the county. But I don't suppose mattered which county they lived in; they still had the same skills.

You could see in Jill's face that she was happy; she was measuring for curtains and carpets and, to be honest, although we had been away a long time, she had always missed her parents and her younger sister. We rounded up the kids and headed back to Jill's parents to give them the good news. Tommy and Doris were over the moon; I think they had been missing Jill and the kids as much as Jill had been missing them.

All the way back down to Yorkshire Jill never stopped talking, how she was going to do this and how she was going to do that. It was nice to see her happy again.

The kids had a little moan about leaving their mates and the football team, but when Jill explained that I was going into hospital and would probably be in for a long time they seemed to accept it. The only problem on the horizon now seemed to be the timing of the operation. I certainly couldn't have it in Yorkshire, not with all the work to do on the house and the way Jill was feeling at the moment about anything going wrong. An operation at this time was out of the question. The next day, first thing, I phoned the hospital to inform them of the situation. They were very nice about the whole thing and understood that if I was moving back north that would be the best place to have the operation. The doctor said they would inform my GP as soon as I got settled in. I would just have to keep my fingers crossed that the house would be suitable to live in before I had to go into hospital. The only things left to do were for Jill to inform the school and for me to tell all our friends.

The day of the move was one of the saddest days of my life. Jill was crying, the kids were in tears, I had that familiar turnip back in my throat again and I'm sure that Charlie and Sharpy had a tear in their eyes. There were hugs and kisses all around, but it was a very sad day, leaving behind some of the best friends anybody could have had and the home that we had known and loved for the past few years.

CHAPTER EIGHTEEN

We had been moved into the new house about six weeks and were just starting to get the hang of things, like not having a bathroom or a big kitchen. The kids didn't seem to mind too much. Having a bath in the old tin bath in front of the fire was a novelty especially on a cold night, but for Jill and me it was a trip to her parents. Jill and the kids seemed happy enough but there was something missing.

The kids had settled in at school and had even made the football team. Jill was happy trying to do up the house and seeing her family again, but I was missing the dogs. The only dog we had was little Milly; we had kept her as a pet. Sally was still down in Yorkshire having cracked a hock and Charlie and I had decided to let a friend of ours have her for breeding, providing she had a home for life. I was missing training the dogs and the excitement of pitting my wits against the wide boys of the game and the bookmakers. It was useless making any plans at the moment with an operation hanging over my head. Nevertheless, I decided to look on the bright side and started to build a kennel.

I was just putting the finishing touches to it and was just about to shout for Jill to come and have a look at my handiwork when she walked down the garden path. "Letter here for you, Tom," she said, "looks like it's from the hospital."

Sure enough it was. I had an appointment to see a Mr. Carter at the Newcastle General Hospital the following week. I looked at Jill. "Cheer up, sweetheart, it had to happen some time and you never know, I might come out of there a new man. Then I can get back to work and we can get back on our feet."

She smiled. "Let's hope so, Tom, but all I care about at the moment is that you come out in one piece." The tears were starting to well up in her eyes as she flung her arms around me giving me a big hug.

"What about the neighbours?" I said, laughing.

"Sod the neighbours," she laughed, hugging me tighter. "If I want to give my husband a hug, then I bloody well will."

The week soon went by and it seemed like no time before we were sitting in a hospital waiting room. We had been there for about 20 minutes when the nurse called out my name. I froze and Jill had to nudge me to stand up. I was shown into a little side room with Jill following close behind. We were introduced to a smartly dressed gentleman standing by a wall. He was sliding x-rays up and down and muttering to himself as he went.

"Right, Mr. Watson, having seen all of your x-rays, I am inclined to agree with my colleagues in Yorkshire that you need surgery and from what I can see the sooner the better. I am also glad that you have brought your wife because I need to talk to you both." Jill was gripping my hand tight enough to stop the circulation she was so anxious. Mr. Carter went on, "This is not a simple operation and the chances of it being a success are only 50-50."

"And if he doesn't have the operation, Mr. Carter," Jill asked, "what will happen?"

"I'm afraid that his back will deteriorate," he explained. "You see, there are three damaged discs and they can only get worse. At least with the operation he has a chance."

I looked from Mr. Carter to Jill and back to Mr. Carter again and said. "Please don't talk about me like I'm not in the room." They both looked suitably embarrassed. "I've made up my mind and I'm going for the only chance I've got. If it has to be the operation, then so be it." Mr. Carter apologised again and Jill just gripped my hand even tighter.

"Well, Mr. Watson," said Mr. Carter, "now that you have made up your mind, would you be prepared to come in next week?"

"Why not," I said. "The sooner we get started, the sooner we are finished."

"Good," said Mr. Carter making some notes in my file. We shook hands as I left and he apologised again.

Jill never said a word on the way home in the van. I don't know whether it was the shock of the operation happening so fast or the slight embarrassment in the hospital, but whatever it was it kept her quiet for the whole journey home. It wasn't until about an hour later when she was preparing the tea for the kids coming in from school that she let it all out.

All her worries about whether or not the operation would be a success and what sort of condition I would be in when I came out of hospital, if I came out of hospital. I tried my best to reassure her that everything would be fine and that she shouldn't be so soft, but the tears were still rolling down her face when there was a knock on the door. It was my old mate, Fred, the lad who had kennelled Sally for me when no-one else would.

He took one look at Jill's face and was nearly on his way out again. "Have I... er ... come at a bad time, Tom. I can always come back later?" asked Fred.

"No, no," said Jill, "you come on in Fred, it's OK."

She was wiping the tears from her face, as Fred asked, "What's up, bonny lass, it's not good to see you so upset." Jill told Fred the whole story. Fred looked up and winked at me. "Do you know," he said, "same thing happened last year to, er, er...Sammy Potts. He had the operation and was as right as rain, strong as a bull, he could even lift a horse. Couldn't do that before!" said Fred trying to look serious.

Jill knew that Fred was telling porkies but at least it had stopped her crying and made her laugh. "Fred you tell more whoppers than Dodger Smith."

"Dodger! Who's Dodger Smith?" said Fred looking all innocent.

"Never mind," she said. "Sit yourself down and I'll put a pot of tea on."

"That's a bit more like it," laughed Fred. "You're not half as bonny when you're crying you know."

"OK," she laughed. "You can cut the patter now, you've got yourself a cup of tea, Fred."

"And a biscuit?" said Fred, winking at Jill.

"Oh all right, and a biscuit." It was nice to see Jill smiling again. At least the thought of the operation was out of her mind for the time being.

All that week we worked hard in the house, trying to keep our minds off the weekend, but I could see in Jill's face that it wasn't far from her thoughts.

I knew, come the day, that the tears would be flowing, and I was right. Monday morning came, I gave all the kids a big hug and made them promise to look after their Mam until I came home from hospital. Jill only just managed to keep the tears at bay until the kids had gone off to school. I had arranged for a mate of mine, Jimmy Thornton, to take me to the hospital but Jill insisted on coming too. I was hoping to leave her at home until after the operation, but she was having none of it. She was determined to spend as much time with me as possible before the operation.

Jimmy dropped a few hints; he was trying to let Jill know, in a polite way, that he had to be going. She took the hint and said that she had to get back for the kids anyway. She gave me a big hug, her eyes full, but trying not to let any of the other patients see that she was fighting back the tears. She turned and walked swiftly away. I could hear her footsteps picking up speed to a steady run along the corridor and out of the hospital.

I made myself acquainted with the other patients and sat on the end of my bed. Jimmy had left me a book to read. I'd never read a book in my life, but I was so bored that I picked it up and started reading. The story was about the life of a man called Ken Payne, a race horse trainer. Once I'd got started into the book I found it difficult to put down; it wasn't unlike the dog racing game, which I could relate to.

I had just finished it when the nurse came towards me with a needle saying, "This won't hurt, Mr. Watson. It's just to make you sleepy," and that's just what it did. I don't remember a thing until I was back in my bed and the doctor was asking if there were any bleeders in my family. I was half in and out of sleep and hadn't quite understood what the doctor meant, and muttered something about my brother being the only bleeder in my family and a right little bleeder too.

The nurse and doctor burst out laughing at this. "No, Mr. Watson," said the doctor, "I think you have misunderstood. Your back is bleeding quite heavily and I wanted to know if there was anyone else in the family with the same problem."

"Not that I know of," I muttered and drifted back off to sleep.

I knew nothing more until I heard voices standing next to my bed. One voice I couldn't mistake. A whispered cockney accent floated above the bed. It was Jack, trying to keep his voice down, but who's ever heard of a cockney that could be quiet (sorry, Jack). Jill and the nurse were discussing my health and why there were so many tubes and bottles after the operation. Apparently, I had lost a lot of blood for one reason or another and had needed an emergency transfusion. My head was still swimming with the drugs and I could only pick up bits and pieces from the conversation. One thing I did understand was that Jack had come to the hospital armed with a large chocolate gateaux. Little did I know it was 9.00 pm and Jack had come prepared to bribe the nurses with something. That something had been three jars of coffee and that huge cake.

I didn't learn the full story until two days later when I was told that Jack had passed himself off as my long lost brother who had travelled up from London. He told the nurses that he had to go back the same night, so there was no point in saying he must leave and come back tomorrow. I also learned the true meaning of friendship. Jack had made a 550 mile round trip just to make sure that Jill and the kids had enough money to get by on until better times. Jack had left two cheques for £200 each, one to be paid that week, the other a month later.   It didn't take a genius to work out that Jack had made himself skint to make sure that we wouldn't be without money. Here was a man I had only known for a short while and who had a family of his own to think about, but who could take the time and effort to care for someone else's family. That was true friendship. If there were more Jacks in the world today, the place would be a lot better off.

As I lay in the hospital bed, looking up at the cracked paint on the ceiling, I was determined not to give in no matter how the operation had turned out. I was from good mining stock, brought up on hard times and I knew what it was like to go without food. I remembered my grandmother and grandfather who had gone without food in order to feed me during the strike. It was memories like that, which were giving me the strength to carry on. No matter how the operation turned out I still had Jill and the kids. With them and a friend like Jack, I knew I'd be OK. If I couldn't go back to working down the mines, I knew the dog game inside out and I was sure that was where my future lay. We never had a lot of money but we'd always got by.

I remembered my first dog, Sandy, and how he had given his all, and his life, just to win a race. I remembered holding his head in my arms as he lay dying on the track where he had loved to run, and in my eyes HE was still the champ. I was back in the North East, back where it had all started and ready for a new challenge with new friends, new dogs, and hopefully a bright and successful future in the years to come.

CHAPTER NINETEEN

It had been six weeks since my operation; no-one could tell me one way or the other if it had gone well or not. All you could get from the doctors or the nurses was: 'It will take time; you must have patience.' I was missing Jill and the kids something terrible. I was doing my best to try and get home, working with the physio until I was sore. I was even trying to exercise when the physio wasn't there; I was so desperate to go home. The exercise must have paid off. It was Monday morning, just after breakfast, when Attila the Hun, or the staff nurse, came to the bottom of my bed, looked in the opposite direction and said, "Right, Mr. Slone, you can go home and you, Mr. Black." I was just about to curse under my breath when Attila turned to me and said, "Oh, I nearly forgot; you, too, Mr. Watson." She walked towards the door, stopped, and with a sly grin gave me a wink. From the day I was admitted to the hospital there had been a love/hate thing between us and this was just a parting shot to say she had the last word.

There was no time to waste; this was the day I'd been waiting for. Six weeks I'd spent in that hospital and I couldn't wait to go home. I'd made arrangements with a friend of mine, Jimmy, to pick me up from the hospital when the time came. Jimmy was like clockwork, always on time. I'd no sooner got back to the ward from the 'phone, dressed and packed, when I heard that distinctive click, clack, click, clack sound of Jimmy's metal walking stick and was I glad to hear it. I said my good-byes to the lads that were left and knew exactly how they were feeling. I'd seen it so many times before. I picked up my small bag and headed for the car park, giving

Jimmy instructions to drop me off at the top of our street. After thanking Jimmy, I walked steadily the rest of the way home. It was fingers crossed to surprise Jill. After all, there was no way she could know I was leaving hospital; we didn't have a 'phone. I opened the outside gate and knocked on the back door. I knocked again. There was no-one in! Instead of me wanting to surprise Jill, the tables had been turned. I had a horrible thought that Attila was looking into a crystal ball somewhere and laughing her socks off!

There was nothing to do but sit and wait. Twenty minutes had gone by when down came the rain. I hurriedly took shelter in the outside toilet and plonked myself onto the seat. It wasn't long before I heard the sneck on the gate lift up and a mad dash to try to escape the rain.

I was just about to open the door when the door was opened from the other side by someone and swiftly closed behind them ; whoever it was must have been desperate. I sat there motionless, not saying a word. The figure of a woman started to undress, what do I do, sing, whistle? I slowly stood up, to screams that nearly took the roof off.

Doris, Jill's mother, who had been bursting to use the toilet had just barged in not expecting anyone to be in there. Once she'd pulled herself together and realised it was me, all hell broke loose. "You ... you stupid ..."

She was just about to start with the language when Jill interrupted. "Mam, Mam, calm down. Tom got just as much a fright as you did and he's not screaming and shouting."

The only reason I wasn't doing those things was because I was too embarrassed. Jill's mother in all the commotion after dashing into the toilet had forgotten to pull up her drawers. Doris looked at me, and then to Jill, pulled me gently from the loo, dashed back in, knickers still round her ankles and hastily bolted the door behind her.

"Why didn't you let me know you were coming home," screamed Jill, more out of temper and shock than anything else.

"Well for a start," I said, "we are not on the 'phone, and if we had been on the 'phone, you weren't in!"

Jill stood there for a second or two, not saying a word, then flung her arms round me and said. "What the hell, you're here now, let's get in the house out of this bloody rain and put the kettle on. Those were the second best words I'd heard all day. The best words were, 'You can go home'. We sat there drinking our tea when Doris emerged from the toilet, still looking flushed.

The next few weeks were spent building up my strength. I had to find out if the operation had been a success or not, plus there were four little mouths to feed and very little money coming in. Tommy and Doris helped out all they could, but they too had a family to keep.

It had been three months since the operation and Jill and I were on our way to see the surgeon, Mr. Carter, fingers crossed that all had gone well. Jill was a bundle of nerves fiddling with her wedding ring and giving me some anxious looks. We arrived at the hospital spot on time. They were just calling out my name as we sat down. "Tom Watson," shouted the nurse, "could you please go straight down to the x-ray department and bring back the results for Mr. Carter." This was it, the moment of truth. I was in the x-ray room for about fifteen minutes, turning this way and then that way. It was more like a photo shoot than an x-ray.

"Right, Mr. Watson," said the nurse, "just sit outside for a few minutes until these x-rays are ready, then you can take them back for the Doctor."

We arrived in the waiting room, x-rays at the ready, desperate to find out the result. It wasn't long before we were called in to see the surgeon, armed with the x-rays. I handed them to Mr. Carter. He slid them up on his screen one by one, asking how I was feeling at the same time.

"Great, just great," I replied, knowing full well I wasn't anywhere near to being one hundred percent fit.

Mr. Carter looked at me, then Jill. "I'm afraid it's not good news, Mr. Watson. The operation was only partly successful." He went on to say that the fusion has only partly worked and he could see there would be problems in the near future. Before Jill or I could ask any questions he proceeded to say that further surgery would be too complicated. In other words there was nothing more he could do.

Jill and I gathered our senses and set off home, barely a word spoken between us, both deep in thought. Someone had to break the ice and it looked like being me. "Right, sweetheart," I said with a big smile, "it's no good worrying about this, that and the other. What's done is done. We can't alter anything so let's get on with it. If I can't work, it's back to the dog game, and this time we'll put the fear of God into those bookies.

Jill looked at me, eyes full of tears and said: "Tom Watson, with an attitude like that, how can we fail? When do we start?"

CHAPTER TWENTY

It was the early seventies, 1974 to be precise. Jill and I had accepted the situation with my back and started to get on with our lives. I'd found work in a kennel working with the dogs I loved, greyhounds; the job was great, but the trainer who owned the kennel was a downright bastard and that was being kind to the man. He was a rough-looking man who could put himself about even if he was in his fifties. He was cruel to his dogs, his staff, but most of all, to his wife. Many times had I seen him give his wife a smack when things hadn't gone right and that turned my stomach, but I, like the other staff, had to turn a blind eye, especially if we wanted to keep our jobs. But deep down, I knew it was just a matter of time before I or someone else said something.

We'd just got back from racing one night, the boss, who was in a different van to me was steaming. He pulled up in the yard screaming and shouting at Joe, who was in charge of about ten dogs, the same as the rest of us. One of his dogs hadn't performed too well and had been expected to win for the well-off, arrogant owner. The boss, Harry Slone, dragged the poor dog from the van and set about it with its lead, then turned on his wife and proceeded to do the same to her.

That was it, the time had come when I could sit back no longer. He was just about to strike his wife again raising his arm in the air, when I grabbed the lead from his hand, "You make me sick, Slone," I shouted, "beating on a defenseless woman and a dog that can't fight back." I didn't like interfering with anyone's marriage, but on this occasion something just snapped. Slone picked up another lead and was lashing out at me. I grabbed the lead, pulled him towards me and smacked him on the nose, to gasps from his wife and staff: a trickle of blood ran down his lip and onto his chin.

"You're ... you're ..." he seemed to hesitate for some reason but it finally came out, "you're finished, Watson," he cried, "and don't ever set foot in this kennel again." I wasn't that bothered, licensed racing wasn't my cup of tea. I was a flapping man, independent racing, and always would be.

As I was leaving the yard Slone turned on Joe, "And as for you, you useless string of misery, sell that dog at any price first thing in the morning, I never want to set eyes on the useless toad again," he screamed.

The owner must have lost face, with the dog running so poorly. From what I could gather, he was a prestige man, and nothing would hurt him more than bragging a dog would win, then seeing it lose. This was my chance to buy an expensive dog for little money. I'd seen the dog run a couple of times and hadn't been impressed, but I'd put that down to the trainer holding the dog up to try and steal a race.

When I arrived home and told Jill about the carry on with Mr. and Mrs. Slone, and the beating of the dog, Jill was in total agreement with what I had done and agreed she'd have done the same thing herself. The next move was to try and buy the black dog that was going to be sold the next day; the only problem was, where would he be sold, and for how much!

I sat down with Jill, worked out how much we could spend, and it wasn't a lot, and then tried to think where I would go if I wanted to sell a dog. There was only one place and that was Highmain Flapping Track. It stood to reason. Slone couldn't sell the dog on a licensed track for two reasons: first, the dog had run badly in his race and would be unlikely to attract a buyer; second, Slone must have thought the dog was lame and if he had been lucky enough to sell the dog on his local track it would be sure to be returned.

I went with my hunch down to Highmain Track, named after the nearby Pit. It was trial day and I was ninety-nine percent sure that

263

that was where Joe and the dog would end up. Trial after trial, and still no Joe. The few people that were there for trials had gone. It looked like my hunch was wrong. I walked slowly to the gate trying to rack my brains as to where Joe could have taken dog, when pulling up in the car park like a mad man was Joe. He jumped out of the van, the dog trailing behind him, and sprinted towards the track entrance: "Wo, wo, what's the hurry Joe, the trials have finished."

"I'm not bothered about a trial, Tom. The Gaffer said not to run the dog if possible, just to try and sell him to the first mug I met."

"You're a bit late for that, Joe, everyone's gone."

Joe popped his head round the corner of the gate. "You're right Tom. The Gaffer will kill me. Mind you, it's his fault I'm late to start with, keeping me back until the last minute."

Joe stood there, a worried look on his face, I asked him if he would mind if I had a look at the dog, which looked as sick as Joe. "No problem," said Joe, handing me the dog's lead. "Mind you, Tom, between me and you, I don't think the dog's all he's cracked out to be."

I slowly went over the dog with a fine tooth comb, looking for anything that may have prevented him from running his best and then, bingo, I'd found it! The dog was just a youngster and one of his testicles hadn't dropped; it was still lodged in his lisk. I was sure that this was his problem, but I didn't want to let on to Joe. "I think you're right, Joe. Maybe this dog's not as good as they think, but he's still a nice dog. He might make someone a nice pet," I hastened to add.

Joe looked at the dog, then at the time, "It's got me beat, Tom. I just don't know what to do." It was plain to see Joe was petrified of Harry Slone.

"Right, Joe, let me try and help you out. What exactly did Slone say to you?"

Joe wasn't the brightest of lads and repeated word for word what Slone had said. "Go to the track and..." he stopped to gather his thoughts, "... oh yes, try not to let the dog run, and sell it to the first

264

mug that want's to buy it!"

"Then it's easy," I said. "You've got to the track and you haven't run the dog, right?" Joe nodded his head in agreement. "That's the first part, the second part is a little more difficult. You have to sell the dog to the first mug that wants to buy it." Joe nodded his head once more. "Well, Joe, I'm prepared to do you a big favour. I'll buy the dog on one condition."

"Anything, Tom, just name it," said Joe, looking for any solution to his predicament.

"Harry Slone is not to know that I've bought the dog, is that clear?"

"No problem, Tom, he'd kill me if he found out that I'd sold the dog to yu. Mind you, he'll kill me if I bring the dog back, and I'd rather you got the poor animal than let him go back to that cruel bastard."

We led the dog to my van and popped him in. Now for the tricky part; the money. "How much did Slone want for the dog, Joe?" I asked.

"Well he ... er ..."

I interrupted. "What Slone said was the first mug that wanted to buy him, is that right, Joe?" Joe nodded his head. "Tell Slone, there was only one punter there and he offered you ten quid, and that way you won't be telling any lies." I thrust the tenner into Joe's hand, strode towards the van and set off. Joe stood there, mouth wide open and a look on his face of pure confusion.

I arrived home feeling like a million dollars. I'd just bought a dog that must have cost a fortune and to top that I'd bought it from a man for whom I had a distinctive dislike. Any man that would beat his wife, his staff and his dogs were the scum of the earth in my book, and deserved all that was coming to him. I must admit I was hurting from being sacked and looking for revenge, but that wasn't going to happen over night.

Jill and I were a good team and I had the feeling things would turn out right in the end. We made sure the dog was lice free, gave him a good feed and bedded him down for the night.

The next morning the kids were arguing as to what to call the new dog; Peter wanted Blacky, Colin wanted Darky, Bobby wanted Shack. "Why Shack?" asked Jill, with a curious look on her face.

"That's easy," said Bobby. "Len Shackleton; he played for Sunderland, the best player that ever put on a pair of boots," said Bobby. "And the new dog will be the same," he continued.

"Don't be stupid," said Peter, "dogs don't wear boots, they'd fall off when they run, silly." Peter was serious.

After we'd all stopped rolling about the floor with laughter we called the dog Socks, because of the one white sock on his left front leg. This went up to about six inches from his toes and was very distinguishable.

Anyone could spot him easily. Something had to be done and I knew what it was. The dog's sock had to be dyed black to blend in with the rest of his body and it had to be done before he went to the vets. It would only take one person to see me with a dog with one white sock and the game would be up. Jill and I waited until the kids had gone off to school and set about the task of dyeing the dog's leg. When the job was done you couldn't tell the difference. Next stop, the vets, to see if he would confirm my hunch about the dog's problem?

We arrived just in time to see Harry Slone driving off with a dog in the back of his car and a strange woman in the front; it wasn't hard to put two and two together. Slone was up to his old tricks; he would tell his wife he was going to the vets, or going to see a dog run, any excuse to be out with one of his bits on the side. Slone had a bad reputation for being a womaniser; kennel girls would only last a few days before handing in their notice, wanting to escape his lecherous advances.

Jill and I waited until Slone was well out of sight before entering the surgery. We were lucky, only one person in, an old lady with her pet budgie. The vet I wanted to see was Mr. Summers who had an excellent reputation and was the best vet there was for greyhounds. It wasn't long before we were called in to see him. "Now," said the vet, looking at the dog, "What seems to be the problem?"

"That's for you to find out, Mr. Summers," I said with a cheeky wink. I wanted to be sure the vet diagnosed the same problem as I did and if he was as good as his reputation, he would do just that.

"Right," said the vet, looking very serious. Starting with his front feet, he picked up the leg that Jill and I had just dyed. This was it. Would he spot it or would he be more concerned with finding the dog's problem? After looking at the dog's legs and then his neck, he said, "So far so good." Then he proceeded to examine his back and down his hind legs right to the tips of his toes. "No problems so far."

I looked at Jill and whispered, "He's not going to find it."

I hadn't got the words out of my mouth when the vet said, "Hello, what's this?" He was right in the problem area. "I'm afraid the dog has a testicle that hasn't dropped and it's causing him some considerable pain. The poor dog must have been in agony," he went on. "Have you had the dog long?" he asked.

"As a matter of fact, Mr. Summers, I came into possession of him a fortnight ago," but hastened to add that I hadn't run the dog.

"Well, whoever had the dog before you should have known the dog was carrying an injury. How the hell he's been running at all is beyond me."

I had to get in quick before he started asking too many questions, like where did the dog come from, who owned him before me? Jill could see the situation and interrupted. "Don't forget, Tom, you have to be at the doctor's shortly and the time's getting on."

With the vet distracted from his thoughts, I asked when would be the best time to bring in the dog for his operation.

"Yes ... er ... yes," said the vet, "... the operation. If you want," he went on, "you can leave him now. I've had a cancellation this morning. A dog should have had a piece of his tail removed, but the trainer thought he could do a better job and took him home." Jill and I looked at each other. We both knew it had to be Harry Slone; the poor dog would be taken back to his kennels, tail strapped up, and made to race in agony.

267

"Right, Mr. Summers, I'll leave this dog in your capable hands then. When would be the best time to pick him up?"

"Let's see now, it's not a big job," said the vet stroking his chin, "call it 2.30 p.m. That'll give the dog time to pull round," and with that Jill and I left.

By the time we got home, Aunt Mary was standing at the gate, arms folded, as if to say, 'You're late. Don't let this happen again!' but she was a kindly soul and never came to our house empty handed. If it wasn't something she had baked, it would be some sweets for the kids.

Since my gran and grandad had passed on Aunt Mary seemed to have taken the role of keeping an eye on me. Jill made a cup of tea while I made sure the kennel was ready for the dog to come back to. When Aunt Mary settled herself into the easy chair it wasn't that easy to shift her! Jill kept looking at the clock then looking at me; someone had to say something to shift Aunt Mary, then Jill and I spoke at the same time, one saying we had to go to the Doctors, the other saying we had to watch the kids playing football and then contradicting each other. It ended up saying we were going to watch the kids play football and if there was anything Aunt Mary disliked it was football. She stood up, put her cup in the sink, and said, "Right, that's me off, can't see the sense in anybody chasing round like silly buggers after a ball," and with that she said her good-byes and was on her way home.

It was just the right time to head back to the vet's. We'd only gone a mile down the road when Jill said, "Tom, we've called the dog, Socks. Don't you think people will think it strange calling a dog that's all black, Socks?" Jill had a point; people might start to get curious and query why the dog was called Socks. We had to change the name.

"You're right, Jill, spot on," I said, "but what are we going to call him and what are we going to tell the kids?"

"Call him Lucky," said Jill, "because he's lucky Slone didn't put him to sleep and as for the kids, tell them Socks had to go back; he was fretting for his owner and this is a new dog from the Riley's in Ireland; they won't know the difference ... I hope!"

We arrived at the vet's to see one of the staff walking Socks round to clean himself. (I mean Lucky!) The dog looked great, as if nothing had happened. Mr. Summers came to the door to watch how the dog was walking, "What do you think, Mr. Watson?" he shouted across the car park.

"Look's good to me," I replied. "How did it go?"

"Sweet as a nut," he replied. "Excuse the pun, no problems at all, in fact the dog should be ready for running in two to three weeks, and, I might add, he'll be a different dog. Put me a few quid on when he's trying," he laughed. It was well known that Mr. Summers liked a bet. We settled the bill and set off home. This, we hoped, was the start we were looking for, but only time would tell.

CHAPTER TWENTY-ONE

Five weeks had past since Lucky's operation. The vet was as good as his word. Lucky was a different dog. We didn't run him round the local tracks, instead we had taken him down to Yorkshire away from prying eyes. It was nice to return to see our old friends, Charlie, Ted and Sharpy among others. Charlie hadn't changed, still gambling mad on anything that moved!

We'd graded Lucky in at one of the local tracks the previous week. Five weeks off and a bit feed to slow him down was just enough to put him in the right grade. He was in a level break; if he couldn't win a graded race he wasn't the dog I thought he was.

Charlie had arranged for a local lad to take the dog in, so that the attention wouldn't be directed at me and the others. Ted and Sharpy were there to help with the betting: it was just like old times.

"How much are thar having on, Tom?" Charlie asked.

It was strange, but warm, listening to the old Yorkshire accent. "No matter how much I'm having on, Charlie," I replied, "I know exactly how much you're having on?" I winked at Ted and Sharpy.

"Come on then, Tom," said Charlie," how much am I hev'ing on then?"

"Same as always, Charlie, same as always ... THE LOT."

Ted and Sharpy burst out laughing. "He's got thee there, Charlie," said Ted, still rolling about with laughter and Charlie not saying a word.

"If you live to be a hundred, Charlie," said Jill, "you'll never change. So how much are you having on?"

Charlie looked at Ted, Sharpy, Jill and me, then burst out laughing.

270

"Thar's right, Tom, I'm hev'ing LOT on."

We settled down to the more serious business of sorting out the money and who was going to which bookie. Jill and I strode onto the track to be greeted by familiar faces, all asking how we were and if we had settled. Matt and Rita were there. The first thing Rita asked was, "Where's the kids?"

"Sorry, Rita," said Jill, "but we couldn't drag them away from their mates back at the old street where we used to live. One of our neighbours is looking after them until we get back."

Rita shrugged her shoulders. "Maybe next time," she said, with a smile.

There were a couple of races before Lucky's, just enough time to make myself familiar with some of the bookies. I was slowly walking down in front of the them when someone tapped me on the shoulder. I turned round slowly to find it was Honest Jim. "Come back tu haunt me, Geordie," he said, standing in a cloud of cigar smoke.

"Depends on your definition of haunt, Jim. If you mean, have I come down to skint you again, that remains to be seen." Jim was visibly shocked, puffing more and more on his cigar, a worried look forming through the cigar smoke. 'Yes,' I thought to myself as I slowly walked away, 'that will keep you guessing, Mr. Honest Jim.'

I met up with Charlie and the lads who had heard a whisper that Honest Jim had a runner in our race. Jim hadn't changed. He was still trying to fleece the punters.

"How good is the information?" I asked.

"As good as tha'll get," said Charlie, a broad smile all over his face. There was something more to this race that was really pleasing Charlie and, no doubt, I would be finding out soon. "Tha'r ken's Billy Evans, Tom, dun't tha'r."

"Yes, Charlie, I know Billy."

"Well, situation is this. Jim has asked Billy to put him £500 on a dog in our race called Banknote and ..." said Charlie, "... Billy's asked us to do the betting!"

This was a great opportunity to have a second bite at Honest Jim for what he had done to us. There was just one problem, how would Billy Evans feel when he found out later that we had a dog in the same race? I put this to Charlie and the rest of the team.

"No problem," said Ted. "Billy had an idea you had a dog in that race and that's why he took the money from Honest Jim. He's thinking on the lines that your dog will be better than Jim's and that he'd rather have a bet on yours than his. Does that mek sense, Tom? It's all mixed up to me," said Ted, with a puzzled look on his face.

"I think I've got the picture, Ted, and if it's all right with Billy, it's OK with me."

It was our race next. We all knew what to do: bet Jim's dog first and then wait for the prices to go out on the other dogs. This was the test. Was Lucky as good as I'd hoped and could we beat Jim's dog?

Jill and I had talked it over about the size of the bet we were having on; it was £300 before we set off and we weren't going to change our minds. It was money I'd saved working for Slone and a few quid I'd won. I'd made the decision not to take part in any of the betting, for obvious reasons, as my conversation with Honest Jim earlier might just make him a little cautious, so my decision was to abstain and keep a low profile. Charlie and the team were regulars and didn't look out of place.

Jill and I stood back to watch the commotion. Honest Jim was forcing out the price on his dog, Banknote, who was out of the Red Jacket. Charlie and co. were betting Banknote with Jim's money all down the line. It wasn't long before the bookies were taking no more bets on Jim's dog. The other dogs were any price: they were all new dogs, and nine times out of ten you would get one or two non-triers, because the people who owned the dogs didn't know how good the other dogs were. One poor thing was that far gone you could have taken his back teeth out and he wouldn't have known. Lucky, who we had called Quick Return was 5-1. As soon as Ted and the lads were ready, they steamed into the bookies again. By this time there was not only total confusion with the punters but the expression on Jim's face was indescribable.

Charlie, who had never forgiven Jim for trying to cheat us out of a race, asked him for £1,000 to £200, "Thar's got that, Charlie." Charlie thrust the money into Jim's hand and stood there. "Thar's got that," said Jim's clerk, writing it down in his book.

"Thar's right, Nobby," said Charlie to the clerk, "but what I haven't got is a ticket!"

Jim looked down at Charlie from the wooden box he was standing on and then looked along the line of bookmakers to see Ted and Sharpy betting all they could on Quick Return. Jim looked at Charlie.

"I think I've been here before," Charlie said, looking up at Jim with a wink and a smile, and clinging onto his ticket as he turned to watch the race.

The hare was starting to move. Jill gripped my hand. We weren't just taking a chance; it was a massive gamble on a dog we knew very little about. Our gut feeling and intuition were telling us it was right. We would soon find out!

Up went the traps. Lucky from trap three and Banknote from trap one came out together, bumping and boring down to the first bend. Then, with an amazing burst of speed, Lucky left the field for dead. The poor dog that didn't look too happy in the paddock was so far back you would have to send out a search party to find it.

It was just likes old times; Lucky had won by eight lengths and done a very fast time to boot.

The best was yet to come ... taking the money from Honest Jim and the rest of the bookies. Charlie stood right at the front of the queue to make sure he got paid and to make sure he had an audience. If Charlie loved anything better than eating it was taking money from the bookies. Sharpy and Ted had drawn their winnings, giving Billy Evans his share; he was more than grateful, thrusting £20 in Jill's hand for the kids.

Charlie was still counting out the winnings when Jim shouted me over. "Do me a favour, Geordie, stop up Durham," he said. "I've only just got over that last caning tha'r gave me. Now I'll be back tu nightmares, wondering if thar's coming BACK."

With that we shook hands and the parting words from Jim were, "I hope ah dun't see thee, Geordie, for a long time ... and that might be too soon!"

We collected our winnings, said our good-byes to the lads, then picked up the dog. After washing Lucky's feet and feeding him, we set off on the long journey home.

CHAPTER TWENTY-TWO

Lucky had turned out to be the dog that Slone was hoping for, but unfortunately for him it didn't turn out his way. His misfortune in writing the dog off and his neglect in locating the poor dog's problem was to be a big mistake in time to come.

The money we had won from the race in Yorkshire with Lucky had been put to good use; Jill had gone on a spending spree, new curtains, new fireside rugs, clothes for the kids and a companion for Lucky; a little fawn bitch that had been badly neglected and bought by a friend of mine, more out of pity than anything else. Jill had called her Mini. She was bought from a villain that thought more about drink than feeding his kids and his dogs. The irony of it all was that the little bitch could run. All she was needing was a good clean out and some good food. It wasn't long before both dogs were winning races all over the place.

Jill, the kids and I were at Highmain track one night when we bumped into my old mate, Joe, who worked for Harry Slone. "How's it going Joe?" I asked.

"Not too well, Tom," replied Joe, with a solemn look on his face that would curdle milk. "I got the sack from Slones place," he went on. I was just about to ask if it was any of my doing when he stopped me in mid stream. "Nothing to do with that black dog, Tom, far from it," he continued. "No, the problem was that I missed the betting on a dog of his at a flapping track."

"What's Slone doing betting dogs on a Flapping Track?" I asked.

"Well," said Joe, "he's got this mate of his who happens to be the Handicapper at a little Flapping track about fifteen miles from here.

It opened up when you left to work in Stoke. Maltwell's its name. When Slone gets a bit short of cash he rings up with the markings of the dog he's going to run and hey presto, it's on the card. Card! That reminds me, Tom, I've been carrying this card round with me for ages; it's the identity card for that black dog you er ... stole ... just kidding Tom." Joe handed me the card. I took a quick glance and from what I could see it was very impressive. "How is the black fellow making out, anyway. I haven't seen or heard of any black dog with a white sock pulling up any trees?"

"You're right, Joe, there hasn't been any dog with a white sock doing much at all." I had to tell a little white lie, not that Joe would say anything, but I couldn't take the chance.

My main line of thought at the moment was how to fix Slone in one of his betting coups. "You wouldn't know if Slone was planning a visit to his friend's track in the near future, would you, Joe? Of course you wouldn't, you've been sacked."

"That might be the case, Tom," said Joe, "that I've been sacked, but it doesn't mean I don't know what's going on at Slones place! If you remember, Tom, Billy the Quiff is still working there."

"And?" I asked eagerly.

"Well, Billy is courting my sister and when he calls to pick her up, I get all the gossip, and it just happens he's running a dog this weekend. The reason I know is because he's in my bleeding race and I've no chance with the class of dog he's got, so Billy tipped me off in case I fancied a few quid on my little fawn bitch."

"Are you sure, Joe, that Slone has a runner at that track and that he's in your race?"

"You can bet money on it, Tom, because Billy the Quiff is taking the dog down to the track and he's asked my sister to go with him."

"Well, Joe, we can both earn a few quid ...with a little bit of luck."

"How's that, Tom?" asked Joe, who, as I mentioned before, wasn't the brightest of lads.

"It's simple, Joe. We get down to the track and nick his market. Nothing to it!"

276

Joe stood there, his usual gaze on his face. "That's no good to me, Tom. The best price Slone's dog will be is 6/4; the rest will be at any price, and at 6/4 that won't do me much good."

"Does the price on the other dogs always drift out?"

"Always," Joe said.

"Do me a favour then, Joe. Take me to where your bitch is kennelled."

"Why?" asked Joe, a real curious look forming on his face.

"It's a long shot, Joe, but maybe, just maybe ..."

We arrived at Joe's allotment, opened the kennel and at first I thought I was seeing things; his bitch was near enough identical to the one I had at home. Joe's bitch was that little bit duller, her coat hadn't been done right, but otherwise there wasn't a lot between them, except the speed. I asked Joe where she had come from. Lo and behold the bitch had come from the same man as my mate's bitch and, according to Joe, the man had bred a full litter and sold the lot.

It wasn't long before the penny dropped, but Joe was still not too happy. "What's the problem, Joe?" I asked.

"The problem is, Tom, I'm not to keen on running a ringer; plus it's me that's got to take it in."

"Stop worrying, Joe. What's to worry about?" I asked.

"Getting caught," said Joe, for a start.

I looked him straight in the eye, "Do you want to get even with that bastard Slone?"

"Er ... er yes," replied Joe.

"Do you want to win a few quid?"

"Er ... yes."

"Well don't sound too enthusiastic then," I yelled at him. "Will you do it or not?"

"On one condition," he yelled back.

"What's that?" I asked, starting to lose my patience.

"Feed my pigeons if I get caught!" I didn't know if he was kidding or not, but either way I was doubled up with laughter and even Joe had a little snigger to himself.

"I'll take that as a yes then, Joe?"

Joe nodded in agreement, then set about brushing the bitch's coat. "Got to get her looking something like yours, Tom, if we are going to pull off this job."

I stood there in amazement; this time it was me that stood there with my mouth open. "JOE," I shouted, "look me in the face and watch my lips. I'll speak very slowly and clearly." Joe stood there, his eye's transfixed on mine, "Your ... bitch ... will ... not ... be ... running. It will be my bitch that will be running!" I felt as if I was talking to someone from another planet.

"Oh, gotcha," said Joe. "I knew all along, Tom. I was ... er ... er just ... er kidding, yes, that's it, just kidding."

By this time I was having second thoughts, but my dislike for Slone was pushing me to the limits. I gave Joe's bitch another check over, ear marks and other details, then left Joe to dream on in a world all of his own.

Jill, who had set off with the kids, was in the house waiting. "I was just about to send out a search party, Tom. It's not like you to take this long to look at a dog. Problem?" she asked.

I just looked at her, slumped myself in the chair and said, "Please, please, don't ask. It's a long story." I just couldn't go through with Jill, what I'd gone through with Joe.

The following day after working the dogs, I set about comparing the two bitches' details. It wasn't as clear cut as I had thought. My little bitch had one or two small scars on her body. If it had been the other way round and Joe's bitch had scars there wouldn't be a problem, but if we were to do the job it had to be right. If my bitch was to beat Slone's dog the handicapper would turn her inside out and Joe would probably need to change his trousers!

'No', I thought to myself, 'this job is not going to go wrong.' I would have to seek the help of an old friend.

Sam Hepple went by the nick name of Slippery, an ex burglar who never did the poor; only food shops and factories, and that was just to feed his kids. More often than not, if he'd had a good night's work, he'd give it to those who were less fortunate than himself.

I made some inquiries as to where Sam was living and found out he hadn't moved in all the years I'd known him. I pulled up at his door to see the curtains twitch, walked up the path and before I could lift my hand to knock, the door flew open. "Tom Watson, me old mate, it's great to see yer," he enthused, shaking my hand until it nearly fell off.

"It's nice to see you, too, Sam. How's tricks?" I asked.

"So, so, but looking at you, Tom, you seem to have a problem."

"We'll I have and I haven't. I need a favour, Sam."

"What sort of favour, Tom?" he asked.

I was becoming very uncomfortable and starting to wish I'd never thought of the idea in the first place. "It's ... it's a bit delicate, Sam," I went on. "Oh, what the hell!" I said, getting up the courage to tell Sam what the job was all about. After explaining all the details and the name of the track, Sam looked at me with a stern look, then burst out laughing.

"You're not going to believe this, Tom," he said, still trying to control his laughter. "I bloody well work at the track. I'm the groundsman," he went on. "There wouldn't be a problem doing what you want. A piece of cake," said Sam, "and I could do with a few quid myself. The money the owner pays me is buttons. Just give me a card with the dog's details on and I'll swap them over. That way, no matter what the Handicapper tries to do, void the race or try to say it's a ringer ... that's if the bitch wins," he hastened to add, "... the card will be identical to the dog that has just run."

I had anticipated Sam's willingness to help and had prepared the necessary details required. With a great sense of relief running through my body, I said my goodbyes to Sam and told him I'd be in touch.

Five days to the race and still lots of work to do and problems to sort out.

Would Joe stand up to the strain at the track? Would he even turn up? And would little Mini be good enough to beat Slone's dog?

All these questions were milling about in my head.

It was a relief that week that the kids were on school holidays. It kept my mind away from the coming weekend. Besides, it was nice to have a few quid for a change to treat the kids. We weren't often flush with a bit of money and it did Jill and the kids the world of good to have a few days at the seaside. Jill had been working hard in the house and the kids were doing really well at school. The break was what everyone needed.

The morning of the race I'd been in touch with Sam and everything was one hundred percent at his end. The card was swapped and no-one the wiser. So far so good. Now the tricky bit; finding Joe. Joe was an essential part of the plan. It was his bitch we were ringing. He was the one that would be taking her in, and we had to make sure that Slone was running his dog. The only way to find that out was through Joe's sister who was courting Harry the Quiff. Harry had this enormous Quiff, thickened with some sort of grease. I would often hear Slone shouting at him that he had more grease on his head than he had on his car.

There was only one thing to do, find Joe; I had a feeling it wasn't going to be easy and my hunch was right. Joe wasn't at home, nor was he at his allotment. If he couldn't be found, we would just have to take the chance that all would go well, hope that Slone had a runner, and try to find someone to take in Joe's bitch. Slone's dog was out of my control. I looked at the alternative, if Slone didn't have a runner, we could still go ahead and run our little bitch. The betting market wouldn't be as good, but we could still win a few quid; now to find someone to take in the bitch!

I shot off to Sam's to see if he had anyone in mind. Using someone from my village was too risky. I arrived at Sam's and told him the story. "No problem, Tom," said Sam. "I've got just the man, an old friend of mine, and a handy lad if things turn nasty."

With that little problem sorted I set off home feeling a lot easier in my mind. If Joe turned up, all well and good; if he didn't, the job would go ahead without him.

I'd been back from Sam's about a couple of hours when who should knock at the door but Joe. He looked as if he hadn't got a care in the world. "Hey up, Tom, how's it going?"

I stood there speechless for a few seconds. "How's it bloody well going? Where the hell have you been?" I shouted. "You've had me pulling my hair out wondering if you'd emigrated."

"No, Tom, I never mentioned I was emigrating," said Joe, looking quite serious. I looked at Joe and thought to myself, 'No, Tom, don't even ask'. Apparently Joe had been working on a fiddle job with a mate of his that had kept him busy all week. Since being sacked from Slone's, money for Joe was in short supply.

The time of reckoning would soon be upon us. We sent the kids down to Jill's mother's, just in case of trouble, and set off for the track. We arrived just in time to see Harry hand Slone's dog over to one of the locals to take in, a handsome brindle dog with a white nose. If Harry was seen to be taking a dog into the track, and him working for a licensed trainer, the game would be up for Slone.

Joe had set off in his own van, well ahead of Jill and me and was parked at the other end of the car-park; for once Joe seemed to be using his head.

Sam was there to greet Jill and me with his mate just in case he was needed; after all he wasn't to know that Joe had turned up. Sam wasn't wrong when he said his mate might be handy if needed; a big strapping lad just over six foot, with one or two battle scars on his face.

"This is my mate, Tony," said Sam, as the introductions went round, after shaking hands. I was glad Tony was on my side. Sam showed me the programme for the nights racing. "I'm only guessing Tom," said Sam, "but I think Slone's dog is giving your mate's dog two yards." The reason, apparently, was because the race consisted of two dogs that had already run and they were known to Tony.

Two of the remainders were dogs that had graded when Sam was working at the track and there was no way Slone would risk a trial when all he had to do was pick up the phone to his mate and have a dog qualified without running. So Sam had it down to trap two, by sheer elimination, as the four dog had to be Mini.

The money was sorted out as we dispersed into the track, £50 for Sam and Tony, £40 for Joe.

Sam kept us right as to which bookies were the best and to how much money they would take. The betting was to be left to Tony, Jill, and myself. Sam was to be left out for obvious reasons.

Two races had gone by and we were in the next race. Tony had noticed a strange team milling about in front of the bookmakers; it had to be Slone's men. They each lined up in front of the book they were going to take, then my heart started thumping. I'd been along to the paddock just to keep an eye on Joe and to have a good look at the dog belonging to Slone. As I got closer my eyes nearly popped out of my head. Slone's dog was a dog I used to train, called Midnight Money, a top class animal. I was beginning to have second thoughts about having a bet as there was no way in this world that my little bitch could beat Monty, which was his pet name, unless Sam had been right and Monty hadn't been round the track. Monty was a lot better dog. If he'd had a look round the track before he was gambled on and as Slone had been told to do by me on several occasions, all would be to no avail.

I went back to tell Jill and the others; we were all agreed we were to stick to the plan.

"ALL DOGS TO THE TRAPS PLEASE," came the announcement. Slone's dog, Happy, was being pushed out to 2-1 by one of the bookies, the rest of the books kept it at 6/4. It was obvious he'd been told by the Handicapper and was in on the job; it wasn't long before the other books followed and all were at 2-1. It didn't take long before Slone's team were in; they were betting Happy like there was no tomorrow. Mini, who Joe had called Joe's Pet, went out to 5-1, it was time that we stepped in. There was no trouble in getting on what money we wanted and left the price at 2-1, so much was the volume of money that had gone onto Slone's dog.

The hare started to move, faster and faster it whizzed passed the traps, when the lids went up. Slone's dog, Happy, who was giving our bitch two yards, was nearly level with her, but Mini was a good railer and wouldn't give an inch. Every time Slone's dog gained on the straits, Mini caught him on the bends. They were neck and neck coming to the last bend. Happy, as expected, ran wide, but not too wide; Mini did her job by sticking to the rails and came out of the bend two lengths clear.

Fifty yards to go and Slone's dog was catching her; twenty yards to go and Slone's dog was only one length behind and catching her with every stride. As they approached the winning line, Mini had just held on by a quarter of a length to screams of delight from Jill, me and the rest of the team.

There was a stunned silence from a section of the crowd and lots of activity from the judge's box. " HOLD ALL BETS — IT'S A PHOTO FINISH AND AN ENQUIRY," came the announcement. This was the crunch time; would Joe's bottle go? The Handicapper made off in the direction of the paddock, followed by Jill, Tony, myself plus a large crowd that were sick of the strokes being pulled by the bent Handicapper.

"What's up this time, Browny," said one of the disgruntled punters to the Handicapper, "lost yer cash?"

"There's no way that this bitch could do the time she's done," said the unhappy Mr. Brown, looking at Mini and Joe as if to say, 'this shouldn't have happened'. He checked everything possible on the bitch, but couldn't find a thing wrong thanks to Sam, then off he marched back to the judge's box.

"Think there might be a problem, Tom," said Tony. "The mood that Handicapper's in and the pressure he'll be under from Slone, it's not looking good?"

"He can't say it's the wrong bitch," said Jill. "he's turned her inside out and can't find anything wrong."

A little old chap who had been cocking his ears spoke up, "This Handicapper does what he wants and don't think because your bitch has won a quarter of a length that that's it; it's not."

"What about the photo?" asked Jill.

"Photo," laughed the old man, "I've seen dogs win by a bigger margin than your little bitch and still lose the race, and before you say 'How?', it's simple. He doesn't give a photo: it's the judge's decision due to the failure of the photographic equipment, and he gets away with it every time," he went on.

"Not this time," said Tony, who hadn't had a lot to say all night. He looked up at the judge's box and caught the eye of the Handicapper, who was just about to give off the result.

"FIRST ... ER ... FIRST ..."

Tony slid his hand into his trouser pocket and pulled out a box of matches, held them up in his hand and shook them at the Handicapper, with the words mimed, "Matches are cheap Browny. I'd like you to bear that in mind."

The Handicapper hesitated for a second or two, his eyes fixed on Tony. "FIRST ... NUMBER FOUR, SECOND ... NUMBER TWO."

There was no doubt in my mind that Tony had swayed the decision of the judge and in no doubt, had the decision gone the wrong way, as to what would happen to the TRACK.

We shared out the money to the delight of Sam, Tony and Joe and made our way out of the track. At the top of the car park, there were some very disgruntled people. It was Slone and his mob. "How the hell did that dog get beat," shouted Slone, "especially by Joe Robson's dog? He hasn't got a dog that could run a bloody message never mind beating a £2,000 dog. All those dogs were hand picked by that bloody idiot Brown. There's no way that shit-for-brains Joe could pull off a stunt like that," raved Slone.

I couldn't resist any longer. I pulled up the van right next to Slone and slowly turned down the window to make sure he could see Jill myself and the bitch. Slone wasn't a stupid a man and soon realised who was behind the little scam.

"You've cost me a lot of money tonight, Watson, and it won't be forgotten," he said gritting his teeth. Jill and I just sat there, not saying a word. The expression on Slone's face spoke for the both of us.

CHAPTER TWENTY-THREE

I suppose if I hadn't had the sack from Harry Slone's kennel I wouldn't have bought Lucky. And lucky was exactly how he and ourselves had been for the past few months, winning enough to go a long way towards buying our own little colliery house.

The Coal Board had decided to sell off most of their terraced houses to sitting tenants and Jill and I were just a fraction away from having the full amount needed to buy the house outright. One more big win and the house would be ours. Jill had set her heart on owning our own home from the first day we were married, though after my accident I didn't hold out much hope.

We were out walking one day, Jill and I, with Lucky and Mini, when we bumped into Fancy Fred. "How's it going?" said Fred, who always had the biggest smile on his face.

"Can't grumble, Fred; we keep getting a winner or two," I replied.

"How's the black feller running," asked Fred? "Not that I'm prying, Tom," he continued. "The reason I'm asking is that there's a big race coming off at Avondale track. There's a new owner and he wants to make a grand opening and according to the crack, the prize money is going to be something else."

Jill's eye's lit up; I could see the balloon above her head (one more big win, and the house is ours).

"Mind you, Tom," said Fred, it's going to take some winning; all the top trainers from the licensed tracks will be there, even if they shouldn't, you know what greedy bast ... ," Freddy stopped himself, remembering Jill was there, "... people there are about. Well, you know what I mean, Tom."

"I think I get the message, Fred, but it's worth thinking about." With that Fred set off on his journey, his grin as broad as ever.

That night I made some enquiries to a very good and trusted friend. I had to be careful, as speaking to the wrong people in the dog game could mean all your best plans were up in smoke. I drove over to see Billy Green. If there was anything happening on the dog scene, Billy would know.

After speaking to him for half an hour and three cups of tea kindly forced on me by Billy's wife, Jean, I'd got to know all that I'd come for and a bit more besides. The race was to be run in ten days time. The prize money was a massive £600 to the winner, but as Freddy and Billy had said, it was going to take some winning.

My first job was to let Lucky have a look round the track. Billy had arranged for a mate of his to take Lucky for a solo run when the track was quiet. Jill and I had decided to stay away from the track, just in case someone connected Lucky to us. If Lucky went round the track in a good time, people would put that down to the man who had taken him on, and, after all, he was just another black dog.

The next day Billy was true to his word, he picked up the dog and set off to meet his mate who didn't know where the dog was coming from. Avondale Track was about forty minutes drive from our house; it was 10.0 am when Billy left with the dog and we had estimated he should be back by about 12.30. It was now 1.0pm. Jill was down to her knuckles.

"It's only just gone one, give the lad a chance, Jill." I was trying to reassure her, when I was worried sick myself. 1.30 pm and you would think Jill was having her fifth baby. I was pacing the floor like an expectant father. 2.0 pm and still no sign. I was fearing the worst when there was a knock at the door. 'Please, please, let this be Billy,' I was saying to myself, and to my delight it was. Jill rushed to the door and straight out to Billy's van.

"Don't panic," said Billy, "he's all right. I thought you might be worrying a little with it being a bit late, but there was an accident on the A45 and everyone was diverted."

"I er ... er ... wasn't worried," said Jill, trying to look calm and collected, "it's just that it's his er ... his ... his feed time, ... that's it ... his feed time," she went on as she hurried Lucky in to wash his feet and make sure he was OK.

"We'll how did it go then, Billy?" I asked, keen to find out what sort of time Lucky had done.

"Put it this way, Tom. He's got a race on his hands." Billy went on to say that Slone was well represented with three good dogs and there were two other good dogs that went round in very good times. "Slone wasn't there, but his man was there, waiting round a side street for the dogs to come back."

By this time Jill was starting to look a bit down in the mouth; she'd set her heart on winning one more big race so we could buy the house.

Billy sat there drinking his tea, deep in thought, "You haven't asked what sort of time the dogs were doing, Tom," said Billy, "and it's not like you!"

"Is it worth telling me, Billy?" I asked half heartedly.

"Well, the best of Slone's dogs was a nice fawn bitch; she went round in 26-54. The other two dogs of Slone's were only three length behind her." Billy stopped for a second or two to drink his tea; he was deliberately taking his time and dragging out the answers, asking Jill if there was any more tea in the pot. By then she had given Lucky his dinner and was just about to sit down. "I'll wait till Jill gets back with my tea," said Billy, "if you don't mind, Tom." Billy was a great one for dragging out any information you were waiting to hear. Jill returned with Billy's tea.

"Now, Billy, is there any chance of finding out the rest of these times?" I asked.

Billy sat there and was just about to dip his biscuit in his tea when Jill stood up: "Don't go too far, Billy, I'm not in the mood."

Billy knew he'd reached the limit and got on with telling us the day's events.

"Right ... er where was I up to," said Billy, placing his biscuit back on the plate. "Ah yes, the dogs that we knew very little about did a similar time to Slone's second string, about three lengths behind his fawn bitch ..."

"...And," asked Jill, "what about Lucky?"

"Ah Lucky," said Billy trying to string out the story until he saw Jill rattling her fingers on the table top waiting for the answer: "Lucky's time was ..." he paused for a moment, stroking his chin, "... 26-44; the track record stands at 26-28 which makes Lucky's run 16 spots off the track record, less than three yards to find. But ..." Billy went on to say, "Slone's bitch is only ten spots behind Lucky, just less than two yards. It's not going to be easy, Tom."

Jill and I were just delighted Lucky had run so well and come off without any problems. We sat down and looked at the situation; we had as much chance as any other dog and we couldn't wait to take on the Slone's and the rest of the big boys of the greyhound world.

All that week we were kept busy with one thing or another; the dogs were kept on their toes, the kids were playing for the school football teams, Jill would be dropped off at one game and I would watch the other, then if possible we would swap round at half- time. The kids had three games that week and it all helped to pass the time. First thing on a morning, Aunt Mary would pop in to keep an eye on the kids while Jill and I would go down to the beach with the dogs. There was nothing like seeing a Greyhound stretching out along the beach at full pace: the majestic way they moved, the agility that their bodies possessed was pure magic. Both Lucky and Mini thrived on their work and would veer off towards the sea, then race back when the tide started to turn. On returning home from exercise the dogs would be washed down to clear the salt from their feet.

Race day, the day of the heats, Billy had travelled over to Avondale track for a race card, the dog had been booked in and paid for by one of Billy's mates and the next step was to see what heat we had drawn. We had drawn heat three. Billy's mate had called Lucky, Trim, after an old dog he'd had years ago.

The kids had opted to stay at home to attend the birthday of one of their schoolmates and Aunt Mary had kindly stepped in to keep an eye on them when they returned. Aunt Mary had never had kids of her own and looked upon me as the child she never had. She had been a widow for the past six years and being lonely she loved to come down to our house for the company.

We saw the kids off to the party, left Aunt Mary the key and set off for the track. Lucky was one of those dogs that as soon as he jumped into the van he was flat out, always the sign of a good dog. We met Billy at the arranged place, gave him the dog, sorted out the money, then Billy was off to meet his mate at another venue. Billy couldn't use the same lad as he used to trial the dog because he'd know how fast Lucky had done round the track and one word in the wrong place could mean a dramatic difference in the price. We had to play it safe.

Jill and I arrived just in time for the first heat and made our way over to the paddock to see what the opposition was like. There were some nice dogs and you could bet money at least half of them were from the licensed tracks and by law they shouldn't have been there. The way I looked at the situation was that a dog was a dog, no matter if it came from a flapping man or a licensed trainer. You were there to take on all comers and may the best dog win!

Billy had arrived at the paddock to see if he recognised any of the dogs. "I think that big brindle dog is one of Slone's," said Billy and that fawn and white dog is one of the dogs we knew nothing about, but he still ran well."

"Well, we are about to find out," said Jill, "they've been called to the traps."

We hurried round to the bookies to see where the money was going. Billy was right, the money was on the brindle dog, Soapy, 6/4 fav; the fawn and white dog, Mouse, was 2-1; only the first two went through to the final.

"PUT THE DOGS INTO THE TRAPS, STARTER," came the announcement.

Soapy had drawn trap 2 and Mouse trap 6. All the dogs were in the traps waiting for the hare — only seconds left.

The hare flew passed the traps and up went the lids. Soapy from trap 2 didn't get the best of breaks, nor did Mouse from trap 6. There was bumping and barging all the way down to the first bend. Mouse, having drawn trap 6, was coming off worst and before you knew it, he was down at the first bend. Soapy, Slone's dog, was having a better run on the inside and soon took the lead to win by two lengths.

"FIRST, NUMBER TWO. SOAPY, SECOND. NUMBER THREE, SPOTLIGHT, AND THE WINNER'S TIME 26-66, DISTANCE TWO LENGTHS. THOSE TWO DOGS GO THROUGH TO THE FINAL NEXT SATURDAY."

"That's one through for Slone," said Jill. "Let's see what he's got in this heat." Meanwhile, Billy was off organising a team to bet Lucky. Jill and I were still keeping our distance from Lucky; as far as anyone knew we didn't have a runner.

Time for the second heat; we followed our pattern as we did in the first heat, walked over to the paddock then down to the bookies. Billy had spotted Slone's fawn bitch in the paddock; she was no oil painting amongst the other dogs, but that would be an advantage to Slone in the betting market — or would it?

I caught hold of Billy's hand and shoved £50 into it. "Get this on Slone's bitch before the betting starts." Billy saw the opportunity to kill two birds with one stone and that was to get the best price and get one over on Slone.

The bookmaker Billy had given the money to had laid him 3-1 and opened up on the boards at evens. Slone's men had no choice but to take the even money that was offered.

"PUT THE DOGS INTO THE TRAPS, STARTER," came the announcement. Slone's bitch, Bambi, had drawn trap one.

The hare flew passed the traps, the lids went up and out came trap one, Bambi, like a rocket. There was no contest; Bambi won comfortably by five lengths and there was no doubt that this was a good bitch. I was happy because I'd won and a bit sick because I knew the time would be fast and if we were fortunate to qualify for the final we would have a race on our hands.

The loudspeaker started to crackle into action. "FIRST, NUMBER ONE, BAMBI. SECOND, NUMBER FOUR, TREETOP. THE WINNER'S TIME 26.33 THE DISTANCE FIVE LENGTHS. FIRST AND SECOND GO THROUGH TO THE FINAL NEXT SATURDAY."

"That's going to take all the beating in the world," said Billy, as he counted the winnings into my hand. "Cheer up, Tom" he said, "you'd think it was a loser you'd backed. You want to see that kid's face that's backed the bitch for Slone; he does look worried."

Time for the third and final heat; you'd think it was the final the way my heart was thumping. Jill was the same, God knows how we'd feel if it *were* the final!

We walked over to the paddock. Lucky looked a picture as he stood out from the rest. I only hoped his looks wouldn't relate to his price. It was obvious Slone's remaining dog was in with Lucky. They had already had two winners and were going for the third, our only chance of a price was Slone's team getting in early before they missed the betting.

"How much are you having on, Tom?" asked Billy. "He's got a right chance of beating Slone's dog. As for the rest ... I'll take my chance with Lucky."

"Put me £300 on, Billy. I've already won £150 on Slone's bitch; might as well go the whole hog."

Jill stood there and never batted an eyelid; she knew if we wanted to win big we had to bet big. "It's no good looking at me, Billy," said Jill. "If you want the best price you'd better get down to them books and quick." Billy didn't stay to discuss the situation and headed off in the direction of the bookies.

It was as we thought, Lucky was 2-1 joint favourite with Slone's dog, Boxer. The man Billy had used to take in Lucky hadn't bothered to change his name. I wasn't too keen on using pet names for the simple reason it had been known for someone from the crowd to shout out the dog's pet name and the dog lose concentration.

Slone's men were lined up ready to take the betting on Boxer when there was a mad rush for trap six, Snowball. Lucky from trap three and Boxer from trap two went out in the betting to 3-1, then Slone's men went in for Boxer and that knocked Lucky's price out to 4-1. This was going to be one hell of a race. We had just turned to gain a good vantage point when there was a rush for trap one, Tess; four dogs heavily gambled on, this was some hot heat.

"TAKE THE DOGS TO THE TRAPS, STARTER," crackled the mike and all the handlers walked off towards the traps. Lucky was as calm as a cucumber, fully alert, ears pricked and ready for the job.

" PUT THE DOGS INTO THE TRAPS, STARTER." This was it. There would be less than a minute to find out our fate.

The hare flashed passed the traps, the break was very even, a blanket start, with Lucky the meat in the sandwich having drawn trap three. It was a mad rush to the bend; something had to give. Jill turned away, not bearing to look. There was an almighty pile-up at the bend, dogs falling all over the place. The crowd were in unison with an almighty *AHH*.

Jill responded to the gasps from the crowd by straining to see the melée at the first bend. "Where's Lucky?" she shouted. "Is he all right; has he fallen?" It was panic stations for a while until we saw Lucky in third place, about four lengths from the leader, Ballpen, in trap five, followed by Tess in trap four. Snowball and Boxer were two of the fallers at the first bend.

If Lucky was to win, or even qualify, he was going to have to do some of his best running, and quick! There were only 300 yards left, Lucky narrowing the gap stride by stride until he was only one length behind the leader, Ballpen, with less than 50 yards to go. It was going to be close: Lucky and Tess, stride for stride; Ballpen hanging on for grim death. There was one last desperate effort to catch Ballpen, but it was no good, Ballpen held on. Tess and Lucky crossed the winning line together: there was no separating them. Some photo finish judges were saying Tess had held on, others were saying Lucky had got up on the line and one good judge saying, you couldn't get a fag paper between them!

"WINNER, NUMBER FIVE, BALLPEN. PHOTO FINISH FOR SECOND PLACE," was the announcement.

There was frantic betting going on with the bookies: some betting on a dead heat, others betting on Tess or Lucky.

The tanoy crackled into action, "LADIES AND GENTLEMEN, AFTER HAVING A SECOND PRINT FOR THE MINOR PLACINGS, THE DECISION IS A DEAD HEAT. THE TIME OF THE RACE WAS 26-48, DISTANCE HALF A LENGTH. HOWEVER," he went on, "DUE TO THE IMPORTANCE OF THE RACE, ONLY ONE DOG FROM THE DEADHEAT CAN GO THROUGH TO THE FINAL. A DECISION WILL BE MADE SHORTLY."

By now, the crowd, including ourselves, were in turmoil, not knowing what decision the judges would come to. "What's going to happen, Tom?" said Jill, just happy that Lucky wasn't injured.

"It's got me beat, Jill. It could be a run off between the two dogs, that's if the owners are agreeable, or the old fashioned way?"

"And what's that?" asked Jill looking curious.

"Win or lose on the toss of a coin."

By this time Billy had put two and two together. He knew the owners of the dogs would be called to the judge's box and had arranged for his friend's wife to sit with Lucky until the situation was sorted out and for his mate to stand by nice and handy.

The Tanoy crackled into action. "LADIES AND GENTLEMAN, THE JUDGES HAVE DECIDED TO HAVE A DRAW. TWO BALLS PICKED AT RANDOM AND PLACED INTO A BAG: THE ONE WHO DRAWS THE HIGHEST BALL WINS. COULD WE HAVE THE OWNERS OF TESS AND LUCKY TO THE WINNING LINE, PLEASE?"

Billy's mate made his way onto the track. If Jill had been the one drawing out of the bag I'd have felt a whole lot better. She was always lucky in that department, but what will be will be!

"Who wants to draw first?" asked the Handicapper. Our man was straight up and hand in the bag before the other chap could take a breath. He brought out the ball and held it up for all to see.

"Shit," said Billy, after seeing the number on the ball.

"What's he drawn, what's he drawn?" asked Jill, jumping up and down, trying to see what was happening.

"Lucky's drawn two," said someone in the crowd.

"Shit," said Jill. Billy was right.

"LUCKY HAS DRAWN NUMBER TWO," shouted the Handicapper.

It was time for Tess's owner to draw. We weren't holding out much hope, after all there's not a lot of numbers below TWO. He slid his hand into the bag, and pulled out the ball, held it up and to his amazement it was number ONE. The gasps from the crowd rang round the stadium.

Jill was like a jack-in-the-box jumping up and down, until she realised she shouldn't be showing any emotion. Billy had taken Lucky from his mate's van and transferred him to our van, knowing we weren't far behind him.

We were pulling out of the stadium, when who should be hiding round the corner, but our old friend, Harry Slone, cap pulled down over his face, the collar of his overcoat turned up. I knew it was Slone; there was something about the man that disturbed me. A cold shiver came over my body as the van approached him. We drove quickly past to avoid Slone or any of his cronies seeing Jill or myself, plus the dog; it was still vital that no-one knew we had a runner, especially Slone.

We arrived home and checked out Lucky to make sure there were no problems after his skirmish at the first bend, gave him his food and locked him up for the night. Aunt Mary, who had been looking after the kids, had prepared home made steak and kidney pie for supper. She was a kindly soul, but very lonely. If Aunt Mary didn't pay her daily visit to see the family, I think she would have wasted away sitting in her little cottage; but it was always nice to see her.

The following morning Jill and I were up at the crack of dawn. We licked our wounds and got down to the business of training Lucky to win a race: a steady walk that day and a stroll along the beach, just to keep him loose from the previous night's racing. We arrived back home to the smell of bacon and eggs; Aunt Mary, who had stayed the night, had heard Jill and I leave early and thought she would save Jill the trouble of cooking breakfast. It was a nice change, especially for Jill, who would normally start breakfast as soon as we got back.

Later that day, after taking Aunt Mary home, I bumped into Norman Walsh, an old mate of mine from when I was working in the pit. After exchanging pleasantries, he proceeded to ask if I had heard the rumours about Harry Slone?

"Rumours, what rumours would they be Norman?" I asked, my curiosity getting the better of me.

"Got the sack," said Norman. This was sounding better by the second. "Got the sack for running a dog on a flapping track in Yorkshire," he went on. "Apparently, he was nearly caught red-handed," said Norman, a slight grin on his face. He, like a few more people in the village, had a huge dislike for Slone, mainly because of the way he treated his wife and because of his womanising.

Norman went on with the tale. It turned out that one of Slone's owners had called in to see his dog only to find that Slone had taken the dog down to Yorkshire to race on a Flapping Track. This was strictly taboo for any NGRC Licensed Trainer.

"How did the stewards find out?" I asked.

"That's debatable," said Norman with a wink and a smile as he carried on with the story. It turned out that the chap who owned the dog had made an excuse to call into Harry Slone's two nights previous on the pretence of seeing his dog, but the true nature of his visit was that he suspected Slone of having an affair with his wife. On finding Slone wasn't at home, he made the excuse to see the dog. By this time Mrs. Slone was suspicious of something, having seen the man's wife at the kennels on several occasions without her husband and decided to confront the man. It wasn't long before the poor man had told Mrs. Slone everything, how he had suspected his wife and her husband for a long time, but had never been able to catch them together. "And by all accounts, Tom, and don't quote me on this," said Norman, "the man broke down and was in a right state. Mrs. Slone took pity on the chap. After all, she knew how the poor man was feeling, being in the same boat herself," he went on.

"Get to the point, Norman," I urged. "How did the stewards know Slone was racing on a Flapper in Yorkshire?"

"Well, Tom, as the story goes, Mrs. Slone told the man it wasn't in her nature to report any trainer to the stewards for racing on a Flapping Track, but, as she turned away from him, she called out: 'But you're not me! And just as a matter of interest, there's a nice race taking place at Lowgate Track in Yorkshire tonight,' and with that she walked away and closed the door behind her."

"But I saw Slone last night at Avondale Track. He couldn't have got the sack. Why would he be hiding?" I asked.

"Well, according to the rumours," Norman went on, "the stewards were there first thing this morning, having just missed Slone by a whisker at the Flapper a couple of nights ago." He went on: "Apparently the Handicapper at Lowgate Track was a bit reluctant to release the ear marks of the dogs that ran that night, hence the delay in Slone's sacking!"

I bid Norman good-bye and set off home to tell Jill the news. Even if the rumours were half true, Slone was in trouble and that suited me fine.

Most of the rumours were confirmed within the next few days, Joe who had been sacked by Slone, had called in to gloat a little and add a bit of exaggeration to the rumour. Harry the Quiff had told Joe that all the kennel staff were on two week's notice and that Mrs. Slone had left her husband and gone to live with her sister, leaving Slone to sort out the sordid mess himself.

The day of the final. 'Would Slone have any runners in the final? Would it be a four dog race?' I asked myself. We wouldn't know until that evening. The conversation on everyone's lips in the village, including our own household, was Slone, Slone, Slone. For the first time ever, Aunt Mary asked if she could come to the races. This was most unusual and had me quite curious. Why would Aunt Mary want to go to dogs and tonight of all nights?

All the arrangements had been sorted out with Billy, where to meet and at what time. Lucky had a hard race on his hands, we all knew that, but the dog was well and he'd had a bit of trouble in the earlier race. With the right draw and a little bit of luck, who knows! Maybe Aunt Mary might be the piece of luck we were needing? There was one more thing to be done. The dye that was keeping Lucky's white foot black had to be replaced by a more soluble dye and fingers crossed it wouldn't rain.

Jill and I placed the container with the water to wash Lucky's feet with the rest of his racing gear at the front of the van, then the kids, and finally Aunt Mary and Lucky, making sure Lucky was well out of the reach of those sprawling legs. We only had a few miles to travel before Lucky was transferred to Billy's van, then from Billy's van to his mate's safe keeping.

We arrived at the track and made straight for the top end of the car park, a bit secluded, but just the right place for what I hopefully had in mind. Aunt Mary was grumbling about her rheumatism as we helped her from the van, but was determined to attend the meeting. As we walked down to the turnstile, there as bold as brass, was Harry Slone with three of his cronies.

"You keep your mouth shut, our Tom," said Aunt Mary. "We want no trouble with the likes of him." And that was before we were within striking distance of Harry Slone.

"I thought you had bad eyes, Aunt Mary?" said Jill, smiling.

"You might be right, Jill pet, but I can see and smell a skunk from a long distance."

"Where's the skunk?" asked Peter, looking all round the car park.

"The only smell I can smell," he went on, "is when our Bobby pumped, getting out of the van." Jill gave him a clip round the ear and told him to behave himself.

We were walking past Harry Slone when he chirped up, "Come to see a good dog in the final, Watson?" he smirked.

"You're right, Slone," I replied. "I have come to see a good dog in the final."

Slone's face lit up, "That's a compliment coming from you, Watson," he replied.

"It might be, if it were directed at one of your dogs."

"Cheeky sod, Watson," he retorted. "You always had a wise-crack answer, but not tonight," he went on. "There's only one winner and that's Bambi."

Aunt Mary shuffled us towards the turnstile, her eyes fixed on Slone's and his on hers. If looks could kill, two dead bodies would be laying outside that track. I have never seen as much hatred in anyone's eyes as I did in those two.

There was a queue forming behind us and getting a little impatient so we hurried through the turnstile and into the track.

Aunt Mary looked visibly shaken and sat down on a small wall inside the track.

"Do you want a drink, Aunt Mary?" asked Jill, looking a bit concerned.

"No, pet," she went on, "it's just that no good excuse for a man, Slone. I'll be all right in a minute or two."

I left Jill with Aunt Mary and the kids and set off in search of Billy; I bumped into him at the paddock looking at the dogs for the first race. "I see your old boss has shown his face then," said Billy. "The rumours must have been true," he went on.

"It's a sore point, Billy. The least said about Slone the better, more importantly, what's your opinion on the draw?"

Billy took the programme from his pocket, turned to race four, the final, rubbed his chin, and gave me a wink. "Lucky has a right chance if he can hit those lids. The race read like this," he went on.

LUCKY	Trap one
SOAPY	Trap two
BAMBI	Trap three
BALLPEN	Trap four
SPOTLIGHT	Trap five
TREETOP	Trap six

"Put it this way, Tom," said Billy, "he's got the draw, all we need now is a little luck!"

Leaving Billy, I made my way to Jill and the family. Aunt Mary seemed to have pulled herself together and even won herself a few quid on the forecast in the first two races, but still gave me the impression she'd rather be at home.

One more race before the final. The excitement was starting to build; everything was going according to plan. The rain had kept off, Lucky had drawn trap one and now it was down to the gods.

The third race completed, this was it.

"CAN WE HAVE DOGS TO THE PADDOCK FOR THE £600 FINAL, PLEASE," came the announcement.

Slone had decided to take Bambi on by himself; after all he no longer worked as a trainer for the NGRC and I suppose he was sticking two fingers up at the establishment. Our man with Lucky was standing right next to Slone who didn't even give Lucky a second glance. Little did Slone realise that Lucky was an expensive buy and was once in his care, only to be sold for a tenner!

After checking all the dogs' ear marks and a quick glance over the rest of their bodies, the Handicapper instructed the handlers to carry on to the traps. Much to my relief, Lucky's darkened foot had passed the test.

"TAKE THE DOGS TO THE STARTING TRAPS," crackled the loudspeaker.

Jill had taken the kids and Aunt Mary to a good viewing point. Billy and I walked down to the bookies; Bambi, as expected, was favourite at 6/4, Lucky was a 3-1 chance. Slone and his men must have thought Bambi was unbeatable; they took all the 6/4 and left her on at 4-6, this knocked Lucky's price out to 4-1. I knew Lucky would find time from last week and was prepared to back my judgement with every penny we had in the house, £400. Billy was of the same opinion as me, his whack was also £400; if Lucky didn't win there were going to be some sad faces going home that night. It was sink or swim, the bets were placed and the announcement was made to place the dogs into the traps. My heart was thumping like a live man trying to escape from his coffin.

The hare was running, gathering speed as it whizzed past the traps. This time Lucky came out in his turn, as did Bambi, and they were neck and neck down to the first bend. Lucky held his place on the inside making Bambi take the long road round; Ballpoint and Treetop were having their own little battle only two lengths behind. Lucky had gained half a length, but Bambi was a gutsy little thing and kept coming back to him. Only 50 yards to go, Lucky still that fraction in front. I could here Jill screaming at the top of her voice with Slone doing likewise: both dogs passed the post together.

Billy came running down to where I was standing, "Has he won, Tom?" asked Billy, desperate for the right answer.

"He's won for me, Billy, by a good neck," I replied.

"PHOTO FINISH," came the announcement, "BETWEEN TRAPS ONE, LUCKY, AND THREE, BAMBI." The betting on the photo told the story, 3-1 Bambi, no price on Lucky.

"FIRST, TRAP ONE, LUCKY. THE DISTANCE, A NECK, AND THE WINNING TIME A NEW TRACK RECORD."

Lucky had broken the old record by two spots, the equivalent of a neck. Slone was standing with his cronies; I'd seen happier faces on the skull and cross bones.

"THE PRESENTATION WILL TAKE PLACE IN FIVE MINUTES," echoed the mike, "WHERE THE WINNING OWNER WILL RECEIVE HIS PRIZE."

After collecting our winnings from the bookmakers, we went in search of Jill and the rest of the family. The handicapper was calling for the owners of the first and second in the final to come to the winning line to be presented with their prize money. Slone had already established himself on the winning line to receive his £100, second prize. I tried to persuade Jill to take Lucky to the winning line, but she was having none of it, saying this was my night and to stand there next to Slone and feel very, very proud.

The look on Slone's face as I walked towards him was a look of sheer murder, his eyes never leaving my face all through the prize giving: anyone in the world could have won that race bar me.

We left the track to congratulations from all the owners except Slone; he left the track skulking with his mates who were conflabbing in the car park. I proceeded to take out the bucket from the van to wash Lucky's feet in full view of Slone, keeping my back to him as I did so. This was the final humiliation for Mr. Slone. I turned, having removed the dye from Lucky's leg, to make sure Slone could see that he'd been beaten by a dog that he'd condemned as useless.

A sheer look of hatred appeared on Slone's face.

Billy had suspected there might be trouble and had tried to persuade Aunt Mary and the kids to travel back in his van, leaving more room in the van for Lucky; the kids agreed but Aunt Mary was having none of it. Billy set off with the kids, leaving me, Jill and Aunt Mary.

We turned slowly towards the van, when Slone shouted: "Watson, you're a thief and a robber."

"Take no notice, Tom," urged Aunt Mary.

"YOU ... YOU ... Tom Watson," he shouted. I was doing my best to keep calm, but finding it increasingly difficult. "And further more, Watson," he shouted, "I think YOU and that shit-head, Joe, planned the whole thing to buy that black dog, or should I say STEAL."

Slone was really getting to me now; I shoved the dogs lead into Jill's hand, with reluctance from Jill. I was just about to forget the whole thing and get into the van when Slone started again.

"It wouldn't surprise me, Watson, if you deliberately doped that black dog to make him run badly the night I backed him."

That was it! He could call me whatever he wanted, but when he accused me of doping his dogs, I had to draw the line. I slammed the door of the van and walked towards him, "Take that back, Slone or I'll break every bone in your wicked, evil body."

"Tom!".... shouted Jill and Aunt Mary. "Hiding behind the women, Watson!" said Slone. That was it, I let fly with a punch that burst open Slone's nose, rage and hatred boiling up inside me. I rained blow after blow until Slone's face was unrecognisable.

"Stop ... stop," screamed Aunt Mary, in near hysterics, "you'll kill him Tom." I stood there covered in blood, hatred filling up once more. I was just about to repeat the dose, when Aunt Mary screamed, "You've got to stop, Tom! He's ... he's your FATHER!"

A numbness came over my body. Blood dripping from my knuckles, I stood there in a trance, Slone moaning and trying to speak, his mouth full of blood, tears streaming down the faces of Jill and Aunt Mary. Slone's men picked him up and carried him to his car, Slone still trying to speak.There was no way I could go straight back home, not the state I was in, not where the kids were. We set off for Aunt Mary's house and I hoped Billy had the sense to realise something was wrong and try to find some way of entertaining the kids.

There were still lots of questions to be asked and answers to be found. We arrived at Aunt Mary's where I cleaned myself up and looked at Aunt Mary for the answers. She broke down before she could start, but pulled herself together with a deep breath. "Tom," she said, her eyes welling up again as she spoke, "I should have told you long ago about Slone, but I thought the least you knew about a man like that the better." She stopped to wipe away the tears rolling down her cheeks. "It made my skin crawl when I found out that you had started working for Slone, and I was so relieved when he gave you the sack. You might think me a bit hard, Tom, but you have no idea what I've had to live with these past years." She took a deep breath, "You see, Tom, Slone's not only your father, but I'm ... I'm ... your Mother."

There was a stunned silence that seemed to go on forever, until I stood up and flung my arms around her. It turned out that Aunt Mary, or mother, had been going steady with Slone until she had become pregnant with me. Slone had used and abandoned her like he had with many others. But at least it explained why Slone hated me so much. The question I kept asking myself was why he had set me on working for him in the first place, but that is something I will never know, as I have no intention of ever seeing or speaking to Slone again.

A lot of the questions in my life had now been answered, some good, some not so good, but then, whose life is perfect? What with Gran and Grandad, who had passed on, and Aunt Mary/ Mother and of course, Jill and the kids, I'd not done too badly. I had good friends who counted. I had a future ahead. And although I'd probably never have lots of money, who cared? With family and friends like these, I knew I was rich indeed.

End